W. Fred Conway

Those Magnificent Old Steam Fire Engines

W. Fred Conway

Fire Buff House Publishers • New Albany, Indiana 47151-0711

Library of Congress Cataloging in Publication Data
Conway, W. Fred

Those Magnificent Old Steam Fire Engines
Library of Congress Catalog Number: 96-083534
ISBN 0-925165-19-0

FBH Publishers, P.O. Box 711, New Albany, IN 47151-0711
© W. Fred Conway, 1997

Printed in the United States of America

Typography and Layout: Pam Campbell-Jones

Front cover art:
"Fire Wagon" by Paul Detlefsen
Art from the archives of Brown & Bigelow, Inc.

Back cover art:
Retired fire horses daydreaming of bygone days by an unknown artist, from the collection of Keith Franz.

The Steam Fire-Engine

"Behold! How she shines in her beauty,
    Resplendent in silver and gold;
Ne'er shrinking from doing her duty,
    When worked by her members so bold;
So peacefully-innocent standing,
    You'd dream not the work she can do;
But when we her aid are demanding,
    She always proves faithful and true.

"We look on her with admiration,
    Well knowing the work she can do;
She's full of life and animation;
    Her duty she seems to know, too;—
She saves us a deal of hard labor,
    Her muscles seem never to tire—
Admired by stranger and neighbor,
    Whene'er she's at work at a fire.

"Oh! dear shall she be to us ever;—
    For she's our companion and friend;
She does her work neatly and clever,
    And labors, with zeal, to the end;
The Steamer! We'll ever adore you;
    In praising you we never tire;
Hand-engines were nothing before you,
    Nor compared with you when at a fire."

(*Fireman's Herald*, March 9, 1882)

Critical Acclaim for W. Fred Conway's Works of Firefighting History

Firefighting Lore

"Overall this book offers an engaging style that is full of little-known facts about firefighting history. It is the kind of book that leaves its readers wanting to share the stories they have learned from Conway. Firefighters can thank W. Fred Conway for taking the time to pass all of them along."

— *Firehouse® Magazine*

"A pure delight to read."

—*The Visiting Fireman*

"This fascinating collection of 'strange but true' stories from firefighting history provides plenty of informative entertainment... a history lesson that's engrossing and fun."

—*9-1-1 Magazine*

Discovering America's Fire Museums

"W. Fred Conway has compiled one of the most helpful traveling companions a fire engine lover could want... it's an actual armchair tour... lots of fun reading. Serious collectors and appreciators of fire fighting history should grab this book!

—*Old Cars Weekly & Marketplace*

"The introduction contains a delightful history of firefighting along with the tools of the trade. Numerous sketches and drawings add both information and charm to the book."

—*Travel Books Worldwide*

"It's a great idea... a fun book... you'll enjoy it."

—*9-1-1 Magazine*

Chemical Fire Engines

"If ever a labor of true love were to need defining, I would commend the person in search of the definition to contact the author of this fine reference text. Mr. Conway's depth of knowledge, liberal use of period photos and drawings not to mention a wealth of original manufacturers' specifications, have come together in fine fashion... a welcome addition to the bookshelf of every serious fire science student and fire buff alike."

—*Harry R. Carter, Ph.D.,*
Columnist and
Fire Protection Consultant

"W. Fred Conway is obviously an avid aficionado of chemical fire engines and his interest and authority come through in this book. Whatever you want to know about this fascinating niche in fire history, it is here."

—*American Fire Journal*

"This book if full of well-researched unusual facts and stories, some of which surprised me. I highly recommend this hard-cover book."

—*Fire Service Digest*

Also by W. Fred Conway

Corydon – The Forgotten Battle of The Civil War

The Most Incredible Prison Escape of The Civil War

Young Abe Lincoln – His Teenage Years In Indiana

Squire – The Adventures of Daniel Boone's Kid Brother

Table of Contents

In 1890 this steamer was called into service at the corner of Free and Cotton Streets in Portland, Maine. The engineer keeps a close watch on the engine's gauges while the stoker feeds it coal.

Photo from the collection of Michael A. LaPlante

Acknowledgements

The eagerness with which America's firebuffing fraternity opened their files for this project has been extraordinary. "This book is long overdue – how can I help?" echoed from every corner of the land. In the mail from fellow fire buffs came rare pictures, catalogs, documents, shipping lists, and an almost priceless copy of the 1876 publication, *"Handbook Of Modern American Steam Fire Engines"* on loan from Richard Adelman, retired Chief of Training, Memphis, Tennessee, Fire Department.

Once the decision was made to tackle this project, the first step was a journey to Oak Ridge, Tennessee, where Tom Scott invited me to peruse his extensive library of fire-oriented books, which is probably the largest such library on the planet. Dr. Scott and his wife Janet graciously opened their home to me, and the material I gleaned on that trip really launched the book you now hold in your hands.

Many of the foremost steam fire engine experts in the country helped in many ways, including John Peckham, who reviewed the manuscript for flaws which I gladly corrected before publication. His own splendid book, *"Fighting Fire With Fire"* is highly recommended for additional reading. Although presently out of print, it is to be enlarged and reissued in the near future.

Other experts include Ken Peterson, Matt Lee, Ed Tufts, Mike LaPlante, Al Wills, Bill Schwartz, Stephen Heaver, Jr., Ken Soderbeck, and Andy Swift. Steamer research done by the late Harold Walker and John Robrecht will hopefully live on through these pages. David Lewis, *"The Little Fire Chief"* of the Fire Museum Network was, as always, extremely helpful and encouraging; and to Curator Nancy Kohnen of the Cincinnati Fire Museum goes credit for many of the facts surrounding that important chapter of steamer history which took place in that city.

Many fire buffs, fire department officials, and museum curators, too numerous to mention, had a vital part in the compilation of this book. But for their help, the book would not be nearly so complete.

Proofreader Evelyn Raymer's eagle eye caught the typos that eluded me.

Pam Campbell-Jones, who did the superb typesetting and layout for this book as well as some of my other books, has become hooked and is now a knowledgeable fire buff herself!

And, my sincere thanks to my wife, Betty, whose editing of the manuscript added a degree of professionalism beyond my capability.

Print from the collection of W. Fred Conway

Introduction

*L*et's turn back the clock for an entire century. Across America – in villages, towns and cities of all sizes are several thousand wheeled behemoths – complex machines weighing from two to eight tons, and requiring two or three large horses to pull them.

Ponderous though these machines may be, they are wondrous to behold, with their intricate brass, copper and nickel brightwork gleaming as they slumber in their firehouses ready to awaken at the first stroke of the gong signaling a fire alarm.

It is their duty, when awake, to pump with unfailing dependability the hundreds of thousands of gallons of water required by their masters to subdue the fires which might otherwise devastate the cities in which they serve. They are America's majestic steam fire engines.

Let's watch one of them as it suddenly awakens. While it has slept, hot water from a heater in the firehouse has circulated through the coils of its huge boiler. On the grate inside the boiler is – first, coal; next kindling wood; and on top of the kindling are kerosene-soaked rags. Asleep in their stalls in front of the engine are the well-trained fire horses, while upstairs the firemen, too, are asleep.

Suddenly, the first loud stroke of the firehouse gong shatters the stillness of the night. The horses, without a command other than the clanging of the gong, rise and back up to the engine as their collars descend from above to encircle their necks. Upstairs, the firemen swing their legs over the side of their bunks, step into their pants which are stuffed down into their boots, hitch their suspenders, and by the fifth stroke of the gong, they hit the brass pole and slide down to the apparatus floor below.

The engineer throws a lighted match into the door of the steamer's boiler and disconnects the water heater, as another fireman opens the firehouse door. The driver hitches up the horses and, then, climbs into his seat. He taps the horses with his whip, signaling them to begin their swift run out into the cool night air.

Anyone who might happen to be up at that hour, or who rouses to peer out of a window, will witness one of the most colorful displays of spontaneous pageantry in America's long standing romance with fire engines.

Two or three gallant steeds with nostrils flaring and flying hooves pounding the cobblestones pass in review as they pull the mighty steam fire engine with its boiler stack belching thick clouds of grey smoke from the fire in its innards that is raising the temperature of the water to the boiling point to produce the steam that will soon drive its powerful pump.

The loud bell on the engine clangs, and the steam whistle on the boiler shrieks its strident warning. The steamer carries no hose or ladders, only the pump; so, following close behind are the horse drawn hose reel and ladder wagon as well as the fire chief in his buggy. In larger cities, steamers from other firehouses are responding as well.

The cacophony of pounding hooves against the pavement, the clang of the bell, the shriek of the whistle, the clouds of smoke and sparks chuffing from the boiler stack, the engine's ornate kerosene main lamp and side lamps illuminating the polished brass fittings and copper air chamber – all combine to produce a thrilling spectacle never to be forgotten by anyone who sees it.

The author, although in his sixties, is not old enough to have witnessed the enthralling pageant just described, but his mother, born over a century ago, often described to him, when he was a child, the wondrous sight he himself has never seen. The very engine she watched is pictured on page 154.

Hopefully, this book will serve, in some measure, to recreate for us those magical moments when passing in review were those magnificent old steam fire engines.

W. Fred Conway
New Albany, Indiana
September, 1996

CHAPTER 1

"I'll Never Give Up!"

During September of 1852, Cincinnati brothers Alexander and "Moses" Latta as well as Abel Shawk had been receiving death threats. The small shop on Ohio Avenue where they labored on their invention had only one entrance, making it difficult for spies, saboteurs or assassins to enter undetected. But Moses Latta, alone in the shop, and engrossed in his work, failed to notice the stranger who had just entered and was staring at him.

The stranger beheld a short, spare, and stoop-shouldered little man totally oblivious to everything except the intensity of his work. Suddenly Moses Latta sensed the man's presence, turned, looked up from his work, and sternly demanded, "Did Mr. Greenwood give you permission to come in here?"

"He did," replied the stranger quickly. "He told me to come and see how the engine was getting on." "Ah! Very well," said the inventor. "Very well! My name is Latta, Moses Latta, and as you come from him, you shall see what few see. Can you in any way or to any extent understand the drawings on the wall?" The stanger confessed that he could not.

*"I'll never give up!
I'll build it, and there are
men enough in this city
to see that it has a fair trial,
and it shall have it.
When it is finished, it will
be heard from at the first fire,
and woe to those
who stand in its way."*

"Well, it is very simple. Let me explain. The engine is intended to throw, at any time, eight streams of water; four from each side, whenever the water can be obtained in sufficient quantity for that number. It is intended, of course, to take the engine to the scene of the fire with horses – about four. As the engine starts out, the furnace is fired up, and, ordinarily, by the time it would arrive at the fire, steam will be up and the engine ready for service. Eight of these large streams, forced out on a fire, with the pressure we shall be able to command, will drown any fire.

Even four of them, well directed, will be of wonderful value. But," added Mr. Latta, "the trouble is that there is no certainty that this, or any other steam fire engine, will ever be allowed to work at a fire.

You are probably not aware how bitter is the feeling of the volunteer firemen against this engine. They say it shall never throw a stream of water on a fire in this city; and I sometimes fear that I shall never live to see this grand idea brought into the service of the world. The recent riots here show what a mob can do in our city. My steps are dogged. Spies are continually on my track. I am worried with all sorts of anonymous communications threatening me with all sorts of ills and evils unless I drop work on this engine and pronounce it a failure."

The old man's eyes flashed as he said, "I'll never give up! I'll build it, and there are men enough in this city to see that it has a fair trial, and it shall have it. When it is finished, it will be heard from at the first fire, and woe to those who stand in its way."

Designing and constructing a new type of fire engine would seem like an innocent enough pursuit. Why the spies and death threats?

When organized firefighting took root in the American colonies during the previous century, the men who formed volunteer fire companies were the pillars of their communities – doctors, lawyers, bankers, merchants, clergymen, and

leading citizens who included men such as George Washington, Thomas Jefferson, John Hancock, Paul Revere, and Benjamin Franklin. Their sole purpose was to protect their own and their neighbors' property from fire.

But over the course of time, many volunteer firefighting organizations deteriorated to the point where they were comprised mainly of lower class citizens – rowdies, brawlers, drunks, and troublemakers. They often lost sight of the true reason for their companies to exist. Protecting property and extinguishing fires often became secondary to fighting and brawling with rival fire companies.

Such a sorry state of firefighting was prevalent in the early 1850's in Cincinnati, which had 14 hand engine companies, three hose companies, and a single hook and ladder company. Together, the membership approximated 1400 volunteers,

Courtesy of The Firefighting Museum of the Home Insurance Company.

If the streets were blocked or had ruts and mud holes that slowed them down, the volunteers would take to the sidewalk, bowling over pedestrians in the process.

Rival volunteer fire companies often gave priority to brawling rather than firefighting, which allowed many buildings, which they were charged with saving, to burn to the ground.

many of them rough and tough bullies who would sooner fight each other than the fires they were supposed to extinguish.

During November, 1851, a newspaper reporter, while walking down a Cincinnati street, heard cries of "Fire! Fire!" His story in the next day's edition enraged the citizenry, including the city council. Here's what the reporter saw:

The blaze turned out to be in a huge old planing mill at the corner of Augusta and John Streets. Firemen dashed to their firehouses, grabbed a section of drag rope, and hauled the little hand-operated pumpers over the cobbled streets as fast as their legs would carry them. Washington Fire Co. No. 1 raced northward from their engine house on Vine between Front and Columbia and began attaching their brass-riveted leather suction hose to the wooden fire plug at Augusta and John Streets. Just then, Western Hose Co. No. 3 arrived, following a mad dash southward from their fire hall on Fifth Street between Mound and Carroll.

The foreman from Western Hose loudly proclaimed that he had arrived before Washington and tried to prevent Washington from using the hydrant. The Washington foreman said his boys had arrived first. The argument soon escalated from shouts to fists and even to hurling bricks and bottles at each other. While all of this was going on, the fire in the planing mill was ignored.

As spectators watched, the flames spread from one end of the mill to the other, leaping defiantly in the air, and they felt the intense heat on their faces. The firemen, absorbed in their bloody brawl, seemed to neither see nor feel the flames and heat. The crowds hesitated to fight the fire themselves, fearing the firemen more than the fire itself. In fact, many spectators retreated to maintain a safe distance from the brawling firemen.

A second alarm brought two more volunteer companies to the scene, but instead of fighting the fire, they, too, promptly joined the mayhem. Soon the brawl escalated into a full scale riot. Third and fourth alarms were sounded, and soon ten volunteer fire companies were on the scene fighting – not the fire but each other. Not one drop of water had yet touched the fire, which was growing to immense proportions.

Next, a general alarm was sounded, bringing in the fire department from Covington, Kentucky, located on the other side of the Ohio River. Could Covington firemen fight the fire while the Cincinniti firemen fought each other? No! The Covington men, arriving on the ferryboat with their engine, took sides with Washington Hose and joined the fistfights.

Finally, Cincinnati's mayor Mark P. Taylor, attempted to end the riot, but his efforts had no effect. The firemen fought all night long, and when dawn came they were too exhausted to fight any longer. The planing mill, meanwhile, had burned to the ground.

The City Council called a special meeting, as citizens clamored for reforms to control the rowdiness of the volunteer firemen. Councilman Piatt opined that "The engine houses have simply become a place for gangs of political parasites to loaf." Councilman Miles Greenwood, himself a veteran volunteer fireman, called Cincinnati's fire companies a "nursery where the youth of this city are trained in vice, vulgarity, and debauchery."

Miles Greenwood, Cincinnati's first paid fire chief, who was the mentor of steam fire engine inventors Abel Shawk and the Latta brothers.

Councilman Joe Ross joined Piatt, Greenwood, and others in proposing a department of paid firefighters to replace the disgraceful volunteers. Yet, since it required 20 to 30 men to operate a single hand engine, of which there were 14, there seemed no way to budget for all of the paid replacements which would be required. But Miles Greenwood knew something that the others didn't.

When he proposed that Cincinnati devise a method of extinguishing fires "without the attendance of the large numbers of men required to operate manual pumping engines," he was well aware of the work Abel Shawk was doing behind closed doors because he had rented Shawk space in his foundry to do his research. Shawk was experimenting with a boiler for a steam fire engine that would require only two men to operate and would pump as much water as several hand engines combined. Miles Greenwood had faith in the idea, and he was ready to push it as hard as he could.

Abel Shawk realized that the key to a successful steam fire engine would be a boiler that could get up steam quickly. Three decades earlier, in Louisville, Kentucky, Dr. Joseph Buchanan had invented and patented a system of spiraling copper tubes, which when preheated, could have cold water injected inside of them with resultant rapid steam. Dr. Buchanan died ten years later, assuming his invention was a failure. But Shawk found an old Buchanan boiler and rented space in Miles Greenwood's Eagle Foundry to experiment with it.

Shawk was able to improve the Buchanan coils to the extent that he filed and received a patent. Greenwood followed his work closely, and realizing that a single steam fire engine could replace several hand engines along with the rowdy volunteers who operated them, he persuaded the City Council to appropriate the sum of $1000 for Shawk to build a prototype for actual testing.

Shawk's forté was the boiler with its coils, but he was not proficient with the steam engines and pumps which would be an integral part of the machine. But, residing in Covington, Kentucky, just across the Ohio River from Cincinnati, were two steam experts. In fact, the Latta brothers had designed and built the first steam railroad locomotive west of the Allegheny Mountains. Soon Latta's shop provided the steam cylinders, steam chests, and all the other necessary components for the prototype fire engine.

But as word of the project leaked out to the volunteer firemen, the death threats began, and Miles Greenwood moved Shawk and Latta, for their protection, to the small shop which had a single door. The inventors worked diligently, obsessed with producing a prototype which would lead to an actual working steam fire engine. They succeeded. During March, 1852, they demonstrated their prototype before the City

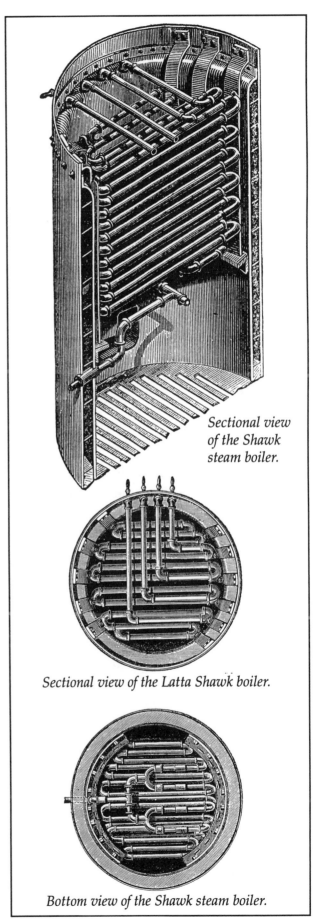

Sectional view of the Shawk steam boiler.

Sectional view of the Latta Shawk boiler.

Bottom view of the Shawk steam boiler.

One of the 14 Cincinnati hand fire engines in use in 1851. Using 30 men on the handles, it could pump up to 160 gallons per minute. Each of the 14 fire companies averaged a membership of 100 firefighters.

Council, as well as 3000 citizens who turned out for the event. The results of the test exceeded all expectations, including those of even the inventors themselves.

From the time a match lit the fuel at the bottom of the boiler, and with only cold water in the coils, steam was generated in four minutes and ten seconds – much faster than even the newest locomotives and riverboats. Within another 50 seconds, water was spurting from the nozzle at the end of 350 feet of fire hose. The City Council was convinced.

Latta and Shawk figured it would take $10,000 to build an actual steam fire engine. Cincinnati city fire engineer Richard Bray promptly pledged $5000 out of his own pocket for the project. Councilman "Uncle" Joe Ross persuaded the council to appropriate the other $5000. A machine that could revolutionize firefighting, not only in Cincinnati and the United States, but throughout the entire world, was in the incubator and on its way to being hatched.

16

Nine months later, on December 22, 1852, the Latta & Shawk engine was ready for a public demonstation. It threw a stream of water, from a huge nozzle 1-1/2 inches in diameter, to the incredible distance of 225 feet. Then, to demonstrate the new engine's superiority, a contest was arranged on January second with the volunteers and their hand engines.

The volunteers showed up with the most powerful hand fire engine in Cincinnati and pumped their hearts out to no avail. Soon six hose lines were connected to the steamer, which shot the water a distance of 175 feet. Next, when three of the hoses were disconnected, the remaining three hoses each sent their powerful streams over the roof of the four-story Broadway Hotel as the shocked volunteers watched in numbed silence. They were unable to throw a single stream as far or as high, so they quietly withdrew in disgrace.

Said Miles Greenwood of the new steam fire engine, "First, it never gets drunk; second, it never throws brickbats, and the only drawback connected with it is that it can't vote." On the spot he recommended that the city purchase the engine and that it be named the *Uncle Joe Ross* for his fellow councilman who had championed its construction, even though Richard Bray had donated $5000. No doubt there was a political motivation. Bray demoted himself from city fire engineer to fire captain, and Miles Greenwood himself was appointed to be the first fire chief of the new paid department to be organized to man the *Uncle Joe Ross*. But troubles with Cincinnati's fire department were far from over.

The volunteers didn't fade away into the sunset. They plotted to destroy the new steamer and, in so doing, resorted to the very demon they were obliged to extinguish – fire. Unfortunately the new paid department was not yet operational, with no driver

"First, it never gets drunk; second, it never throws brickbats, and the only drawback is that it can't vote."

having been hired for the four horses required to pull the ponderous *Uncle Joe Ross*, which weighed in at an incredible twelve and a half tons. It was stored at Miles Greenwood's foundry.

One of the workers in the foundry had a brother named Larry, who was in the teamster (horse-driving) business in Vermont. Larry arrived in Cincinnati on a Saturday evening in February to visit his brother, and what happened the next morning is recounted in Larry's own words:

"Yes sir. I drove the team that hauled the first steam fire engine ever built to the first fire on which streams were played by steam power. I'll tell you how it was. My brother worked in Miles Greenwood's foundry in Cincinnati, and I lived at Island Pond,

The "Uncle Joe Ross," America's first successful steam fire engine.

Vermont, and in May, 1852, I believe, I went to Cincinnati to see him, arriving there Saturday evening. We were on our way to church Sunday morning when the fire bells struck. My brother said, 'Now we'll see what they will do with the steam machine,' and we started for Miles Greenwood's shop, where the steam fire engine was.

It was built by Greenwood, the first ever on wheels. There the engine stood, steam up, four large grey horses hitched to it, a crowd looking at it, and Greenwood as mad as the devil because he couldn't get a man to drive the horses. You see, all the firemen were opposed to this new invention because they believed it would spoil their fun, and nobody wanted to be stoned by them, and then the horses were kicking about so that everybody was afraid on that account. My brother says, 'Larry, you can drive these horses, I know.' And Greenwood said, 'If you can, I wish you would. I'll pay you for it.'

My business was teaming, you see. And just as I was, with my Sunday clothes on, I jumped on the back of a wheel horse, seized the rein, spoke to the horses, and out we went kiting. Miles Greenwood went ahead, telling the people to get out of the way – the streets were full of people. The horses went on a fast run nearly all the way, and when we got to the fire we took suction from the canal and played two streams on the building, a large frame house, and put the fire out.

That was the biggest crowd I ever saw in my life, and the people yelled and shouted, while some of the firemen who stood around the hand fire engines jeered and groaned. After the fire was out, Greenwood put on two more streams and four were played. Then the city hired me to drive the four-horse team with the steamer, paying me seventy-five dollars a month. It was a great, long, wide affair, with a tall, heavy boiler – it was bigger than this room and run [sic] on three wheels, two behind and one in front to guide it.

After a few weeks a fellow offered to do my work for fifty dollars a month, and they turned me off and hired him. The second fire he drove to he was run over and killed."

Larry left out part of the story. After the hoses were stretched and the Uncle Joe Ross was pumping water onto the fire, a cry rang out, "The hose is cut!" The volunteer firemen arsonists and saboteurs having disabled the steamer, next tried to disable its operators, but this time the crowd was not afraid to act. They quickly subdued the volunteers, and new hoses were connected to the steamer, which went on to drown out the fire. The City Council voted to abolish the volunteer fire companies, and the new fire department was officially established with paid, trained professional firefighters.

Thanks to Abel Shawk, the Latta brothers, Richard Bray, Uncle Joe Ross, Miles Greenwood and others, including the volunteers whose disgraceful conduct led to their own demise, a new age of firefighting was born as Cincinnati became not only the first all paid fire department in the United States, but the first all steam fire department in the world.

➤➤◄◄

Note: "Moses" was evidently a nickname for one of the Latta brothers. The story of "Moses" and the stranger first appeared in an 1897 book, and has often been repeated although its authenticity has been questioned.

Note: By way of comparison, Cincinnati's most powerful hand engine, using 30 men, could pump 160 gallons per minute. The *Uncle Joe Ross* with only two men – a driver and an engineer – could pump 1000 gallons per minute. This equates to about 5 gallons per minute per man for the hand engine, and 500 gallons per minute per man for the steamer – an increase in efficiency of 100 to 1!

Note: The *Uncle Joe Ross* was the first *successful* steam fire engine, but others had been constructed and/or designed previously: George Braithwaite in London, England in 1829; P.R. Hodge in New York City in 1840; and John Ericsson, who designed the Civil War vessel *Monitor*, designed a steam fire engine in 1841 which was never built. William L. Lay of Philadelphia designed a steam fire engine in 1851 which was also never built.

CHAPTER 2

A New Industry Prospers

$\mathcal{T}$he initial development and use of steam fire engines in the Queen City of Cincinnati did not by any means bring to a close Cincinnati's involvement with these marvelous firefighting machines – far from it. From the *Uncle Joe Ross* in 1852 until the last Ahrens-Fox was built in 1916, the succession of steamer manufacturers in Cincinnati turned out one in every five of the 5000 steamers manufactured in America.

The evolution of Cincinnati steamers and steamer manufacturers is somewhat complex, but hopefully the following chronology will untangle the knot.

In 1854, after Abel Shawk and the Lattas had received the final payment for the *Uncle Joe Ross*, they failed to agree on the design for their next engine, so they parted company and went their separate ways. The Lattas built 30 more steamers. Then, in 1863, they sold their patents to the firm of Lane & Bodley.

Meanwhile, Abel Shawk's new company, "Young America," brought out reliable light weight steamers, but after building only five of them, the company folded.

In 1902 the American Fire Engine Company merged with still another steamer manufacturer, LaFrance, to form the most celebrated name in fire apparatus — American LaFrance.

Lane & Bodley, who had bought out the Lattas, hired one of their apprentices, a young German immigrant named Chris Ahrens, to become their factory superintendent. Young Ahrens, just 18 years of age, was destined to become one of the most famous names in the manufacture of fire apparatus – not only in building steamers but subsequent motorized engines as well.

Ahrens, who also had joined the Cincinnati Fire Department, guided Lane and Bodley into building steamers with steel rather than iron frames, which greatly reduced their weight. Yet, these engines were still, like the original *Uncle Joe Ross*, self-propelled by the steam, and horses were required to assist in getting them to the fire.

In 1867 Lane and Bodley, fearing the intense competition of some ten other steamer manufacturers that were springing up throughout the east, decided to spin off their fire engine division and concentrate on their core products for sawmills. Their fire engine patents were purchased by none other than Chris Ahrens.

The C. Ahrens Fire Engine Company eliminated the cum-

A.B. & E. LATTA

The original and only successful
STEAM FIRE ENGINE BUILDERS.
BUCKEYE WORKS, CINCINNATI, O.

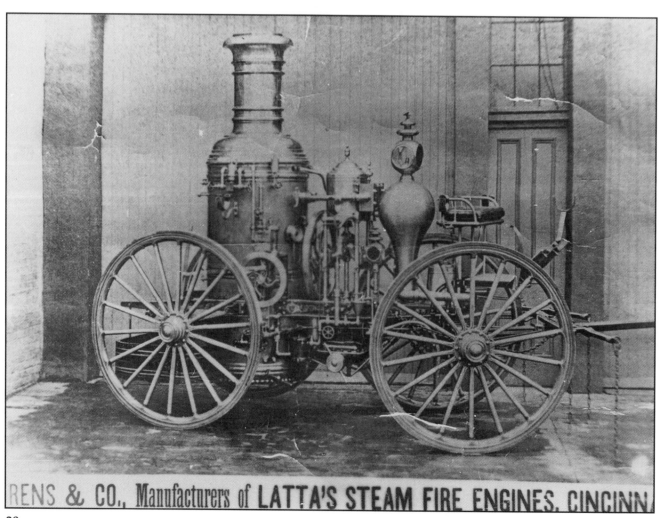

RENS & CO., Manufacturers of LATTA'S STEAM FIRE ENGINES, CINCINN

A Lane & Bodley Engine.

Photo from the Collection of W. Fred Conway.

bersome self-propeller gear, and added a fourth wheel rather than following the Latta three-wheel design. Ahrens advertised his engines as "Improved Latta Engines."

During the next eight years, Ahrens pursued a dual career as a Cincinnati city fireman and a fire engine manufacturer, but in 1875 he resigned from the fire department, renamed his firm "Ahrens Manufacturing Co.," and resolved to become America's premier fire engine manufacturer. With aggressive marketing, his business grew and thrived. Chicago, Louisville, and St. Louis, as well as Cincinnati, were but a few of the large midwestern cities protected from fire by Ahrens steamers.

For 16 years Ahrens dominated the midwest market, while back east, competitors Silsby, Amoskeag, Clapp & Jones and Button dominated the market. Then, in 1891, Chris Ahrens received an offer he could not refuse.

A group of businessmen saw an opportunity to corner the entire market for steamers in the United States by merging Ahrens, Silsby, Clapp & Jones, and Button to form the "American Fire Engine Company" with Chris Aherns offered the presidency of the consortium.

Ahrens accepted the offer, and the resultant consolidation closed all of the manufacturing plants except Ahrens in Cincinnati and Silsby in

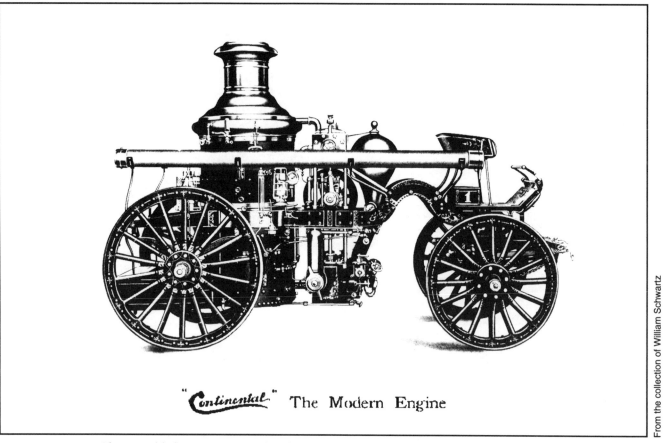

"*Continental*" The Modern Engine

Above and below are pages taken from an Ahrens Fire Engine Company catalog.

FLEXIBILITY FOR THE ROAD AND RIGIDITY FOR ACTION—both are desirable in a steam fire engine. Each taken alone is quite simple. In the "CONTINENTAL" we find the two successfully combined.

We illustrate the "Improved Ahrens Equalizing Front Gear." Embracing the best features of the ordinary "platform gear," the further advantages of a "Three Point Mounting" are also afforded.

In effect, the Equalizing Gear permits the pumping machinery to maintain its alignment with the boiler in a natural and unrestrained manner. The four wheels follow the surface of the road quite independently, and—over humps and through ruts—no twisting stresses are transmitted to the main frames. It follows therefore that the engine mechanism which is mounted thereon is effectually shielded from strain.

THE CONTINENTAL "RIDES" WITH WONDERFUL EASE, YET NO STEAMER STANDS MORE FIRMLY WHEN WORKING AT MAXIMUM SPEED.

Page 35

Seneca Falls, New York. In these two plants, all four brands of engines were manufactured. Chris Ahrens was now able to bring into the business his two sons, George and John, as well as his son-in-law, Charles Fox. The Fox name was also destined to become part of the legend.

The evolution continued. In 1902 the American Fire Engine Company merged with still another steamer manufacturer, LaFrance, to form the most celebrated name in fire apparatus – American-LaFrance.

By this time, however, Chris Ahrens was ready to retire. His sons George and John, along with their brother-in-law, Charles Fox, withdrew from the American-LaFrance combine and formed Ahrens Fire Engine Company. They continued to manufacture steamers in Cincinnati under the brand name "Continental."

In 1898 Ahrens introduced the "Metropolitan" model, which was the "Cadillac" of steamers. With 421 feet of 1-1/4" tubing inside the Metropolitan boiler, the water could be brought to a boil from a cold start within an incredible two minutes. When a Metropolitan was delivered to

Springfield, Missouri, in 1903, *The Springfield Republican* reported "That the engine throws water high enough for any fire in Springfield is evident from the fact that the stream was thrown from the square over the National Exchange bank building; over the Heer dry goods company; across Olive Street and down upon the roof of the building occupied by the Mint Saloon." The stream was calculated to have been 210 feet high. The engine remained in active service in Springfield well into the 1930's.

Some 144 Metropolitans were built until the final one was constructed in 1917, as America's fire departments began the vast transition from steam to gasoline. Correctly forecasting the new trend, John Ahrens and Charles Fox had, in 1911, designed a new line of eminently successful motorized fire engines. Again the company was reorganized and renamed Ahrens-Fox, another of the most celebrated names in fire apparatus.

The company remained in business until 1958, when its demise spelled the end of Cincinnati's proud history as a fire engine manufacturing center. Some 987 steamers had been produced in the Queen City over a span of 64 years.

THE

METROPOLITAN
STEAM
FIRE ENGINE

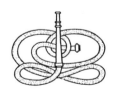

AMERICAN-LA FRANCE FIRE ENGINE CO.

ELMIRA, N.Y.

FACTORIES : ELMIRA· SENECA FALLS ·CINCINNATI

BRANCHES

NEW YORK· BOSTON ·BALTIMORE ·ATLANTA ·CHICAGO ·PORTLAND ORE. ·SAN FRANCISCO

COPYRIGHT, 1906, BY AMERICAN-LA FRANCE FIRE ENGINE CO.

A page taken from a Metropolitan Steam Fire Engine catalog.

Metropolitan Steam Fire Engine

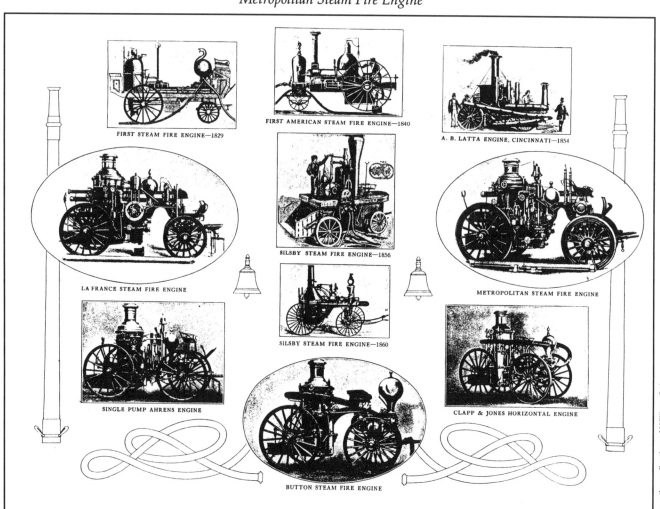

FIRST STEAM FIRE ENGINE—1829

FIRST AMERICAN STEAM FIRE ENGINE—1840

A. B. LATTA ENGINE, CINCINNATI—1854

LA FRANCE STEAM FIRE ENGINE

SILSBY STEAM FIRE ENGINE—1856

METROPOLITAN STEAM FIRE ENGINE

SINGLE PUMP AHRENS ENGINE

SILSBY STEAM FIRE ENGINE—1860

CLAPP & JONES HORIZONTAL ENGINE

BUTTON STEAM FIRE ENGINE

Both photo and artwork above are taken from a rare Metropolitan Steam Fire Engine catalog.

CHAPTER 3

Two Steamers Named Sherman

By 1871, nearly two decades after the invention of the Uncle Joe Ross, all of America's principal cities were protected by steamers, with about 1400 of the engines in use nationwide. But not all of these were in major cities. Smaller cities, towns, and, in some instances, even villages enjoyed the superior fire protection offered by steam fire engines.

This chapter will contrast a steamer in one of America's largest cities with its country cousin that protected a small village some 700 miles away. These two engines have been chosen because they shared the same name.

It was common practice for steam fire engines to be given proper names, just as ships are christened and named. Steamers were named for mayors, political figures, famous persons, cities, Indian tribes, or for their perceived firefighting ability. The first of the two engines in our story was named not for Civil War General Sherman but for his brother, Frank, a Chicago notable.

Realizing early on that his fire department with its 15 working steamers was not equal to controlling the raging conflagration, Mayor Mason sent the following telegrams: CHICAGO IS IN FLAMES. SEND YOUR WHOLE DEPARTMENT TO HELP US.

The *Frank Sherman*, an 1864 first size Amoskeag, was one of 15 steamers protecting Chicago, Illinois, on October 8, 1871. Of Chicago's 17 steamers, two were out of service for repairs, and some of the rest were very tired – long past due to be overhauled. Of course, the Chicago Fire Department in 1871 consisted of only paid firemen – 185 of them, but some of them were out sick on that fateful night. It was up to about 150 men with 15 steamers to protect an area of 18 square miles, encompassing a population of around 300,000.

The previous evening a traveling author and lecturer, George Francis Train, in addressing a crowd at Chicago's Farwell Hall, made an incredible prediction:

"This is the last public address that will be delivered within these walls," he declared. "A terrible calamity is impending over the City of Chicago. More I cannot say. More I dare not utter."

Whether Train feared a conflagration or some other calamity or pestilence is unknown. The *Chicago Times* termed him "The Prince of Blatherskites." But blatherskite or not, within the next 72 hours the Chicago Times building, along with Farwell Hall and 17,000 other stuctures, had burned to the ground. Over 300 persons had perished in the flames.

The same day as Train's speech, Chicago firemen had been run ragged and had fought a mill fire for 17 hours. There had been scarcely any rain for 14 weeks.

The next day, at about 8:30 p.m., 35-year-old Catherine O'Leary, who lived with her husband and children in a cottage on Chicago's west side, carried a lantern to the small barn back of her cottage to milk her cow. Setting the lantern on the

Mrs. O'Leary's neighbors had formed a bucket brigade to fight the fire, but no one had thought to alert the fire department.

barn floor, she began her milking when, for reasons unknown, the cow let loose with its right hind foot, which connected with the lantern. The fire which resulted soon engulfed the barn in flames.

In the third floor fire dispatching center at the Courthouse a mile to the northwest, Fire Alarm Dispatcher William J. Brown was busy playing his guitar for his sister Sarah and her friend Martha Dailey. Sarah noticed a glow to the southeast, but Brown continued to play his guitar, assuming it was but a rekindle of the previous fire and of no importance.

Meanwhile, Mrs. O'Leary's neighbors had formed a bucket brigade to fight the fire, but no one had thought to alert the fire department. Fi-

Thousands fleeing the conflagration clogged the city's bridges.

As the fire spread out of control, Chicagoans stuffed bags with personal belongings and fled in terror.

nally William Lee ran past a nearby fire alarm box all the way to Box 296 three blocks away. It was locked. In those days all fire alarm boxes were kept locked to discourage false alarms. Lee got the key from the corner druggist, unlocked the box, and pulled the lever. It was now 9:05 p.m.

Fire Dispatcher Willam Brown kept on strumming his guitar. Somehow the alarm didn't get through. No lights flashed, no bells rang — only the melodious strains of the guitar filled the alarm room.

At 9:21 p.m., nearly an hour after the fire started, with the glow on Chicago's night sky getting ever brighter, a watchman screamed at Dispatcher Brown, "Strike Box 342!" Brown obeyed, but Box 342 was more than a mile south

of the fire. Three engines, two hose wagons, and two hook and ladders turned out — all heading in the wrong direction.

Realizing he had given the wrong location, the watchman again screamed at guitar-strumming Brown to strike the correct box, but this time Brown refused. He felt it would only compound the confusion.

Someone again pulled Box 296. Obviously it was out of order — no alarm was received by Brown, who by this time had laid his guitar aside, realizing that he had a big problem. He took it upon himself to strike a second alarm, followed by a third alarm, and then a general alarm, calling out the entire Chicago Fire Department.

One of the first steamers finally to respond to the long-delayed and confused alarm was the *Frank Sherman*. But the *Sherman*, like the other 14 which fought the fire, could not prevail against the overwhelming odds. They kept retreating and repositioning themselves until they finally ran out of city and ended up at the docks on Lake Michigan. With the steamers constantly changing locations and with their stacks spewing smoke, sparks, and cinders, the story was told of two Irishmen, newly arrived in the United States, who were spending the night in a Chicago hotel.

Awakened by the commotion, one of them peered out the windows as two steamers dashed by. "Pat, wake up!' he shouted. "They're moving hell! Two loads have gone by already." Anyone in Chicago that fateful night could well have likened it to hell.

The *Frank Sherman* was positioned on Ewing Street on the northern border of the fire, but the fire began to eat back against the wind, endangering new areas to the south and west. The *Sherman*, aided by the *Long John*, couldn't hold its ground and moved south, attempting to halt the fire on its northern and eastern perimeters. But it had to keep retreating.

Fleeing from still another position on Taylor and Clinton Streets, it took up a position on Polk Street as the flames approached Ewing. As the situation deteriorated, the whiskers of stoker George Leady and engineer John Hohn were scorched, and the horses' legs were blistered.

Chicago's Little Giant *steamer pumping at the Chicago fire.*

When their hose began to smoke, they fled down Polk Street toward the river.

They ended their flight of terror out on the Goodrich Docks at Michigan Avenue, where the street ended at the river. George Leady, the stoker, was on the dock when the water supply failed. Only he and fireman Johnny Reis were left. When the smoke became unbearable, Leady and Reis jumped aboard the *Sherman*, and its four horses pulled them to safety. Finally they reached an area of relative safety, dropped the suction hose into Lake Michigan, and supplied water to wet down the smoldering ruins.

Lecturer Train's uncanny prediction had proved all too accurate – Chicago had just been wiped out.

Realizing early on that his fire department with its 15 working steamers was not equal to controlling the raging conflagration, Mayor Mason sent the following telegrams: CHICAGO IS IN FLAMES. SEND YOUR WHOLE DEPARTMENT TO HELP US. Special trains were quickly chartered to bring steamers and hose carts from Milwaukee, Cincinnati, Dayton, Louisville, Detroit, Port Huron, Bloomington, Springfield, Janesville, Allegheny, and Pittsburgh.

By coincidence, a delivery engineer, named Walker, who worked for the Clapp & Jones steam fire engine manufacturer of Hudson, New York, was in Chicago en route to Racine, Wisconsin, and Pentwater, Michigan with two brand new steamers. When he saw the fire, he decided to help without even being asked. A group of railroad employees under Walker's direction unloaded the steamers from a flat-car and placed them into action. They saved a grain elevator.

Just before 6:00 P.M. on October 9th a special train pulled into Chicago from Ohio. On it were three steamers from Cincinnati and one from Dayton. Soon Chicago Fire Chief Robert A. Williams felt a hand on his shoulder, and someone said, "Chief Williams, I've always wanted to meet you." The white-haired gentleman who had sought out Chief Williams was Cincinnati's fire chief, Miles Greenwood.

They shook hands firmly. Although the Chicago Fire Department never had, up until that time, purchased a steam fire engine manufactured in Cincinnati, Miles Greenwood was one of the first out-of-town fire chiefs to answer Chicago's desperate plea for assistance. But beginning in 1880, Chicago purchased no less than 124 steamers manufactured in Cincinnati.

Each year in the United States, Fire Prevention Week is observed during the week in October which marks the anniversary of the Great Chicago Fire.

> *"Chief Williams, I've always wanted to meet you." The white-haired gentleman who had sought out Chief Williams was Cincinnati's fire chief, Miles Greenwood.*

Three years later, 700 miles northeast of Chicago in upstate New York, the quiet village of Port Henry, nestled on the shore of Lake Champlain with a population of 1,401 was devastated by fire. Port Henry's hose reel and *"Little Giant"* chemical engine were no match for the flames that ravaged the business district, taking out the entire Van Ornam block along with the Lewald Store, the Mulkern Clothing Store, and Bien's Jewelry Store. In attempting to save the stock of the jewelry store, A.B. Huntley was burned to death.

Such a catastrophe must never occur again. Ordinarily a village as small as Port Henry could not afford a steam fire engine with accompanying hose cart and equipment – an expenditure of around $6,000, which is comparable to a quarter million dollars today. But two of Port Henry's leading citizens were well-to-do business partners – J.G. Witherbee and George Riley Sherman.

Witherbee built a water system for the village, and Sherman built a firehouse for a brand new fourth size Clapp and Jones steam fire engine. Although the village floated a bond issue, it is safe to assume that Mr. Sherman helped to underwrite the cost of the engine since on September 13, 1875, the Board of Trustees of the Village of Port Henry voted to name the new steamer the *"G.R. Sherman."*

In fact, the new engine company formed to man it was named the "G.R. Sherman Engine Co.," while the hose company became the "Witherbee Hose Co." It is interesting to note that Witherbee and Sherman brought a telephone sys-

The G.R. Sherman is shown in the engine house donated to the village of Port Henry, New York by its leading citizen – G.R. Sherman. This picture, taken about 1883, shows the men of the G.R. Sherman Engine Company. Could the man at the extreme right be G.R. Sherman himself?

Photo from the collection of the Port Henry Historical Society

tem to Port Henry as well and that these gentlemen had the first two bathtubs in the village.

On January 8, 1877, little more than a year after the arrival of the *G.R. Sherman*, fire again struck the village of Port Henry. The following story appeared in the local newspaper:

"A fire broke out in an uninhabited tenement owned by Pat McQuillan on 'Hog Alley' last Monday evening at half past six o'clock. A thick snow was falling and the wind, which had been blowing quite hard in the afternoon, was still blowing moderately. The fire alarm was at once sounded and the steamer brought out.

Owing to the great depth of the snow – three feet on level, and embanked still higher by the sidewalks – it was fully twenty minutes before Chief Engineer Wyman could impress sufficient help to get the steamer in position at the fountain in Witherbee's grounds, the nearest available source of water supply. The hose companies after floundering through the snow, laid about 1,000 feet of hose, and it was 30 minutes after the alarm sounded that two streams were brought to bear on the fire through two 1-3/4" nozzles.

By this time McQuillin's building had fallen in, and the entire gable end of the adjacent house was in flames. The nozzles being too large to throw effectively at the same time,* one was closed and the other at once brought a powerful stream to play over the entire burning gable, which speedily

...after 14 months of painstaking work by Andy Swift, the G.R. Sherman emerged in pristine condition, just as it would have appeared when it left the Clapp & Jones factory in 1875.

quenched the flames, leaving the main portion of the house intact."

In spite of the snow and the distance to the water supply, the *G.R. Sherman* had proved its worth – the Village of Port Henry had been saved. The *G.R. Sherman* continued to protect Port Henry for another 30 years.

But that's not quite the end of the *G.R. Sherman* story. Somehow it escaped the fate of most steamers – the scrap drives of World War II. Sometime after it was replaced by a motorized engine in 1917, it was sold to a gentlemen who stored it at the end of his fishing pier on Lake Champlain. Next, it was sold to a fire buff in New Jersey whose efforts to restore it floundered. Then, it went to an antique dealer in Florida whose restoration efforts also bogged down. Next it was purchased by the author of this book, who had it shipped to Firefly Resorations in Jonesport, Maine,** where, after 14 months of painstaking work by Andy Swift, the *G.R. Sherman* emerged in pristine condition, just as it would have appeared when it left the Clapp & Jones factory in 1875.

After being exhibited at the International Association of Fire Chiefs convention in Louisville, Kentucky, the steamer was delivered to its new home at the Conway Fire Museum in New Albany, Indiana, where it joined more than a dozen other hand and horse drawn fire engines on display.

---

* The *G.R. Sherman* was a small fourth size village engine rated at 500 gallons per minute. Pumping through 1000 feet of hose it could not be expected to supply two 1-3/4" nozzles. It acquitted itself well.

** Firefly Restorations is now located in Hope, Maine.

Photo from the collection of W. Fred Conway

At left:

For years the G.R. Sherman was stored at the end of a fishing pier on New York's Lake Champlain.

Below:

Restored during 1994 and 1995 by Andy Swift of Firefly Restorations, The G.R. Sherman is on display at the Conway Fire Museum, New Albany, IN.

Photo from the collection of W. Fred Conway

CHAPTER 4

How Did They Work?

*L*ittle more than a decade after the *Uncle Joe Ross* had been invented in Cincinnati, the Civil War ended, and the various manufacturers of steam fire engines (quite a few had jumped on the bandwagon) had pretty well settled on standard designs which were so efficient and reliable that there would be no major improvements for another half century.

That steamers were not difficult to operate is attested to by an article in the *Mount Desert Herald* (Bar Harbor, Maine) dated October 8, 1881, explaining how a group of men who had never before operated a steamer, fired up the town's newly acquired engine and saved a hotel:

"Last Tuesday night was the coldest we have had this fall. A northerly wind had been blowing a gale nearly all day, increasing in violence as night fell, and the evening was as cold, rough, and disagreeable as possible. At about 8:30 P.M. fire was discovered in the Hotel St.

"Old firemen who were present declared they had never seen a machine better handled, even by fully organized and experienced companies. It was the steamer which did the business, and even the doubtful ones of those present were ready to admit before the fire ended that the Steam Fire Engine was a success" ...

Sauvier. Water was thrown upon the fire from buckets, and hose attached to waterpipes, but without avail, and a general alarm was given. A company for the new steam fire engine had just been organized, but the needful arrangements for getting promptly to work had not yet been perfected. Nevertheless, by the aid of stout horses and willing hands, the big machine was very quickly got to work, and did noble service.

In less than fifteen minutes from the time the first alarm was given, flames were bursting through the roof, and it was apparent to any one the least conversant with fires that the handsome hotel was doomed to total destruction. The steamer was taken to the nearest reservoir, and a stream got on between the burning building and Lyman's Hotel, next west, the piazza of which was only twenty feet distant. The steamer is a first-class double engine built by Hunneman &

Co., of Boston. When she arrived here she was tested, under the direction of J.C. Hunneman and was accepted. Since that time she had not been handled by any one up to the night of the fire. The Company had not taken her in charge and nothing was in readiness for a fire. Thus the engine was in the worst possible condition for prompt service.

Nevertheless, within fifteen minutes from the time the first alarm was given, the engine had been taken from the house, run to the reservoir on Mount Deseert Street, a distance of some eighty rods, fired up, the hose attached, and she was playing on the fire, with a pressure of twenty-five pounds of steam, which was quickly run up to eighty, throwing water through a 1-1/2 inch nozzle, and thoroughly drenching the exposed buildings. She threw a stream completely over the highest portion of the Lyman Hotel. Old firemen who were present declared that they had never seen a machine better handled, even by fully organized and experienced companies. It was the steamer which did the business, and even the doubtful ones of those present were ready to admit before the fire ended that the Steam Fire Engine was a success, and had gone a good ways towards paying for itself on this one occasion. The fire was a fierce and quick one, and when at its height presented a sight of awful grandeur not soon to be forgotten."

The sixty years from 1853 to 1913 marked the heyday of steam fire engine manufacturing in the United States, with only a few built in 1914, 1915, and 1916 and the final one built in 1917.

The principal variations in the design of the steamers were the pumps: single piston, double piston, and rotary; the frames: straight, or crane neck, with variations; and the configuration of the tubes and/or coils within the boiler.

The sixty years from 1853 to 1913 marked the heyday of steam fire engine manufacturing in the United States, with only a few built in 1914, 1915, and 1916, and the final one built in 1917. By that time another revolution in fire engines was sweeping the country as cities and towns converted from steamers to motorized engines powered by gasoline.

But during the six decades of steam fire engine manufacture, more than 80 firms turned out around 5000 of them, of which some 80% were built by only eight manufacturers, each of whom accounted for 100 or more. Only one firm turned out more than 1000. The principal manufacturers, with their histories, are outlined in Chapter Six, as well as a list of all of them. Some companies built only one or two before folding or moving on to other pursuits.

It is surprising that so few persons today, including firefighters themselves, have even a basic understanding of how steam fire engines operated. The big vertical boiler on the back is a mystery, thought by many to be a tank of water with which to fight the fire. Not so – it's just a big hot water heater, not unlike the one in your home.

The boiler gets the water in or around its tubes and coils so hot that it produces steam, which is what drives the fire pump at the middle or front of the engine. The boiler was often sheathed in brass or nickel to help transform the engine from a mundane piece of machinery into a dazzling showpiece. Many fire companies spared no expense such as adding gold leaf trim and ornate lamps, to create a spectacle that would outclass the engines of neighboring or rival fire companies.

Another sometime mystery is the gleaming inverted-pear-shaped dome on many steamers which are often of polished copper. These domes are not tanks to hold extra water, nor are they, as one puzzled fireman postulated, a reservoir of oil for the engine lamps, atop of which the "main" lamp sits. It is really an air chamber which evens out the pulsations of water flow from the pistons driving the pump so that the water is discharged in a smooth steady stream rather than in intermittent spurts.

Here is an illustration: picture an old-fashioned automobile tire pump pumping air into a tire. The air goes into the tire in spurts – one spurt for each downstroke of the pump. But now, punch a hole in the tire, and a steady stream of air will come out, even if you continue pumping more air in, a spurt at a time.

The tire serves the same function as the air chamber on the steamer. Water coming into the engine, either under pressure from a fire hydrant or sucked up into the pump through a rigid hose dropped into a cistern, river, pond etc., is forced up into the air chamber, and, acting like the tire

The boiler was often sheathed in brass or nickel to help transform the engine from a mundane piece of machinery into a dazzling showpiece.

in our illustration, it compresses the air in the top of the chamber, which works as a shock absorber, evening out the flow of water through the fire hoses, even though the piston pump is pumping in spurts.

Village size engines often had a single piston, which could be either in a vertical or horizontal configuration. Larger engines usually had double pistons. Yet, many steamers were equipped with rotary, rather than piston pumps, and both types of pumps did an excellent job.

Regarding the different styles of frames, many smaller village size engines had straight frames, which restricted the turning radius of the front wheels so that they had difficulty rounding sharp turns. The crane neck frames allowed the front wheels to turn beneath an arch in the frame, allowing very tight turns when neccessary. Most larger engines were of the crane neck style. There were variations of these styles, such as the "U" or the harp, but they were rare.

In summary, the fire in the boiler heated the water in or around the boiler tubes or coils, turning it into steam to power the piston or rotary fire pump. A pear-shaped air chamber evened out the pulsations of the piston to produce an even flow of water through the fire hose and out of the nozzle onto the fire.

The following drawings and diagrams depict the various styles of pumps, frames, and boilers, and will enable the reader to envision the operation of steam fire engines.

STEAM PISTON PUMPS

Single Piston Pump in Vertical Position
Third Size Steamer

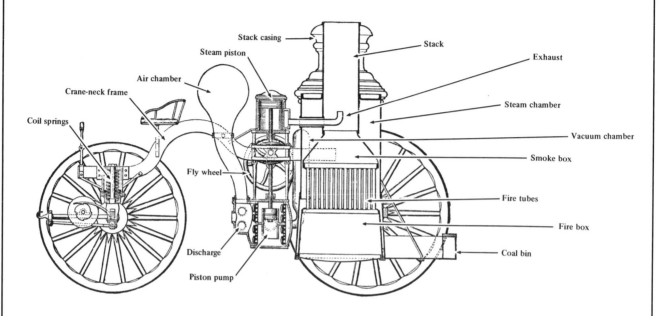

Stack casing · Stack · Exhaust · Steam piston · Steam chamber · Air chamber · Vacuum chamber · Crane-neck frame · Smoke box · Coil springs · Fire tubes · Fly wheel · Fire box · Discharge · Coal bin · Piston pump

Single Piston Pump in Horizontal Position
Second Size Steamer

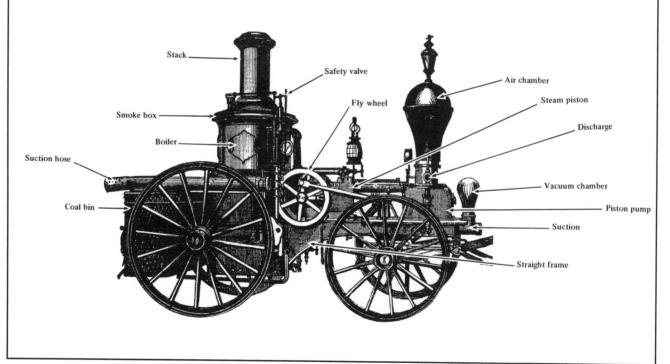

Stack · Safety valve · Air chamber · Fly wheel · Steam piston · Smoke box · Discharge · Boiler · Suction hose · Vacuum chamber · Coal bin · Piston pump · Suction · Straight frame

Double Vertical Piston Pumps

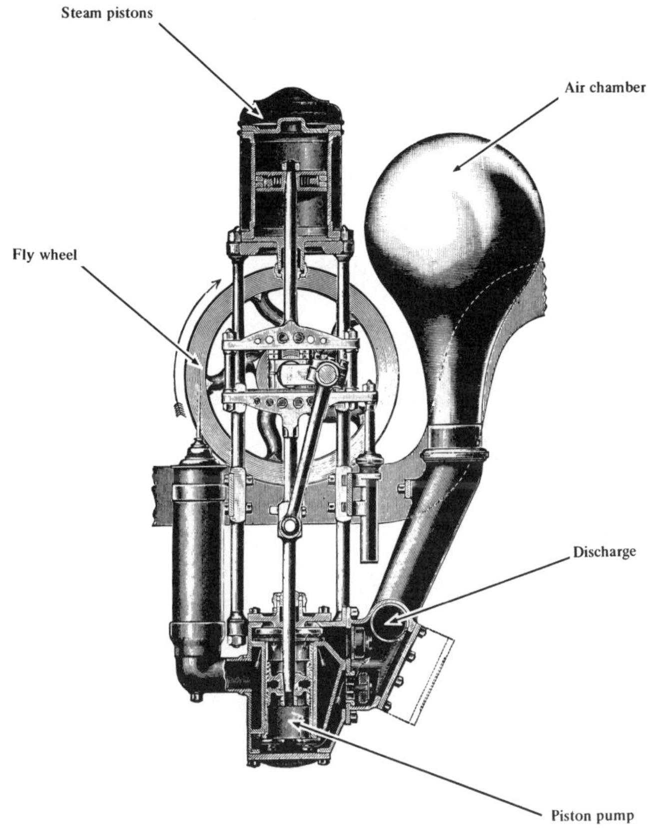

Steam pistons

Air chamber

Fly wheel

Discharge

Piston pump

Side View

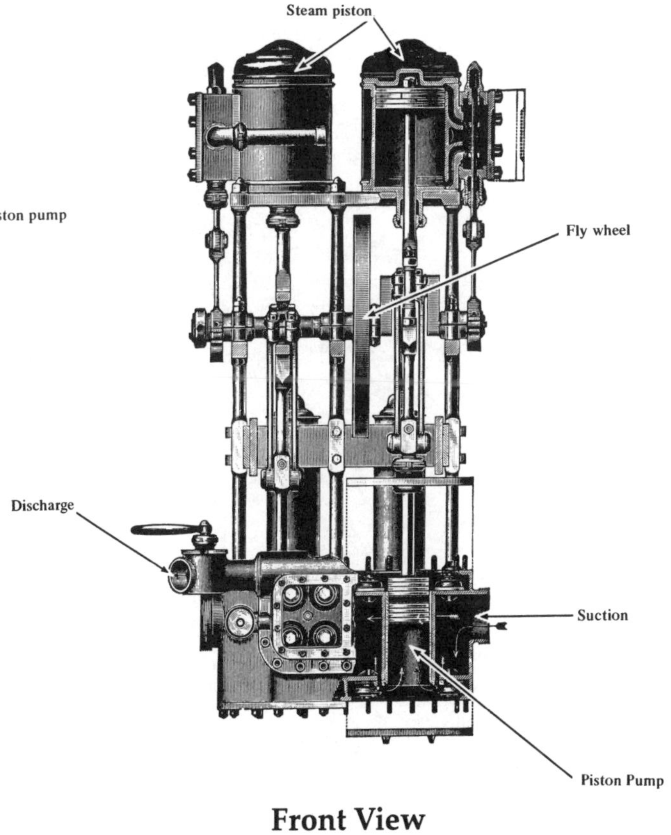

Steam piston

Fly wheel

Discharge

Suction

Piston Pump

Front View

Hotizontal Rotary Pump

Crane Neck Frame

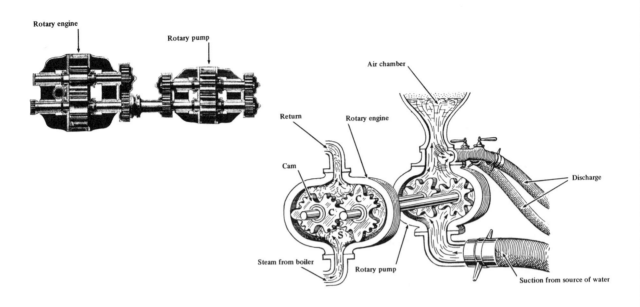

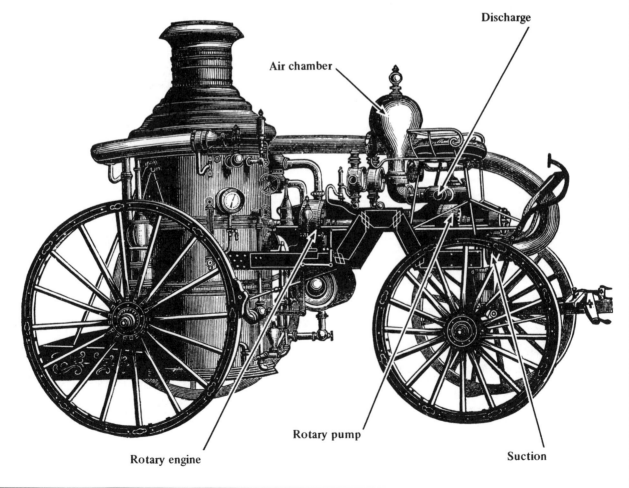

Horizontal Rotary Pump

Straight Frame

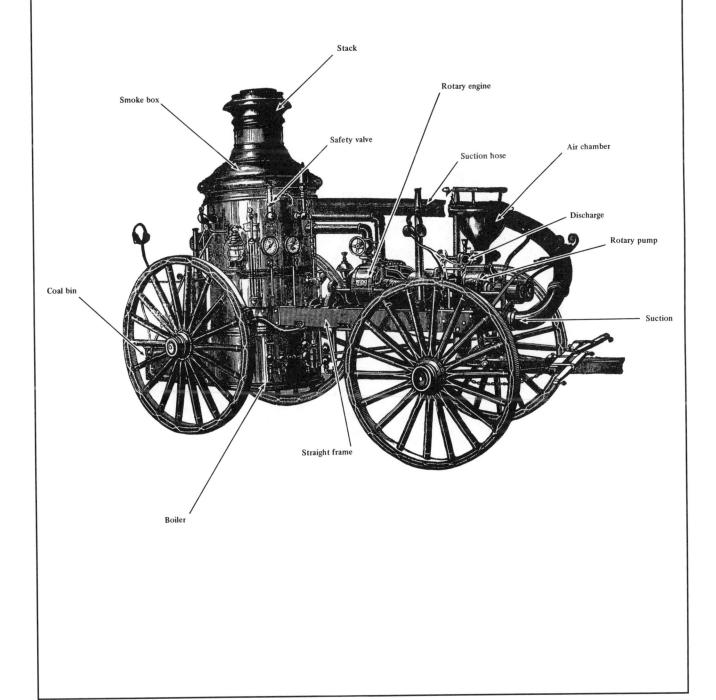

Stack

Rotary engine

Smoke box

Safety valve

Suction hose

Air chamber

Discharge

Rotary pump

Coal bin

Suction

Straight frame

Boiler

Types of Boilers

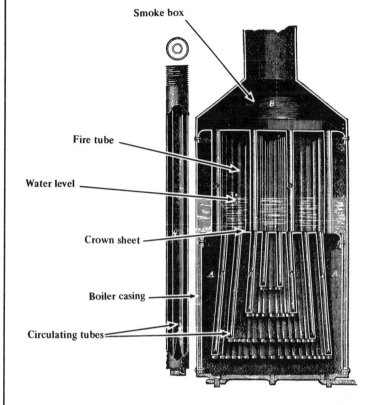

Smoke box

Fire tube

Water level

Crown sheet

Boiler casing

Circulating tubes

Fire Tube Boiler

Water Tube Boiler

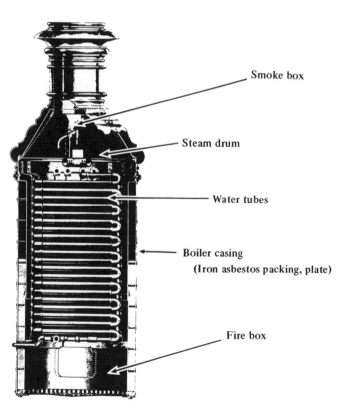

Smoke box

Steam drum

Water tubes

Boiler casing
(Iron asbestos packing, plate)

Fire box

SIZES OR CLASSES OF STEAM FIRE ENGINES

Not until 1906, as the age of steam fire engine manufacture was close to the end, did the various manufacturers finally agree on the standardization of engine sizes or classes (the two terms are used interchangebly). So, for the first fifty years of the steam fire engine era, one manufacturer's "first size" engine might be rated at 950 gallons per minute of pumping capacity, while the first size of his competitor might be rated at only 800 gallons per minute. Comparing engine pumping capacity by size or class was difficult, because it was not a case of comparing "apples to apples."

To illustrate this, the engine capacities of four of the leading manufacturers are compared in the following chart.

The figures, which were often exaggerated, are from manufacturers' literature.

To show the vast difference in size between the biggest – the double extra first size Amoskeag, weighing 17,000 pounds, and the smallest – the tiny (by comparison) American-LaFrance Cosmopolitan model weighing only 1,500 pounds, the two models are pictured on the following page.

Size	Ahrens	Amoskeag	LaFrance	Silsby
Double extra first	1,000	1,350	—	—
Extra first size	900	1,100	1,100	1,100
First size	800	900	900	950
Second size	700	700	750	800
Third size	600	550	650	700
Fourth size	500	350	550	600
Fifth size	400	—	450	500
Sixth size	300	—	375	400
(Pump output in gallons of water per minute)				

The biggest — Double extra first size Amoskeag. Self-propelled. Weight 17,000 pounds.
Note the fire alarm box on a pedestal with lamp atop at the right of the engine.

The smallest — Sixth size American-LaFrance Cosmopolitan. Weight 1,500 pounds.

CHAPTER 5

Steamers In Action

$\mathcal{B}$y the end of the Civil War, the manufacture of steam fire engines was in full swing, but photography was still in its infancy. Although posed pictures of early steamers with their crews are found in the archives of many fire departments, pictures of steamers actually responding to and fighting fires are rare.

But, with the kind assistance of fire historians, fire chiefs, and fire buffs throughout the United States, a number of these photographs have been assembled to present this picture gallery of steamers in action.

This photo of Ft. Wayne, Indiana, steamer No. 1 was taken Sunday, May 3, 1908.

The Aveline Hotel Fire in Fort Wayne, Indiana on Sunday, May 3, 1908. Eleven people perished.

Photo from the collection of the Fort Wayne Fire Museum

The locale of this steamer in action is unknown.

Photo from the collection of Jay McGuire

Photo from the collection of Matt Lee

This 1914 blaze at the Federal Electric Sign System Company in Detroit went to three alarms before being brought under control. The fire occurred at 63 State Street near Washington Boulevard and shown in the photograph is a mixture of horsepower and gasoline propelled apparatus. In front of the building is an American-LaFrance engine working two lines under a full head of steam.

Photo from the collection of Matt Lee

Note both the smoke and steam eminating from this steamer. The location is unknown.

Photo from the collection of Matt Lee

Engine No. 22. Buffalo, New York.

Photo from the collection of Matt Lee

This Detroit steamer appears to be producing more smoke than the fire itself. Note the bags of coal behind the steamer.

47

Engine No. 1 on the run in Milwaukee in 1910.

Engine No. 20 on the run in Milwaukee. Note the dog chasing the steamer.

A Portland, Maine Amoskeag working at a block fire in Freeport, Maine, 1908.

Photo from the collection of Michael A. LaPlante

Photo from the collection of Boston Sparks Association

At left:

In January, 1898, Engine Company 35 of Boston got this self-propelled steamer, which was built by the Manchester Locomotive Works, successor to Amoskeag.

Below:

A Milwaukee steamer in action. Note the pile of coal, ready for use at the five alarm fire.

A 1902 theatre fire in Portland, Maine.

Photo from the collection of FDNY

At left:

An American-LaFrance steamer pumping from a hydrant at a New York fire.

Photo from the collection of Michael A. LaPlante

These steamers are all drawing from a slip to fight this lumberyard fire in Milwaukee, Wisconsin.

52

Two steamers are drafting from a cistern in Milwaukee. A third steamer (far right) is just arriving.

Steam fire engines supply hoselines at this multiple-alarm fire around 1900 in downtown Los Angeles.

Photo from the collection of Captain Bob Foster, LAFD

At left:

Hoselines are tangled like spaghetti along the 400 block of South Broadway in Los Angeles, as the city's fire engines and a Gorter water tower battle a 1913 blaze in a commercial building.

Photo from the collection of Paul Ditzel

Flames destroyed the Mutual Life Insurance Company building at California and Sansome Streets in Los Angeles in the financial district because of a lack of water caused by a quake-shattered water system.

Photo from the collection of Michael A. LaPlante

*The engineer takes a short break from shoveling coal for this photo
taken in 1902 in Portland, Maine.*

Photo from the collection of the Portland, Maine Fire Department

*The steamer in the foreground is supplying 2-1/2" hose lines at this Portland, Maine fire in 1908.
Note the coal piled next to both steamers – the fire was expected to last a while.*

CHAPTER 6

Principal Manufacturers

Their Engines and Their Stories

LA FRANCE ROTARY

LA FRANCE PISTON

AMOSKEAG

SILSBY.

AHRENS.

AMOSKEAG

CLAPP & JONES.

Silsby Manufacturing Co.

*T*he only firm which built more than 1000 steam fire engines was the Silsby Manufacturing Co. (originally known as Silsby, Mynderse & Co.) of Seneca Falls, New York. All 1150 of their engines were built at "The Island Works," on a tiny, five acre island in the Seneca River in upstate New York.

The firm, which first manufactured hand pumped fire engines, was established in 1845 by Horace C. Silsby, who was born in Connecticut in 1817. His first experimental steam fire engine was built in 1856, utilizing the rotary pump patented a year earlier by an employee who had the unlikely name of Birdsill Holly.

Silsby steamers were eminently successful and were manufactured until 1892, when the company was merged, along with its principal competitors, into the American Fire Engine Company, which was a conglomerate put together to create a virtual monopoly on fire engines.

Silsby advertised his engines to be so free of vibrations while pumping that a glass of water could be placed on one of the wheels without a single drop being spilled.

Silsby, along with competitors Clapp & Jones, also of New York state, and Amoskeag of New Hampshire, supplied most of the steam fire engines in the north and east, while Ahrens of Cincinnati (successor to Latta & Shawk and Lane & Bodley) supplied most of them in the midwest. These four firms, together, produced two of every three steamers ever built in the United States.

A Silsby steamer responds to an alarm.

The first Silsby engine, the "Neptune," was built in 1856 and was exhibited at the Crystal Palace in New York City. When tested there, it shot six streams of water 150 feet, and four streams 200 feet, using 1-1/8" nozzles. The rotary pump could draft water up to 29 vertical feet without the use of a check valve.

CROSS SECTIONS OF SILSBY ROTARY PUMP AND BOILER

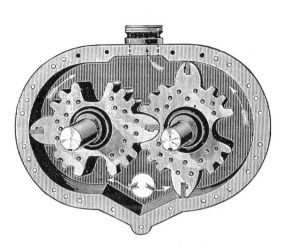

Rotary Steam Cylinder

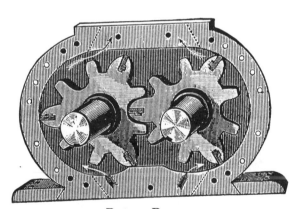

Rotary Pump

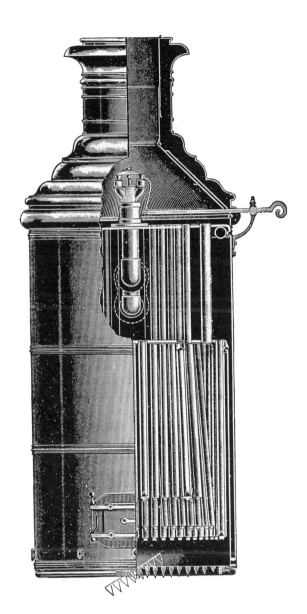

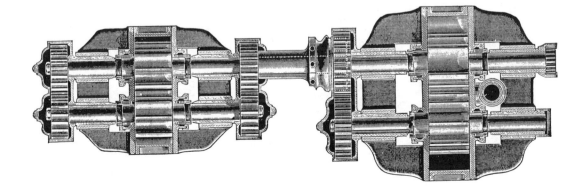

SILSBY STEAMERS

Photo from the collection of Matt Lee

An early Silsby steamer being tested.

*A restored 1886 Silsby steamer on display at the
American Heritage "Big Red" Fire Museum in Louisville, Mississippi.*

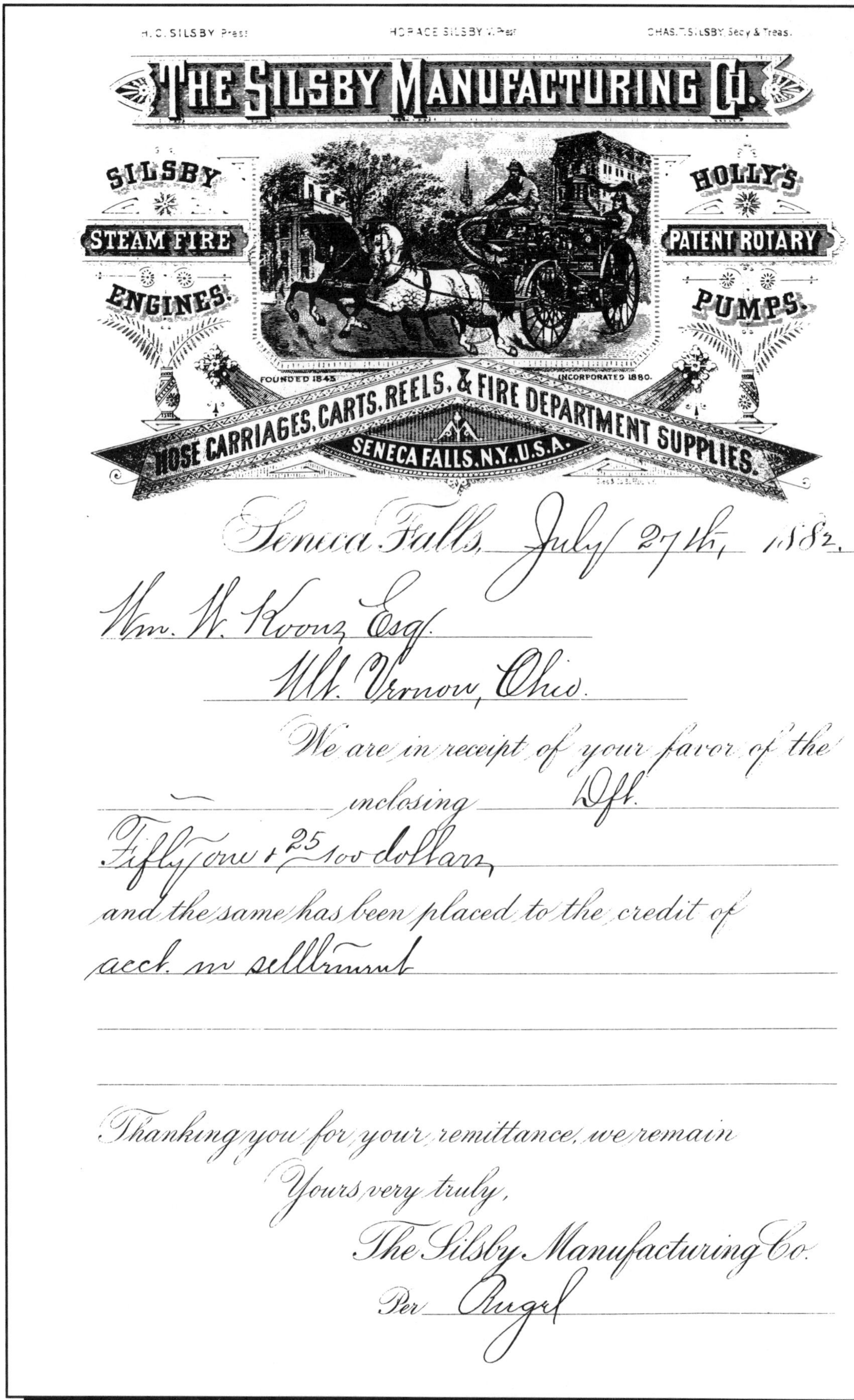

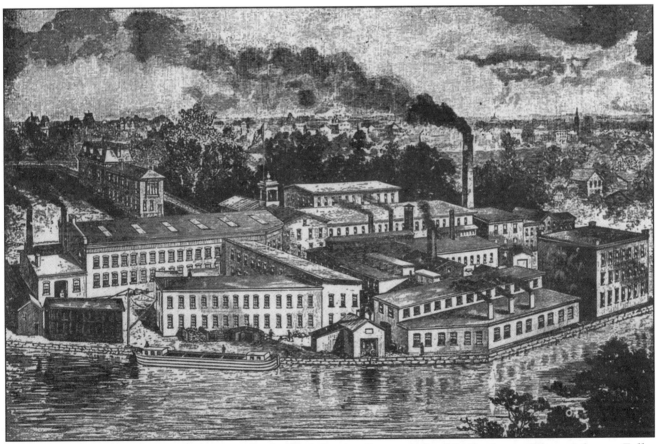

The Silsby Manufacturing Company completely filled the tiny five acre island in the Seneca River at Seneca Falls, New York. It was known as the "Island Works."

Riveting a boiler in the Silsby plant.

A pump is being assembled.

A rotary pump is installed on a frame at the Silsby factory.

A craftsman is shown hammering out a copper air chamber for a Silsby steamer.

A Silsby engine is tested before it leaves the factory.

⇀AHRENS↽
STEAM FIRE ENGINES.

↧COMBINING ALL MODERN IMPROVEMENTS.↧

The Simplest, Most Powerful and Durable Steam Fire Engine Built.

The Champion and only Engine making the full run of ten hours with 120 lbs. of Steam at the trial November 30, between the AHRENS, the Amoskeag and Clapp & Jones Engines, made by order and under the supervision of the New York Fire Commissioners.

Ahrens (et al)

$\mathcal{T}$he firm(s) which we are ranking as No. 2 represent an exercise in the genealogy of the steamers manufactured in their birthplace – Cincinnati, Ohio. By considering them together, they manufactured 987 steamers, from 1852 to 1916.

From 1852 through 1861,	31 steamers were manufactured in Cincinnati under the Latta name.
From 1855 through 1856,	5 steamers were manufactured in Cincinnati under the Shawk name.
From 1863 throught 1867,	24 steamers were manufactured in Cincinnati by Lane & Bodley, who bought out Latta.
From 1869 through 1892,	376 steamers were manufactured in Cincinnati by Ahrens & Co., who bought out Lane & Bodley.
From 1892 through 1903,	354 steamers were manufactured in Cincinnati by the Ahrens Division of the American Fire Engine Company, who bought out not only Ahrens, but Clapp & Jones, Button, and Silsby as well.
During the year 1904,	38 steamers were manufactured in Cincinnati under the American-LaFrance name. American had merged with LaFrance to form American-LaFrance.
From 1905 through 1912,	134 Ahrens (Continental model) steamers were manufactured in Cincinnati, as Chris Ahrens had withdrawn from the American-LaFrance consortium, preferring to go it again on his own.
From 1911 through 1916,	25 steamers were manufactured in Cincinnati under the Ahrens-Fox name (Continental models) as Chris Ahrens founded a partnership with his son-in-law Charles Fox.

It is interesting to note that both American-LaFrance and Ahrens-Fox went on to become powerhouses in the motorized fire engine era, as both firms pioneered motorized fire apparatus, building probably the best and most reliable fire engines available during the first half of the 1900's.

SIZES OF AHRENS STEAMERS

Double Extra First Size	1300 gallons per minute
Extra First Size	1100 gallons per minute
First Size	1000 gallons per minute
Second Size	750 gallons per minute
Third Size	600 gallons per minute
Fourth Size	500 gallons per minute
Fifth Size	300 gallons per minute

1907 Ahrens in service at Valdez, Alaska until 1935. Beautifully restored by Andy Swift.

Cross Sections of Ahrens Boiler

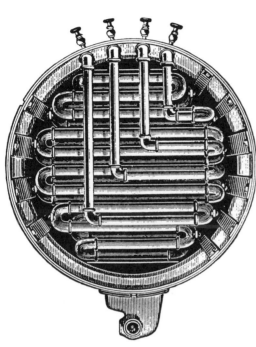

Top View of Ahrens Boiler

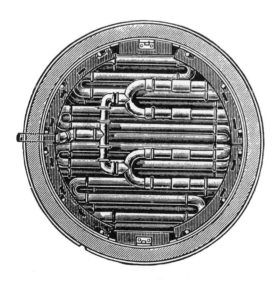

Bottom view of Ahrens Boiler

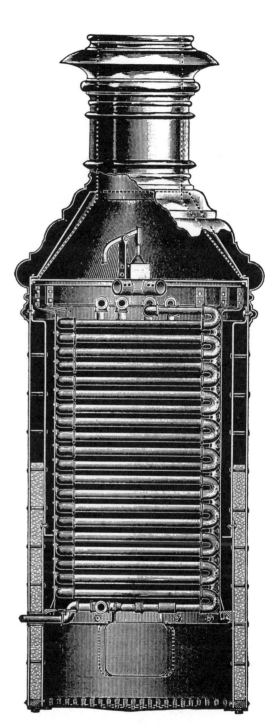

Ahrens Boiler

Ahrens Steamers

Single Pump Ahrens

Double Ahrens Engine

Ahrens Steam Fire Engine

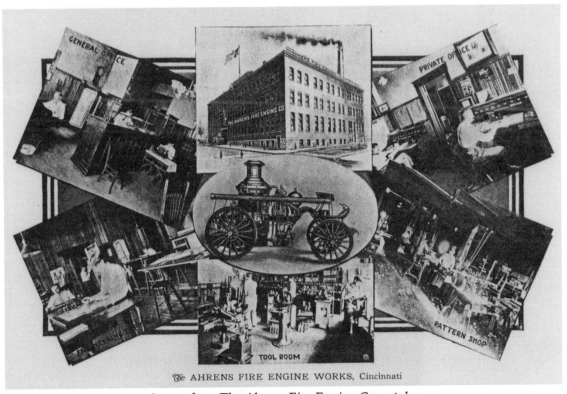

A page from The Ahrens Fire Engine Co. catalog.

73

Amoskeag
Manufacturing Company

*P*roducing a total of 853 steam fire engines between 1859 and 1913 – the third most of any manufacturer – the Amoskeag Company of Manchester, New Hampshire, was originally in the textile weaving business, including the manufacture and repair of the machinery used in that industry. This somehow evolved into building railroad locomotives, with fire engines sandwiched in between.

Their first engine, designed by employee Nehemiah S. Bean, was built in 1859, and was sold for $3000 to the city of its manufacture, where it remained in faithful service for the next 17 years.

In 1872 Amoskeag brought out a self-propelled engine, also designed by Bean, wherein the steam powered the wheels to propel the engine to the fire, supposedly without horses. However, horses were sometimes also needed to move the huge engines, which weighed 17,000 pounds. They were the largest steam fire engines in the world.

Although they were moderately successful, only 22 of the giant self-propellers were built. They could reach a top speed, without horses, of ten miles per hour. Regarding the Amoskeag self-propellers, the May 6, 1897 issue of *The Fireman's Herald* ran an article titled *The Dangers Of A Steam Propeller*, which read, in part, as follows:

"A steam propelled fire engine is a thing of terror. It seems to us that a steam propelled fire engine is a terrific menace to life and property. The fire engines, in rushing through the streets, are dangerous, but the horses act as a fender in case a person is unfortunate enough to get in the way. But with the steam propeller tearing down the street it would be like an express train ploughing its way through the streets.

Any person who has seen Jumbo No. 1 of the Hartford, Connecticut Fire Department – a steam propeller – knows what a thing of terror it is. Jumbo has several names on its death roll. Its first driver met death in turning a corner, teams have been run into, and it was only a year ago that at an exhibition a horse and its rider met their death under its crushing wheels."

Although the few steam propellers that were manufactured remained in service for many years, they never gained popularity and accounted for only a tiny fraction of all of the steam fire engines which were ever manufactured.

In 1877 the firm was acquired by the Manchester Locomotive Works, who, as the name implies, made railroad locomotives. Around the year 1900, a deal fell through that would have resulted in their being acquired by International Fire Engine Co. (renamed American-LaFrance in 1903). But, in 1908, the firm again changed hands and became known as A & B Manufacturing. Under the A & B name the company made only 15 more engines, however, since the age of steam fire engine manufacture was drawing to a close. Their final engine left the factory in 1913.

AMOSKEAG MANUFACTURING CO. MANCHESTER, N. H.

Amoskeag Steamers

Size	Capacity	Weight	Length	Width	Height
Double Extra 1st (self-propelling)	1350 gpm	17,000 lbs.	16'6"	7'3"	10'
Extra 1st	1100 gpm	9,000 lbs.	24'9"	6'5"	10'
1st	900 gpm	8,000 lbs.	24'6"	6'2"	9'2"
2nd	700 gpm	7,000 lbs.	24'3"	6'	9'
3rd	550 gpm	6,000 lbs.	24'	6'	8'10"
4th (horse-drawn)	350 gpm	4,200 lbs.	20'3"	5'10"	8'3"
4th (hand-drawn)	350 gpm	4,000 lbs.	16'	5'10"	8'3"

EARLY AMOSKEAG STEAMERS

Amoskeag Steamers

DOUBLE STRAIGHT FRAME ENGINE
Built by the Anoskeag Manufacturing Company

Self-propelled model en route to a blaze in Boston.

AMOSKEAG STEAMERS

DOUBLE STRAIGHT FRAME ENGINE.
Built by the Amoskeag Manufacturing Co.

SINGLE PUMP U TANK ENGINE.
Built by the Amoskeag Manufacturing Co.

Amoskeag Steamers

EXTRA FIRST SIZE DOUBLE STEAM FIRE ENGINES.
Crane-Necked Frame. Horse Draft.

FIRST, SECOND AND THIRD SIZE DOUBLE STEAM FIRE ENGINE..
Crane-Necked Frames. Horse Draft.

AMOSKEAG STEAMERS

FOURTH SIZE SINGLE STEAM FIRE ENGINE.
Horse Draft.

FOURTH SIZE SINGLE STEAM FIRE ENGINE.
Hand Draft.

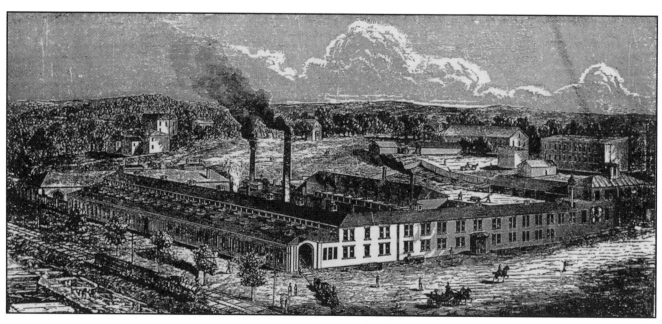

MANCHESTER LOCOMOTIVE WORKS

Manchester, N.H.

A horse-drawn Amoskeag, Detroit Engine #809, June 1906.

The "Pride of Hartford" was a self-propelled Amoskeag steamer.

STEAM FIRE ENGINES

Clapp & Jones

Manufacturing Company

Hudson, N.Y.

IMPROVED WATER WORKS MACHINERY, TENDERS
HOSE CARRIAGES, FIRE DEPARTMENT SUPPLIES, ETC.

AVERY COMPANY, PRINTERS
BOSTON, MASS.

Clapp & Jones

$\mathcal{B}$y producing over 600 steamers between 1862 and 1892, when he was acquired by the American Fire Engine Company, Mertilew R. Clapp and his financier partner Edward D. Jones became the fourth largest steam fire engine manufacturer in terms of the number of engines produced.

Their factory was located in the quaint town of Hudson, New York, on the Hudson River south of Albany, but many years ago it embarrasingly burned to the ground. Today, Hudson is home to one of the largest and most prestigious fire museums in the world, housing dozens of vintage fire engines, including four steamers, two of which are Clapp & Jones, originally manufactured only a mile or two from the museum.

M.R. Clapp was an employee of the Silsby Company when he decided to strike out on his own. He was very innovative, and his novel designs for piston pumps and boilers made his engines extremely reliable. They were manufactured in six sizes, ranging from the extra first size down to the village fourth and fifth sizes, which were hand drawn. Stunning examples of restored Clapp & Jones engines are displayed at the New York State Museum in Albany, New York, the Conway Fire Museum in New Albany, Indiana, and the Woodland Fire Department in California, as well as the American Museum of Firefighting at Hudson.

Attesting to the advantages of Clapp & Jones steamers was a committee from Port Huron, New York, who had been sent in 1867, by the mayor and city council, to visit various cities for the purpose of examining the steam fire engines of different manufacturers so as to select the best one for Port Huron. Their report to the mayor and council read in part as follows:

"We would recommend the steam fire engine built by Messrs. Clapp & Jones as the best adapted for the use of a small city for the following reasons: it has less machinery than any other seen, and is less liable to get out of order; it is so constructed that in case of any trouble with the pumps it can be taken apart and put together again in from five to eight minutes, while most other engines would take several hours. It is very light and works without any jumping. The boiler is very small but is capable of making all the steam wanted. We recommend its purchase."

Port Huron took the committee's advice, and when the Clapp & Jones engine arrived it was put through its paces. The Port Huron Press reported as follows in its August 21, 1867, edition:

"After attaching 1000 feet of hose, steam was gradually worked up to to 120 lbs., and with this pressure she threw 197 feet with apparent ease, the water guage showing 225 pounds. After this, through 500 feet of hose, she threw 219 feet with 110 pounds of steam. This, the boys think, will do for a machine weighing only 4800 lbs., and if there is any engine in this state that can beat it, they would like to be informed at an early day."

CLAPP & JONES STEAMERS

Clapp & Jones Village Engine

Sections of Clapp & Jones Village Engine.

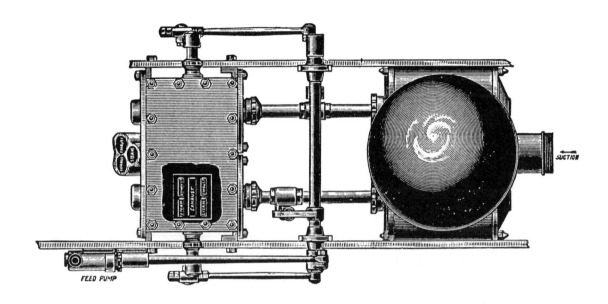

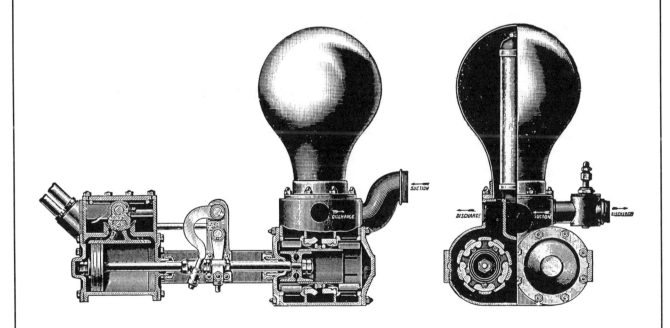

Clapp & Jones Steamers

Double Clapp & Jones Engine

Sections of Clapp & Jones
Double Vertical Engine.

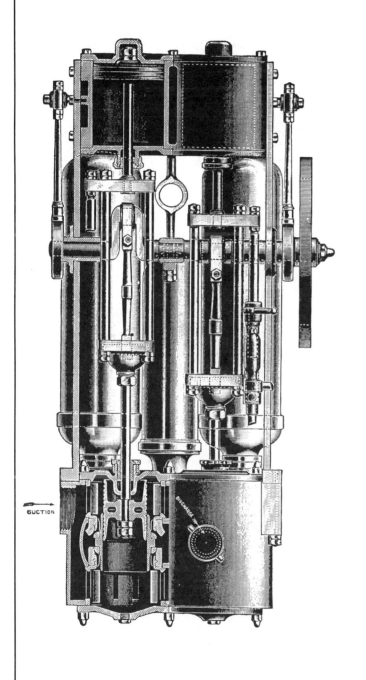

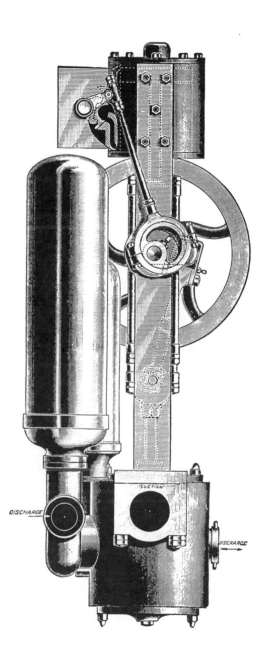

CLAPP & JONES BOILER

Section of Clapp & Jones Pump

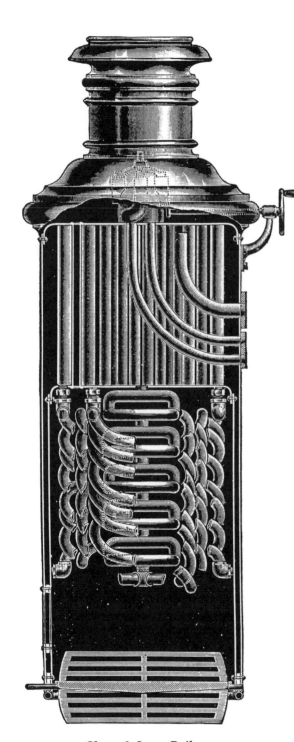

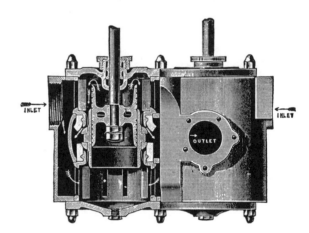

Section of Clapp & Jones Pump

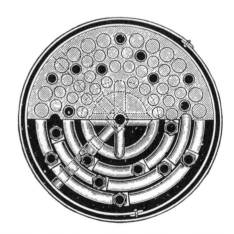

Clapp & Jones Boiler

Bottom Section of Clapp & Jones Boiler

CLAPP & JONES MANUFACTURING COMPANY

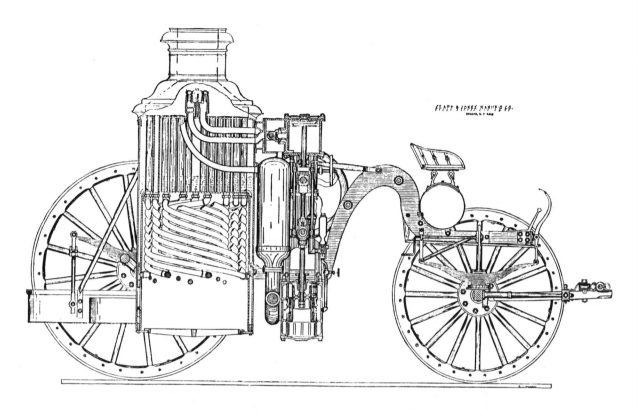

Above and below are diagrams from the Clapp & Jones Manufacturing Company catalog.

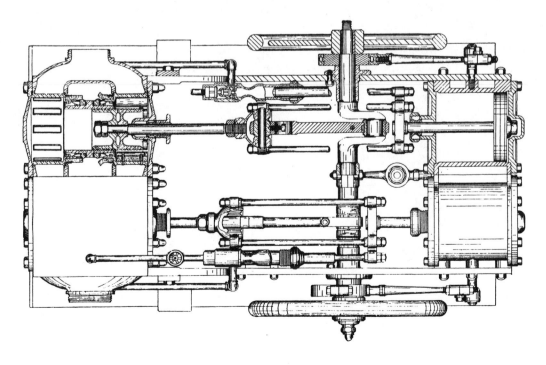

Photo from the collection of Ken Bechthold

RESTORED
CLAPP & JONES ENGINES

1875 Clapp & Jones fired up and pumping at the Woodbury, California Fire Department 120 years after it was manufactured.

Courtesy of the New York State Museum, Albany, New York

1875 fifth size engine on display a the New York State Museum, Albany, New York. This engine was used as late as 1940 for thawing out frozen fire plugs.

1874 fourth size engine restored by the Frenchtown, New Jersey Fire Department.

This restored Clapp & Jones engine is on display at the American Fire Museum at Hudson, New York, the town where it was manufactured.

LaFrance Manufacturing Co.

$\mathcal{P}$roducing 539 steamers between 1873 and 1904, Truckson LaFrance turned out the fifth largest number of steamers of any manufacturer, at his plant in Elmira, New York. In 1904, LaFrance Manufacturing merged with American Fire Engine Co. to form the most prodigious fire engine company of them all – the celebrated American-LaFrance, which, through a succession of owners, is still in business, today, providing chassis to other fire truck manufacturers.

Truckson LaFrance

Truckson Hyenveux was a descendent of a French Huguenot family which came to America for religious freedom. When the Hyenveuxs arrived in America, they found that the English settlers could not pronounce their last name, so, being from France, they changed it simply to LaFrance, according to *The History of American-LaFrance* published in 1972.

After obtaining patents on his improvements to rotary steam engines, Truckson LaFrance, along with several partners, formed the LaFrance Manufacturing Company on April 17, 1873. In addition to building steam fire engines, they also turned out such diverse products as corn shellers, cotton pickers, rail fence machines, and even railroad steam locomotives.

That same year, they built their first stream fire engine, which included the rotary pump Truckson had perfected. Truckson's brother Asa, a well known cornet virtuoso, was employed as a travelling salesman for his brother's fire engines. Asa, also turned inventor, eventually patented a spring raised aerial ladder.

In 1884, the firm included piston pumps in their line of steamers, and the rotary pumps gradually faded out of the picture.

Truckson LaFrance died in 1895, and in 1900 the LaFrance Fire Engine Company merged with the American Fire Engine Co. (which had already combined Button, Silsby, Ahrens, and Clapp & Jones) to produce the International Fire Engine Co., whose name changed in 1903 to the most famous name in fire engines – American-LaFrance.

LaFrance Steamers

LaFrance Rotary Engine

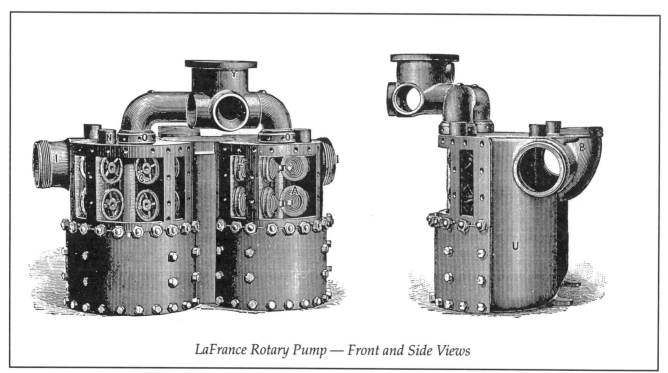

LaFrance Rotary Pump — Front and Side Views

LaFrance Steamers

LaFrance Single Piston Engine.

LaFrance Double Piston Engine.

LaFrance Steamers

Double Piston

Single Piston

LaFRANCE PISTON FIRE ENGINES

SINGLE PUMP AND STEAM CYLINDER

Comprising engines with full nickel-plated finish, mounted on half-elliptic springs over front and hind axles, or mounted on spiral springs; wooden wheels, seat, pole and whiffletrees, hand tongue and rope reel when required, suction hose, tools and fixtures complete.

IN THREE SIZES.

	4TH SIZE	5TH SIZE	6TH SIZE
Height over all	9 ft. 2 in.	9 ft.	9 ft.
Length over all	24 ft.	22 ft.	22 ft.
Width over all (ordinarily)	6 ft.	6 ft.	6 ft.
Weight without supplies, about	5500 lbs.	4700 lbs.	4000 lbs.
Capacity: Gallons per minute	550	450	375

DOUBLE PUMP AND STEAM CYLINDER

Comprising engine with full nickel-plated finish, mounted on half-elliptic springs or platform springs over front axles, and half-elliptic springs over hind axles; seat, pole and whiffletrees, hand tongue with rope reel when required, suction hose, tools and fixtures complete.

These engines are built with extra heavy steel axles and running gear, also extra heavy wooden wheels, with eighteen spokes in front and twenty spokes in hind wheels, for service in cities with rough pavements.

These engines are built with extra heavy steel axles and running gear, also extra heavy wooden wheels, with eighteen spokes in front and twenty spokes in hind wheels, for service in cities with rough pavements.

IN FOUR SIZES

	EXTRA 1ST SIZE	1ST SIZE	2ND SIZE	3RD SIZE
Height over all	9 ft. 6 in.	9 ft. 6 in.	9 ft. 6 in.	9 ft. 4 in.
Length over all	25 ft.	24 ft. 6 in.	24 ft. 3 in.	
Width over all (ord'n'ry) .	6 ft. 3 in.	6 ft.	6 ft.	6 ft.
Wt. without supplies, abt	8500 lbs.	7300 lbs.	6500 lbs.	6000 lbs.
Capacity: Gals. per min ...	*1100	900	750	650

**The extra first-class engine will throw a
1 3/4 inch stream 300 feet, or a 2 inch stream 275 feet.**

THE LA FRANCE FIRE ENGINE COMPANY, ELMIRA, N. Y.

THE LaFRANCE

PATENT

NEST-TUBE BOILER.

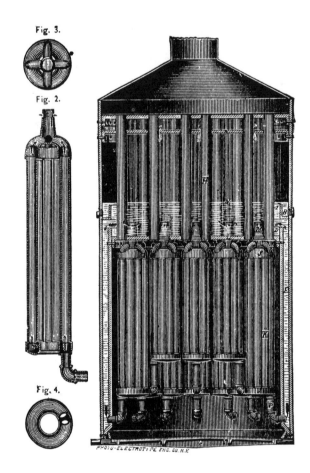

Figure 1 is a sectional view of the boiler.

Figure 2 is a sectional view of a cluster or "nest" of water-tubes, comprising nine 1¼ inch tubes, connected by right and left threads to malleable iron "headers."

Figure 3 is a view of the water "header" at top of Fig. 2, which screws into the crown-sheet.

Figure 4 is a view of the "water ring" at bottom of Fig. 2, which connects with leg of boiler.

THE LaFRANCE

FIRE ENGINE COMPANY

ELMIRA, N. Y., U. S. A.

MANUFACTURERS OF

LaFRANCE'S NEW IMPROVED PISTON

STEAM FIRE ENGINES,

IN SEVEN SIZES.

Manufacturers of LaFrance's Patent Rotary Steam Fire Engines, and Sole Manufacturers of Hayes' Extension Ladder, Truck and Fire Escape, and Manufacturers and Dealers in Hose Carriages, Carts, Reels and General Fire Department Supplies.

ELMIRA, N. Y.
ADVERTISER ASSOCIATION, PRINTERS.
1885.

Button
Fire Engine Co.

*T*urning out 229 steam fire engines during the three decades between 1862 and 1892, when he merged with American, Lysander Button became America's sixth largest producer of steamers.

Located at Waterford, New York, his Button Fire Engine Works, which began as a manufacturer of hand fire engines in 1834, made the successful transition to steamers when the market dictated such a move was necessary for survival.

The firm, which was later known as Button & Blake, had an untarnished reputation for superb fire engines, both hand and steam operated. Button steamers were built in six sizes: first class – weight 7000 pounds; second class – 6000 lbs.; third class – 5000 lbs.; fourth class – 4000 lbs.; fifth class – 3000 lbs.; and sixth class – a real lightweight at only 2500 pounds.

All of the sizes had crane neck frames, allowing sharp turns, and all pumps were piston, with both horizontal and vertical configurations.

In 1891, Button, along with his competitors Silsby, Ahrens, and Clapp & Jones, combined to form the American Fire Engine Company.

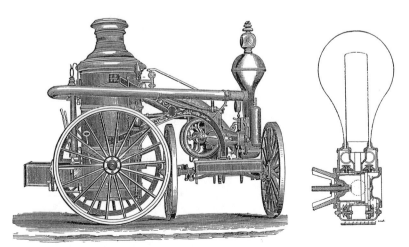

Button Fire Engine. The view at the right shows a cross section of the pump used on this engine. Button engines were 12 1/2 feet long, 6 feet wide, and 9 feet high.

103

First Size Double Engine (Pat. 5/4/1864)

Capacity: 696 cu. inch, or 3 gal. per revolution. Arranged for four streams. Will throw a 1-1/2 inch stream 300 feet or a 1-3/8 inch stream, 325 feet, horizontally. Furnished with driver's seat and pole, brake, 4 discharge pipes, full assortment of nozzles, 3 pressure guages, water guage, 3 service lanterns, a silver-plate cutglass signal lamp, 3 silver-plated name plates, poker, shovel, 12 feet of small hose, an oiler, steam whistle, safety valve, two blow-off cocks, a feed pump, relief valve, spanners and a complete set of tools.
Weight: 1000 pounds.

Second Size Double Engine (Pat. 5/4/1864)

Capacity: 530 cu. inch, or 2.75 gal. per revolution. Arranged for three streams. Will throw a 1-1/4 inch stream 275 feet, or two 1 inch streams, 220 feet horizontally. Furnished with driver's seat, pole, drag rope reel and hand tongue, three discharge pipes and other equipment as for first size engine.
Weight: 6000 pounds.

Third Size Double Engine (Pat. 5/4/1864)

Capacity: 372 cu. inch or 1.61 gal. per revolution. Arranged for two streams. Will throw a 1-1/8 inch stream 250 feet horizontally. Furnished with or without a driver's seat or pole, two discharge pipes and other equipment as for first size engine.
Weight: 5000 pounds.

Second Size Single Engine (6/20/1871 - 9/26/1871)

Capacity: Variable - the smaller being 423 cu. inch or 1.81 gal. per revolution the larger, 699.8 cu. inch or 3.03 gal. per revolution. Arranged to discharge four streams and will supply four 1 inch streams effectively. It will throw a single stream more than 300 feet. Furnished with seats for the driver and captain, a pole for two horses and other equipment. It can deliver from 800 to 900 gpm and it can sustain a stream 100 feet high through a half a mile of hose.
Weight: 6000 pounds.

Third Size Single Engine (Pat. 6/20/1871 - 9/26/1871)

Capacity: 397.6 cu. inch or 1.72 gal. per revolution. Arranged for two streams. Will throw water through 1-1/4 inch stream, 230 feet and 1-1/8 inch stream 250 feet. It will throw two 7/8 inch streams, 180 feet. Furnished with equipment similar to other models.
Weight: 5000 pounds

Fourth Size Single Engine (Pat. 6/20/1871 - 9/26/1871)

Capacity: 322.9 cu. inch or 1.39 gal. per revolution. Arranged for two streams and equipped in the same manner as other engine.

> The 1875 catalogue states that "this is a very powerful engine for its weight, and just the thing for volunteer village departments. It will throw as much water through one or two thousand feet of hose as any engine. We will warrant it to play 170 feet through 1000 feet of hose and a 1-1/4 inch nozzle. It will generally get to work quicker than a hand engine."

Button Pump & Boiler

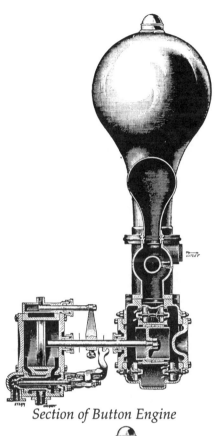

Section of Button Engine

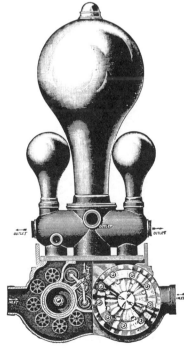

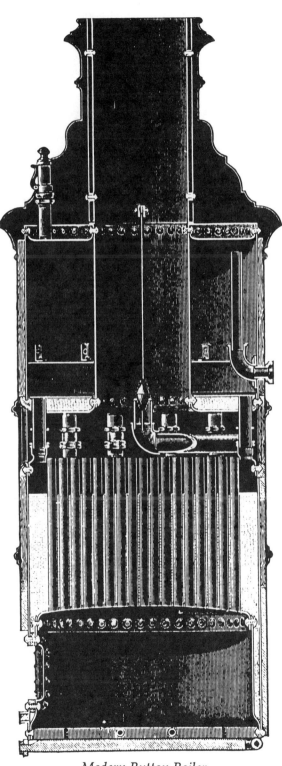

Modern Button Boiler

BUTTON STEAMERS

Model of L. Button & Son

Modern Double Button Engine

Button Steamers

The Button Steam Fire Engine

Warren No. 12, Boston, Massachusetts
Built by Button & Blake

107

Waterous
Engine Works

*T*he Waterous Engine Works of St. Paul, Minnesota, and Brantford, Ontario, Canada, known today as one of America's premier manufacturers of pumps for fire trucks, produced at least 106 steam fire engines between 1886 and 1913.

Charles H. Waterous, Sr., originally from Burlington, Vermont, moved to Buffalo, New York, and at age 34 migrated to Brantford, Ontario. His occupation was that of an engineer on the Great Lakes shipping systems, but when he moved to Brantford in 1848, he purchased a quarter interest in the Van Brocklin Foundry, which manufactured machinery for saw mills, including steam engines to power the saws.

A decade later, in 1858, Waterous was able to purchase a controlling interest in the foundry, and it was renamed the Waterous Engine Works, Ltd. Soon the thriving business employed 250 workers. The foundry continued to grow under Waterous' management and exported saw mill steam engines all over the world. It was only natural that this successful steam engine company would diversify into steam fire engines, and a second factory was built in St. Paul, Minnesota, to produce them for the United States, with the Brantford plant building them for Canadian fire departments.

Deals for the Waterous steam fire engine division to merge with first American-LaFrance, and next with the Seagrave Corporation, failed to materialize, and Waterous remained independent. Although they no longer build fire engines per se, many of the pumps on today's fire engines are built at the Waterous factory in St. Paul.

Waterous steam fire engines were sold primarily in the states of North and South Dakota, Minnesota, and Wisconsin, as well as the provinces of Ontario and Quebec in Canada. However, two of them were sold in Kentucky, and two went to Charles Waterous' former city of residence – Buffalo, New York.

Waterous became the pioneer manufacturer of horse-drawn, gasoline-powered fire pumps, producing them concurrently with steamers. Although 106 Waterous steamers have been identified, serial numbers indicate that the number may have been closer to 150.

Waterous Engine, Pump, Boiler

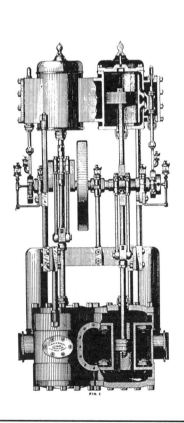

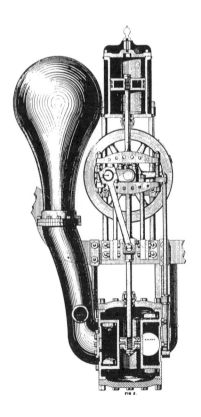

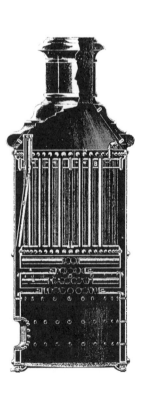

WATEROUS STEAMERS

Nos. 1 and 2 Waterous Engine.

No. 3 Waterous Engine.

WATEROUS STEAMERS

*The Waterous Improved Piston Steam Fire Engine.
Built in 4 sizes.*

Nos. 4 and 5 Sizes Waterous Engine.

1912 Second Size Waterous steamer on display at the Conway Fire Museum, New Albany, Indiana. Restoration by Andy Swift. Note the solid rubber tires, indicating that the engine was built near the close of the steamer era. It fought its last fire in Ottawa, Ontario, Canada in 1931.

113

The Cumberland No. 3 of Portland, Maine, 1870. This was the last engine ever built by James B. Johnson/Portland Co. The horizontal pump engine is typical of a Johnson. See J.B. Johnson on page 119.

Other Prominent Steam Fire Engine Manufacturers

Who produced fewer than 100 engines —
in alphabetical order.

Cole Brothers

Between the years 1867 and 1880, Cole Brothers of Pawtucket, Rhode Island,
turned out 60 steamers in three sizes: first size – 6500 lbs.;
second size – 5500 lbs.; and third size – 4500 lbs.
Prices ranged from $4,000 to $5,000.

Cole Brothers Double Engine.

W.C. Hunneman and Company

*W*illiam C. Hunneman, an apprentice of Paul Revere,
founded his firm in Boston in 1790. He and his sons were to produce more than
700 hand fire engines over the next 90 years. Seeing the end of the hand engine business
on the horizon, the Hunnemans began to build steamers in 1866.
When they went out of business in 1883, they had build 28 steamers.
Sadly, their steamers, although excellent machines,
did not enjoy the enthusiastic acceptance of their hand engines.

Photo from the collection of J.R. Hunneman, Jr.

Hunneman No. 678 "Somerville No. 1." This engine purchased by Somerville, Massachusetts, was the first steamer ever built by the Hunneman Company.

Above is Hunneman No. 724, A double engine sold to the Boston Fire Department November 19, 1872. Below is Hunneman No. 690, sold to Newton, Massachusetts on October 19, 1868.

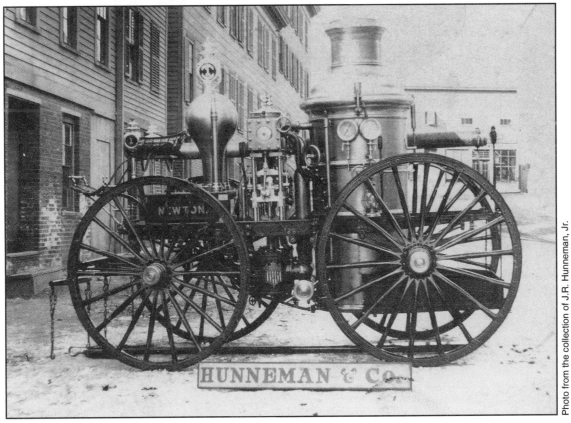

Photo from the collection of J.R. Hunneman, Jr.

Photo from the collection of J.R. Hunneman, Jr.

William Jeffers

*T*he Pawtucket, Rhode Island firm of William Jeffers
manufactured and sold a total of 71 steamers between 1861 and 1878.
Jeffers had built 63 steamers when he sold his business to
P.S. Skidmore in 1875. Skidmore went on to build eight more
before the factory, including his patterns, was destroyed by a fire in 1878.

Single Pump Jeffers Engine.

J.B. Johnson

*J. B.*Johnson of Boston,
and later of Portland, Maine,
produced about 30 steamers
between 1859 and 1869.
Johnson engines were comparatively
light in weight, and were considered
to be handsome in appearance.

Johnson Engine Casco No. 5, Portland Maine.

Thomas Manning, Jr. & Company

$\mathcal{B}$etween 1886 and 1900, the Thomas Manning Company
of Cleveland, Ohio, built about 30 steamers and was becoming
such a well-known manufacturer that it was acquired by the
International Fire Engine Co. (soon to be renamed American-LaFrance).
Manning engines were built in four sizes: first size – 6650 lbs.;
second size – also 6650 lbs.; third size – 5820 lbs., and the fourth size 5400 lbs.

Built by Thomas Manning, Jr., & Co.

Mansfield
Machine Works

*T*he Mansfield Machine Works of Mansfield, Ohio,
had for thirty years built steam and pumping machinery
prior to producing their first of eventually about 50 steam fire engines,
in 1883. Their engines were very plain and were priced
well below the cost of the major brands.
Mansfield was acquired by the
International Fire Engine Company in 1902.

A Rotary Engine built by the Mansfield Machine Works.

THIS OLD BOY

CAN BE

REJUVENATED

AND ITS EFFICIENCY INCREASED

FULLY 100 PER CENT

The Oldest Active Steam Fire Engine in U.S.A.
Built 1859. Greene N. Y, Fire Department

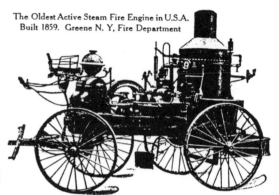

By Replacing Its Boiler with One of the

NOTT SPIRAL WATER TUBE TYPE

The most scientific heating surface, the quickest steaming the most positive circulation, the most consistent in volume, the most elastic, the most easily repaired.

The extraordinary steaming and pressure holding properties of this boiler are such that a marine type of same has been used by the U. S. Navy, and is being placed on vessels requiring high horse power.

Many rebuilds are carrying the Nott Boiler, to the satisfaction of their users. If you contemplate renewing the boiler or rebuilding any engine in your Department, look carefully into its merits.

NOTT FIRE ENGINE CO.,   Minneapolis, U. S. A.

W.S. Nott & Company

Producing at least 100 steamers and probably as many as 150, the story of the W.S. Nott Company is perhaps the most incredible of all.

W.S. Nott

*A*lthough passed in 1890, the Sherman Anti-Trust Act was not yet stringently enforced. It was designed to prevent the very thing that transpired in the steam fire engine industry at the turn of the century - the amalgamation of all of the principal manufacturers into a combine to monopolize the industry, excluding the smaller and weaker players, thus forcing them out of business. But in the case of the fire engine "trust," one of the smaller players had the temerity to come against the trust. An Irishman, William S. Nott, was not about to watch his company be eclipsed or forced out of business by the new combine. He fought back, and by some accounts, actually won.

Just as today we watch mergers and acquisitions of manufacturers taking place at an almost frantic pace, so it was a century ago. By the year 1890, some 15 firms had emerged as the nation's primary manufacturers of heavy duty or specialized fire apparatus - steamers, aerial ladders, chemical engines, and water towers. Steamer builders were Silsby (Seneca Falls, New York), LaFrance (Elmira, New York), Clapp & Jones (Hudson, New York), Button (Waterford, New York), Ahrens (Cincinnati), Amoskeag (Manchester, New Hampshire), Manning (Cleveland), and Waterous (St. Paul).

Aerial ladder trucks were manufactured by LaFrance, Preston (Chicago), and Gleason and Bailey (Seneca Falls, New York). The primary manufacturers of chemical engines were Babcock (official name - Fire Extinguisher Manufacturing Co.) of Chicago; Champion (Louisville), Holloway (Baltimore), Macomber (Worcester, Massachusetts), and Gleason and Bailey. America's only water tower builder at that time was Hale of Kansas City, Missouri.

In the early 1890's mergers and acquisitions among these 15 leading fire apparatus builders really heated up. In 1891, steamer manufacturers Silsby, Clapp & Jones, Ahrens, and Button combined to form the American Fire Engine Company. About the same time, chemical engine manufacturer Babcock took over competitors Preston, Champion, and Hale. (Hale water tow-

ers were raised by the pressure of carbon dioxide generated from a chemical engine tank mounted on the apparatus.) Thus, the merger of the 15 principal fire apparatus manufacturers left only nine companies.

The rapid pace of merger activity continued. On December 14, 1899, the New York firm of Alexander and Green incorporated the International Fire Engine Company, with privately held stock valued at $9 million. Their purpose was to dominate and, in fact, monopolize the fire apparatus industry in America by eliminating all competition. International attempted to purchase the assets of no less than 11 leading fire apparatus manufacturers, including those who produced steamers: American, LaFrance, Manning, Amoskeag, and Waterous. Although both Amoskeag and Waterous were considered part of "The Trust," during negotiations the deals fell through, and they remained independent.

The trust also gobbled up chemical engine manufacturers Babcock, Holloway, and Macomber, as well as apparatus builders Gleason and Bailey, S.F. Hayward, and Rumsey. The trust was now well on its way to achieving its purpose - total control of the fire apparatus industry in America with a single corporate entity.

Outside of the trust, now, were only Amoskeag and Waterous (who didn't join after all), as well as relatively small Seagrave (Columbus, Ohio), Peter Pirsch (Kenosa, Wisconsin), and W.S. Nott (Minneapolis, Minnesota). Nott was to become the David who came against and slew Goliath - "The Trust."

William S. Nott was born in Dublin, Ireland, on May 5, 1853. At age five his parents immigrated to Chicago, where he attended school and then accepted employment with a manufacturer of leather belting and rubber goods. Staying long enough to learn the business from top to bottom, Nott moved to Minneapolis and established his own business manufacturing the same products. It is interesting to note that he became the world's

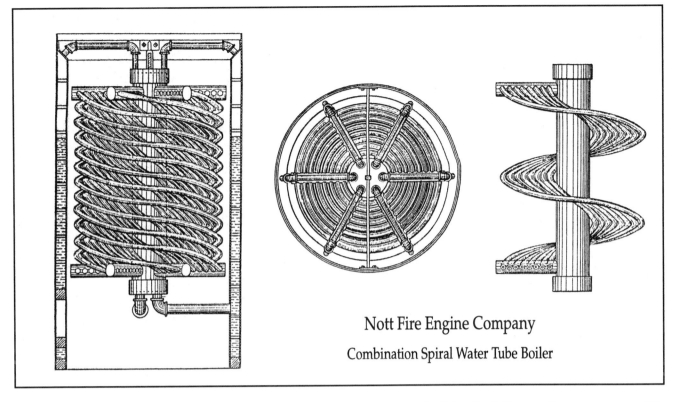

Nott Fire Engine Company
Combination Spiral Water Tube Boiler

largest manufacturer of leather dice cups. Other items coming from the Nott plant included threshermen's supplies, pipe and boiler covering, and even rubber tires for recently invented automobiles.

Still another division of Nott's enterprises successfully manufactured chemical fire engines and hose carts and acted as a distributor for fire apparatus manufactured by others - specifically companies within the trust. But soon after its formation, the trust dropped Nott as a distributor for fire apparatus. Oops! Nott, no slouch, fought back. A man to be reckoned with, he was a director of the Security Bank of Minnesota and part owner of several other businesses, including an adding machine company and a firm which manufactured crematories. A biographer stated, "He wielded a great influence for good, and no man in this city [Minneapolis] stood higher for integrity and sterling worth."

Although his fire engine division was only a small part of his total enterprise, Nott determined to fight the trust by building a full line of his own fire apparatus. He acquired another building in

1900 in which he built his engines in secrecy. He hired the Minneapolis Fire Department's steam engineer and mechanic, H.E. Penney, to design and supervise construction of Nott steamers, which were soon named "Universal," competing with the trust's "Continental" and "Metropolitan" models. He also continued to build or assemble chemical engines and hose carts.

In secret, Nott put together a network of sales agents, and by the time his first steamer was completed in January 1902, he already had orders from Oklahoma, New Mexico, Pennsylvania, Montana, and even the Philippine Islands. The only steamer manufacturer outside the trust (Amoskeag and Waterous were still thought to be in the trust) was Nott, and he used that independence to help sell his steamers.

Incredibly, the success of his new steamers quickly mushroomed until he had more orders than he could timely produce. He underbid the trust on price, trying to buy market share, a strategy which worked. He offered his steamers for as little as $3700, with a five year guarantee. The orders poured in, and he contracted out the manufacture of the boilers to speed production; still, he could not keep up.

Meanwhile, the trust, annoyed by this upstart, determined to force him out of business. A Nott salesman, determined to place a Nott steamer in Montana, said "It was the hardest fought battle that I ever got into, and [I] have been in quite a few since my career on the road." The agent priced the steamer at only $3500, took in a badly worn LaFrance in trade, and threw in free freight. The salesman continued, "The trust did not want us to have an engine in the West as a reference, and they used every means in their power, both honorable and otherwise, to get their steamer in."

But Nott's turnaround time became too long, which caused fire departments to wait months for delivery. The trust played up these delays with negative advertising, but Nott fought back. If his sales representatives had to pass "rewards" under the table, they would do it. One of his reps wrote, "You may judge from the price we get for this engine that it is not all 'clean turkey.'"

In spite of late delivery and sometimes questionable workmanship, as the motorized era was dawning, Nott had turned out at least 100 steamers with a unique spiral tube boiler designed by Penney. Although Nott customers for the first two or three years were small towns and cities, the large cities began to take notice. Additionally, Nott acted as a distributor for Seagrave apparatus, and conversely, Seagrave, who didn't build their own steamers, sold the Nott.

Meanwhile, the trust was having problems of its own. They were undercapitalized and could not raise additional money. Ahrens pulled out of the trust, which fell into receivership. Although

This 1902 W.S. Nott steamer is located in Royalton, Minnesota.

Photo from the collection of Ken Peterson

Photo from the collection of Ken Peterson

This 1912 W.S. Nott steamer was originally delivered to Kenora, Ontario, Canada.

its demise may not have been totally attributable to Nott, it appeared that David had slain Goliath. A Nott salesman commented, "It has taken a long time to circumvent the octopus, but we finally landed."

Yet, the trust, in a weaker form, continued as the entity of American-LaFrance. As late as 1910, F.S. Seagrave, who was to become American-LaFrance's fiercest competitor, still referred to that company as "The Trust."

By 1905 Nott had delivered 50 steamers to 48 fire departments and had nine more under construction. Production was now at the rate of 30 to 50 steamers per year, with sales to the larger cities taking off. Seattle, Los Angeles, Milwaukee, Minneapolis, Atlanta, New Orleans, Chicago, and New York City were now customers. Sales were so strong, in fact, that Nott passed up exhibiting at the 1909 conference of the National Association of Fire Engineers.

But after nearly a decade of success in battling the trust, the curtain fell in 1910 when it became clear that steamers were destined to be replaced by motorized fire engines. Not to be defeated by a new type of pumper, however, Nott developed his own line of motorized fire engines and, in 1912 sold them to Minneapolis, St. Louis, Chicago, and New York City.

Although the new Nott motorized engines sold well, they were plagued by design flaws. Coupled with the head start of other motorized fire engine manufacturers, the poorly designed engines finally brought "David" to his knees, and in 1915 Nott ceased production. Yet, "David" was still not through.

Not willing to give up, Nott became a distributor for first Seagrave, and then, capitulating, he became a distributor for his arch enemy, American-LaFrance. In this context, the trust might be perceived to have been the ulti-

Photo from the collection of Ken Peterson

mate victor. American-LaFrance, Seagrave, and Ahrens-Fox went on to become the three power-houses of the fire engine industry and remained so through World War II. Ahrens-Fox finally folded in 1958, American-LaFrance ceased production in 1995*, and Seagrave, as this chapter is written in 1996, is still an industry leader.

H.E. Penney, who designed the Nott steamers, rejoined the Minneapolis Fire Department,

and Nott had motorized pumpers for small towns built under his name by Luverne Fire Apparatus of Minnesota. He was still selling fire apparatus with the Nott name at the time of his death in 1923 at age 70.

Did William S. Nott really break the trust? His biographer, Richard L. Heath, wrote… [he] fought the 'fire engine trust' at the turn of the century - and won."

---

*The new owner of American-LaFrance, Freightliner Corporation, is scheduled to resume production in 1997.

An ad taken from The Fireman's Herald, *June 30, 1906.*

NOTT ENGINES

A privately owned first size W.S. Nott steamer.

Photo from the collection of Ken Peterson

Reaney & Neafie

*R*eaney & Neafie, later known as Neafie & Levy,
produced steam fire engines only during the span of a single decade
from 1857 to 1868, but during that time they turned out some 40 steamers
from their Philadelphia factory. Their engines were sold
throughout the United States. Only two of them are known to still exist.
One has been beautifully restored and is on display at
CIGNA Museum in Philadelphia.
It is considered to be the oldest steam fire engine still in existance.

Photo courtesy of CIGNA Museum and Art Collection

In the forefront is the Pioneer, an 1857 Reaney & Neafie steamer. It is probably the oldest steam fire engine still in existence.

131

The Test of Time

METROPOLITAN STEAM FIRE ENGINE

1897 Nine Years of Active Service 1906

The first Metropolitan Engine ever built was placed in service in the St. Louis Fire Department in 1897. ¶ It is now and always has been in the congested district of the city and averages about thirty runs a month. ¶ There has been no trouble with this, the first Metropolitan Engine and Boiler, since it was placed in service. ¶ The City of St. Louis has now in service thirty-three engines of this type, of which fifteen are new Standard Metropolitan Engines and eighteen are rebuilt with new boilers to conform as nearly as possible to that type.

AMERICAN-LAFRANCE FIRE ENGINE CO.
ELMIRA, N. Y.

FACTORIES: Elmira, Seneca Falls, Cincinnati
BRANCHES: New York, Boston, Baltimore, Atlanta, Chicago, Portland, Ore. San Fran

An advertisement from The Fireman's Herald, *June 30, 1906.*

American-LaFrance Metropolitan

*S*pecial mention is made of the approximately 800 American-LaFrance Metropolitan model steamers manufactured from 1898 to 1917, which are often considered to have been the ultimate steam fire engines ever produced. Two restored Metropolitans are pictured below.

Manufactured in 1903, this Metropolitan steamer pumps 700 gallons per minute. It served in Sacramento on front-line duty until 1920, and in reserve status until 1924, when it was sold to Fox Studios, where it was featured in the film "Gone With The Wind."

This 1911 American-LaFrance Metropolitan steamer took 2000 hours to restore to its former grandeur and is on display at the Jeff Morris Fire Museum, Portland, Oregon. This steamer was in service until 1922 or 1923.

AMERICAN-LAFRANCE SPOTLIGHT

*I*t was rare for steam fire engines to be manufactured or used for purposes other than pumping water at fires. But both of the engines illustrated below were designed to generate electricity to power spotlights and floodlights to illuminate night time fire scenes.

Other uses for steamers included thawing out frozen fire hydrants and hose, and in cities such as Cincinnati and Louisville they pumped water from the basements of city buildings during the 1937 flood.

Photo from the collection of William Schwartz

Instead of Horses...

Christie
Front-Drive Tractors

*I*t was an idea whose time had come. By around 1912, progressive fire chiefs realized that, in the future, gasoline engines rather than horses would propel fire engines to fires and that gasoline engines would replace steam in powering the fire pumps. In fact, a number of motorized engines were already in service.

As devoted as the firemen were to their horses, there were never-ending feed bills and veterinary bills to pay, not to speak of the mess and smell in the firehouses, which the horses shared with the firemen, even if on different floors. A team of horses might cost $660. to maintain for a year, with gas and oil for a motorized engine only $85.

And, what about the millions of dollars invested in the dependable steamers? City fathers could not be expected to retire the 3000 to 4000 steamers in use at that time and order new motorized fire engines.

The obvious solution was conceived by Walter Christie, a driver and designer of racing cars for the Indianapolis 500. He proposed to design and manufacture two-wheeled gasoline-powered tractors to pull the steamers (and ladder wagons and water towers as well) to fires, instead of having to use horses. This arrangement would get the steamers to the fires faster, eliminate the expense and mess of the horses, and keep the investment in the steamers intact. Quite a concept, but would it catch on?

Did it ever! After receiving extensive newspaper coverage on the delivery of his first tractor to the New York City Fire Department during December, 1911, orders for tractors began to flow in from across the country. During the next six or seven years, Christie produced more than 600 tractors for the nation's fire departments. Soon, competitors, including American-LaFrance, were producing similar tractors as well.

By around 1920, however, steamers were being phased out on a large scale, and a frenzy of orders for motorized fire engines was in progress.

There was only, therefore, a narrow window of opportunity for Christie – from about 1912 to 1920 – to capitalize on his idea, and he used that brief time to become a legend in firefighting history. Even so, he is probably even better remembered for the army tanks he designed, which were used in both World Wars I and II. Christie died in 1944 at the age of 77.

A Christie tractor pulls Pittsburgh's Steamer No. 2.

These firemen take a few moments to pose with their Christie tractor-drawn steamer.

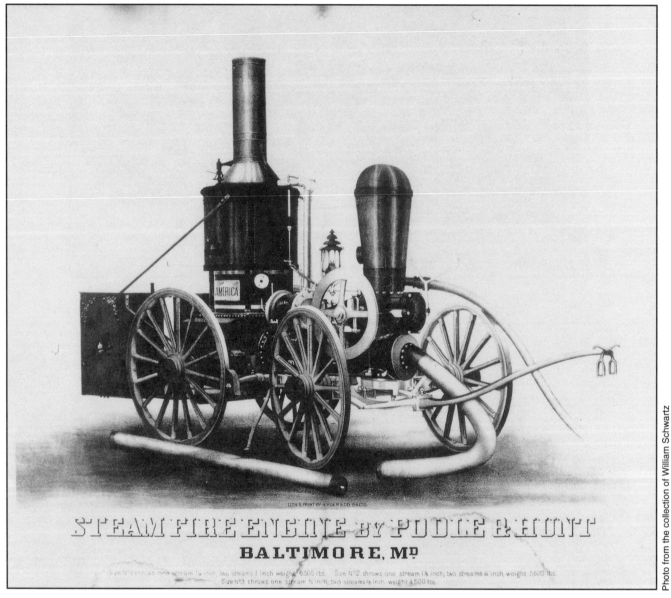

Photo from the collection of William Schwartz

Additional Steam Fire Engine Manufacturers
including the number of engines produced if known

John Agnew	Philadelphia, PA	4
Allen Supply Co. Works	Providence, RI	3
Allerton & Stevens	New Haven, CT	1
Allerton Iron Works	South Norwalk, CT	5
Arlington Iron Works	Waverly, IA	?
Arthur, Burham, and Gilroy	New York, NY	1
Joseph Banks	New York, NY	6
Bean & Scott	Lawrence, MA	1
George M. Bird & Co.	East Boston, MA	1
George F. Blake	Boston, MA	?
Campbell & Rickards	Philadelphia, PA	6
Campbell & Whittier	Roxbury, MA	3
G.J. & J. L. Chapman	Philadelphia, PA	7
Thomas M. Corbett & Co.	Milwaukee, WI	1
Watts G. Cory	Amsterdam, NY	1
John N. Dennison	Newark, N.J. & Reading, PA	5 or more
Ettenger & Edmond	Richmond, VA	5
R.J. Gould	Newark, NJ	70
Richard Harrell	Paterson, NJ	30
Haskell & Jones	Albany, NY	?
Jacob L. Haupt	New Brunswick, NJ	5
A.E. Heaton	New York, NY	2
Hill & Moorlen (Frank Moorlen & Co.)	Augusta, ME	2
Hinckley & Drury (Boston Locomotive Works)	Boston, MA	2
Hunsworth & Eakins	Philadelphia, PA	2
John A. Ives & Brother	Baltimore, MD	5
Jucket & Freeman	Roxbury, MA	5
Kimball Carriage Works	San Francisco, CA	1
Knapp Machine Works	Pittsburgh, PA	1
Knowlson & Kelly	Troy, NY	1
Knowles Steam Pump Works	Warren, MA	2
John L. Knowlton	Sharon Hill, PA	6
J.W. or S.W. Landell & Co.	Philadelphia, PA	3
Lee & Larned (Novelty Iron Works)	New York, NY	30
Joseph L. Lowry	Pittsburgh, PA	2
McKay & Gallagher	East Boston, MA	1
E.V. Merrick & Son	Philadelphia, PA	2
Issac P. Morris & Co.	Philadelphia, PA	1
Murray & Hazelhurst	Baltimore, MD	4
James Nelson	Pittsburgh, PA	1
B.S. Nichols	Burlington, VT	3
John Nichols	Paterson, NJ	1
Joseph Nussey	Paterson, NJ	2
Philadelphia Hydraulic Works	Philadelphia, PA	2
Poole & Hunt	Baltimore, MD	14
Sheppard Iron Works	Buffalo, NY	6
E.B. Sintzenich	Rochester, NY	1
James Smith	New York, NY	15
A.B. Taylor & Son	New York, NY	3
Union Machine Co.	Fitchburg, MA	12
William H. Van Ness	New York, NY	4
S.A. West	San Francisco, CA	1

Seems as if I could see Flash a-mopin' along here now,
Feelin' that he was simply an assistant to a cow;
But sometimes he'd imagine he heard the alarm-bell's din,
An' jump an' rear for a season before they could hold him in;

If ever I see an old hoss grow upward into a new -
If ever I see a milkman whose traps behind him flew,
'Twas that old hoss, a-rearin' an' racin' down the track,
An' that respectable milkman a-tryin' to hold him back.

An' if, as some consider, there's animals in the sky,
I think the poor old fellow is gettin' another try;
But if he should sniff the big fire that plagues the abode o' sin,
It'll take the strongest angel to hold the old fellow in.

From: "Flash: The Fireman's Story" by Will Carleton ©1885

CHAPTER 7

Those Incredible Fire Horses

*O*ccasionally, today, a steamer will participate in a parade, pulled by plodding draft horses. No....that's not the way it was! Fire horses were special – often Percherons, Belgian draft horses, Morgans, or a mixture of those breeds. Any horse could pull a milk wagon, but fire horses, often bred for that specific purpose, were the cream of the crop. They were fast, agile, and intelligent.

These horses are racing to a fire along this Boston, Massachusetts street, in 1908.

Photo from the collection of Michael LaPlante

Three graduates of Detroit's fire horse college race to a fire. Note the matched size and coloring.
The steam at the rear of the engine indicates that the engineer is blowing the whistle to clear the way.

Fire horse candidates were thoroughly examined by the department veterinarian, and then field tested by having them pull a carriage. If they passed, it was either on to fire horse college or to on-the-job training at a firehouse. Cities such as Detroit had training schools for fire horses. When they graduated, they were ready for duty.

Often the horses in the two or three-horse hitch were of matched sizes and coloring so as to make a striking appearance when pulling the elaborate, smoke-belching engine. Either two or three horses were assigned to each steamer, depending on the weight of the engine, and the steepness of any hills in the district. Firehouses were more likely to be located at the top of a hill rather than at the bottom. The horses, weighing at least 1400 pounds each, maintained perfect step.

Stalls for the horses were beside the engine, so that the horses could back into place within seconds of the house gong striking the alarm, even if they were fast asleep. The fastest steamer companies prided themselves in being out the door within 13 or 14 seconds after the first stroke of the gong, although 40 to 60 seconds was the norm.

The following account is from a history of the New York City Fire Department written in 1888:

"Suddenly the electric current causes a bell to sound, the measured strokes being given in quick and startling succession. The men spring from their beds simultaneously, as if they had been lying awake waiting for this summons. Ten or twelve pairs of legs are at one and the same time thrust into the trousers and boots, and are pulled on with two hitches. There is a terrific racket below. The bell is still sounding, repeating

Photo from the collection of W. Fred Conway

the signal five times over. Down a brass rod, in one corner of the room slide the firemen in rapid succession.

On the ground floor they find the horses already hitched to the engine, the driver on the box, and the furnace lighted. Each man jumps to his place on the rig, the doors are flung open, and in one minute from the first sound of the alarm the company is on its way to the fire. In fact, it is not unusual for an engine to be out of the house within 40 seconds of the moment when the bell first strikes.

At an alarm of fire at the Clarendon Hotel, in Fourth Avenue near Seventeenth Street, a stream of water was turned upon the building by an engine within two minutes and thirty-five seconds, the engine having been manned and brought four blocks in the meantime."

The history goes on the describe the automatic hitching of the fire horses:

"The time in hitching is wonderfully quick. Automatic machinery does the work quick enough to make your head swim. The instant the operator at Fire Headquarters opens the circuit to send an alarm, the current drops a metal ball right beside the gong. The ball strikes, presses down a bar of brass, and pulls a steel wire that automatically unhitches the springs at the sides of the stalls that hold the halters of the horses. The harness is always suspended over the shaft by an automatic iron 'hanger.' It is held in position by three springs. When the driver grabs the reins the tension loosens the springs, the harnesses drop down upon the horses, the watchman snaps the collars around the horses' necks, and automatic weights attached to little pulleys in the ceiling carry the framework of the 'hanger' up overhead out of the way."

Fire horses were the pets not only of the firemen who cared for them but of the entire neighborhood where the firehouse was located. Carrots, apples, and sugar lumps were treats the fire horses often enjoyed.

144

As fire horses were phased out and motorized tractors and engines were phased in, the horses were either put out to pasture or sold for other uses such as pulling delivery wagons. The final run for the fire horses was always a memorable and sad event, which the media usually played up beforehand. An alarm box on a prominent street corner would be struck by the fire chief of the city, and while thousands of spectators lined the streets on the route from the fire station to the box, the horses would pull the steamer (and ladder wagon) on their final run. Some of the crusty firefighters could not hide the tears in their eyes.

Stories about former fire horses bolting to fires, pulling their milk wagons behind them are true. They would fall in behind the new motorized engines, the milk wagon driver being unable to halt them. The oft-heard expression, "Like an old fire horse," is well-deserved.

Of the many true stories about the noble deeds of fire horses, perhaps the one about Dan, the fire horse who once refused to respond, is the most poignant. It is repeated here from an 1897 edition of *The Fireman's Herald:*

"Dan is the pride of the New York Fire Department. He is probably eighteen years old, and has been attached to Company No. 4 the greater part of his life. He will "shake hands" as a greeting to visitors, and he displays wonderful masculine instinct in his preference for fair womankind when he is asked for a kiss. He will kiss a beautiful lady with evident relish. He has never been ill during all these years, and he has run with the machine to 3,600 fires, and there has never been a fire below Houston Street to which he has not responded.

Dan is exceedingly amiable in disposition. Even little children play with him. Dan is within a few yards of the street, and youngsters used to timidly approach him and pat him on the nose, "shake hands," kiss him, and then scamper away. Dan was their favorite. One day a little tot more bold than the others entered Dan's stall, and the nice, soft bedding prompted the child to sit down, and in a few moments it had fallen into a peaceful slumber.

At this moment an alarm sounded on the fire gong. There was a hurrying of feet, a rush of the horses to their posts, and every man to his place. But Dan did not move. He was seen anxiously peering out of his stall, and all the men looked in wonder, this being the first time that Dan had failed to respond in fourteen years. One of the men ran to the horse, and then did he discover the cause of the trouble. Dan realized that had he moved he would have crushed the life out of the little child. The sleeping baby was picked up, and only then did noble Dan dash to his place."

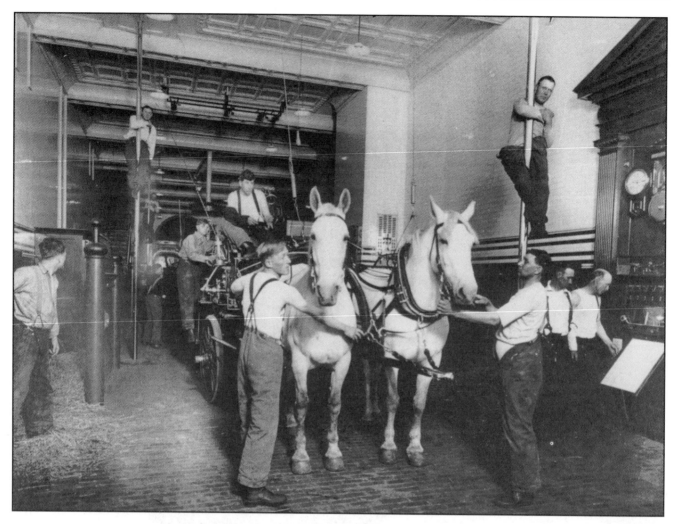

At top:

Los Angeles Engine 23 firefighters show how fast they can answer a night alarm in May, 1915. As the gong over the watch desk strikes the alarm box number, chains across the horses' stalls drop. The horses quickly take their places in front of the engine before the firefighters slide down the poles. The driver pulls a rope and the quick-hitch harness drops onto the backs of the horses. A system of ropes and counter-weights then pulls up the harness holders as the firefighters complete the hitch.

The fire horses in this painting are peering outside, perhaps wondering if they will be summoned to pull the engine through the snow.

Cincinnati's Engine No. 39 is shown above in 1914 before the wreck. The photo below shows the steamer after the wreck. Note the horse down in the foreground. He has been struck by an automobile.

Notice how the boys at the right are running as if they can keep pace with these three powerful steeds. Hook & Ladder Co. No. 1 thunders down Olive Street in New Haven, Connecticut in about 1900.

These two photos depict perfect examples of "out with the old and in with the new." The motorized fire engines soon replaced horse drawn apparatus.

CHAPTER 8

Where Are They Hiding?

*O*f the approximately 5,000 steam fire engines built between 1852 and 1917, less than 400 are known to survive.

$\mathcal{W}$hat happened to all of them? Many, of course, were junked or scrapped, but others were converted to other uses – to power threshers, dredgers, pile drivers, power plants etc. But the biggest exodus of the once proud steam fire engines occured during the World War II scrap drives. Hundreds of steamers kept in storage by fire departments were donated to the war effort. To have held them back would have been considered unpatriotic.

After a year-long search to locate the survivors, 331 of them have surfaced. Yet, there are probably others that remain hidden, defying the efforts of the many fire buffs, fire department officials and museum curators who have graciously assisted in the project to ferret them out. The author will welcome any additions, changes, or corrections to this list, which will be amended accordingly in future editions.

The picture below shows 1877 Ahrens No. 176 leaving the Uniontown, Pennsylvania, central fire station during the early 1940's on its final response, to be recycled into guns, shell casings, or whatever, for the war effort.

ALABAMA
Mobile: Phoenix Fire Museum
    1904 American-LaFrance, Metropolitan No. 3019,
           900 gpm
    1904 American-LaFrance, Metropolitan No. 3020,
           900 gpm
    *Note: These two engines are identical and are consecutively
        numbered.*

Montgomery: Municipal Building Lobby
    1910 American-LaFrance No. 3330, 1st size, 1000 gpm

ALASKA
Valdez: Valdez Museum & Historical Archive
    1907 Ahrens No. 131, 2nd size 700 gpm
    Note: Beautifully restored by Andy Swift.

ARIZONA
Phoenix: Hall of Flame Fire Museum
    1870 Shand & Mason (manufactured in England)
    1878 Silsby, 3rd size, No. 548
    1890 Shand & Mason (manufactured in England)
    1904 American, 2nd size 700 gpm, No. 2969
    *Note: The Hall of Flame is the largest and most
        comprehensive fire museum in the world.*

Scottsdale: Museum
    1877 Silsby, 3rd size, No. 548

Tucson: Tucson Fire Department
    1904 Nott, 3rd size, No. 737

CALIFORNIA
Anaheim: Anaheim Fire Department
    1903 Metropolitan, 700 gpm

Blue Jay: Private owner Howard Schneider
    1913 Waterous 4th size, 500 gpm

Burbank: City of Burbank Fire Department
    1905 Steamer w/Christie tractor

Chico
        Metropolitan

Coto De Caza: Private owner Dave Hubert
    1902 American, 2nd size, No. 2823
    *Note: A recent offer of $150,000 for this steamer was not
        accepted.*

This 1880 Silsby is on display at the Firefighters' Museum of Nova Scotia.

A restored 1861 Jeffers at the Middleburg Fire Department in Middeburg, Vermont.

This 1870 Clapp & Jones is on display in the American Museum of Fire Fighting, Hudson, New York. One of her old-time engineers said, "She vibrated or 'walked' so much that she was all right so long as we staked her down or tied her to a tree." At its first fire (in 1878) it shot a stream in the back of the burning building so powerful that it went clear through the structure, burst the shutters on the front, and hurled them across the street.

The Hero, a 1910 American-LaFrance on view at New England Fire & History Museum in Brewster, Massachusetts.

Eureka: Eureka Fire Department
1904 American-LaFrance, Extra 1st size, No. 3006

Long Beach: Long Beach Firemen's Museum
1894 Amoskeag

Los Angeles: Travel Town Museum
Steamer

Los Angeles: Los Angeles City Fire Department Museum
1893 Amoskeag, 2nd size, No. 690

Los Angeles: County of Los Angeles Fire Museum
1903 American Metropolitan, 700 gpm
Note: This engine was featured in the motion picture Gone With The Wind.

Napa: Napa Fire Museum
1904 Nott

Sacramento: Sutter Museum
 1862 Silsby, 1st size, No. 39
 Note: This is one of the oldest surviving steamers in the United States.

San Bernandino: San Bernandino Fire Museum
 American-LaFrance
 Clapp & Jones

San Diego: The Firehouse Museum (Pioneer Hook & Ladder Co.)
 1904 American-LaFrance Metropolitan, No. 2991
 1100 gpm

San Francisco: Hook & Ladder Museum
 LaFrance, No. 386

San Jose: San Jose Fire Department Muster Team
 1899 American Metropolitan, 2nd size, No. 2676
 Note: Display includes a 1914 Martin-Knox tractor.

Santa Fe Springs: Santa Fe Springs Fire Department
 American Metropolitan, 3rd size, No. 2900

Stockton: Pioneer Museum & Haggin Galleries
 1862 Neafie & Levy, 2nd size
 Note: This is one of the oldest surviving steamers in the United States.

Stockton: Stockton Museum
 1874 Amoskeag, 2nd size, No. 469

Suisan City: Suisan City Fire Department
 1898 American w/Knox-Martin tractor

Woodland: Woodland Fire Department
 1874 Clapp & Jones, 3rd size
 Note: Beautifully restored. In first line service until 1892, it came out of reserve to fight a large fire in 1937.

Yermo: Calico Ghost Town
 Ahrens

COLORADO
Colorado Springs: Pike's Peak Ghost Town
 1898 American, 2nd size, No. 2606

Denver: Denver Firefighters Museum
 1890 Ahrens

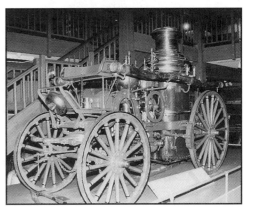

An 1889 Ahrens, No. 577 on display at the Yakima Valley Museum, Yakima, Washington.

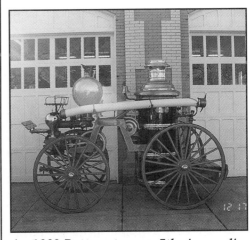

An 1889 Button steamer, 5th size on display the Union Fire Co. No. 1, in Belmar, New Jersey.

A 1906 Ahrens Continental, 500 gpm is located at the Firefighters Museum in Everett, Washington.

A 1912 Waterous steamer on display at the Conway Fire Museum in New Albany, Indiana. This 2nd size 800 gpm steamer served Ottawa, Ontario, Canada in front line duty from 1912 to 1920, when it was placed in reserve. It fought the Ottawa City Hall Fire in 1931.

Parker: Braehead Ranch Fire Brigade
1864   Amoskeag, 1st size

CONNECTICUT
Brantford: Museum
1878   Silsby, 4th size 500 gpm, No. 588

Hartford: Hartford Fire Department
Steamer w/tractor

Manchester: Connecticut Firemen's Historical Society Museum
1864   Johnson, 4th size, hand-drawn

Norwich: Yantic Fire Company
Silsby

Vernon: Rockville Fire Company
Steamer

Wilson: Wilson Fire Department
Amoskeag, self-propelled

DISTRICT OF COLUMBIA
District of Columbia: Engine Co. No. 18
Metropolitan, 3rd size

District of Columbia: Smithsonian Institution
1878   Clapp & Jones
Note: This engine is on loan to the Fire Museum of Maryland.
Two additional steamers

FLORIDA
Fort Myers: Edison Museum
1909   American-LaFrance

Gainesville: Florida State Museum
1886   Ahrens, 4th size, No. 459

Jacksonville: Jacksonville Fire Museum
1898   American-LaFrance
1902   Steamer

Orlando Fire Station No. 3 Museum
1908   American-LaFrance Metropolitan, No. 3352

GEORGIA
Atlanta: Atlanta History Center
American-LaFrance

Augusta: Museum
Steamer

Hawkinsville
LaFrance

Marietta: Fire Station No. 1
1879   Silsby, 3rd size, 600 gpm, No. 655
Note: This engine was disassembled and hidden during World War II to escape the scrap drive. Beautiful restoration by Robert L. Johnson of "Whistles in the Woods."

IDAHO
Boise: Idaho State Historical Society
1902   American Metropolitan, 3rd size, No. 2910

The G.R. Sherman, an 1875 Clapp & Jones steamer on display at the Conway Fire Museum in New Albany, Indiana. It is a 4th size 500 gpm steamer that served the village of Port Henry, New York, on the shore of Lake Champlain. The authentic restoration was done by Andy Swift of Firefly Restorations.

Photo courtesy of the Fire Museum of Maryland

This 1905 LaFrance with Christie tractor is on display at the Fire Museum of Maryland.

159

An 1884 Button No. 156, 5th size, owned by the Nebraska City Volunteer Fire Department, Nebraska City, Nebraska.

ILLINOIS

Chicago: Museum of Science & Industry
1869 Amoskeag, 1st size, No. 313
Gould

Chicago: Fire Department Repair Shop
1893 American, 3rd size, No. 2142
1907 Ahrens, 2nd size, 700 gpm, No. 135

Elgin: Elgin Fire Barn No. 5 Museum
1869 Silsby #207, 3rd size
Note: The original price of this steamer was $5,000.

Hampshire: Shireland Amusement Park (now closed)
American

Morris: Morris Fire Department
1868 Steamer

New Salem
1904 American-LaFrance Metropolitan, 2nd size, No. 2955

Rockford: Private owner Matthew Spinello
1883 Amoskeag, 2nd size, No. 580

INDIANA

Evansville: Museum of Arts & Sciences
1902 American Metropolitan, Extra 1st size, No. 2946

Fort Wayne: Firefighters' Museum
1893 Amoskeag, Extra 1st size, 1100 gpm, No. 701

Lafayette: Private owner John R. Gambs
1868 Silsby, 3rd size

LaPort
1873 Silsby, 3rd size, No. 412

New Albany: Conway Fire Museum
1875 Clapp & Jones, 4th size 500 gpm, No. 131
1912 Waterous, 2nd size 800 gpm

Rushville: Rush County Historical Society
1893 American (Ahrens), 4th size, No. 2250
Note: The original cost of this engine was $4,350. It's last alarm was January 25, 1924 at Rushville Odd Fellow's Hall.

Seymour: Seymour Fire Department
1885 Ahrens, 5th size, No. 433

1904 American-LaFrance Metropolitan at the Crum Lynne Vauclain Fire Company, in Crum Lynne, Pennsylvania. It is painted green.

Brass and nickel were used to the utmost in the restoration of this machine.

The Eagle.

Builders plate of Ashland No. 1.

The Ashland No. 1.

Pressure gauge of the Ashland No. 1.

The Eagle and Ashland No. 1 are on display at the White Mountain Central Railroad Fire Station in Lincoln, New Hampshire.

The DuPont, an 1872 Amoskeag of Portmouth, New Hampshire, on view at the New England Fire & History Museum in Brewster, Maine.

Washington: Davies County Historical Society
   1878   Ahrens, 4th size, No. 202

IOWA
Belle Plaine: Belle Plaine Fire Department Museum
   1891   Ahrens, 5th size, No. 641
   Note: On March 7, 1905, this engine was loaded onto a special train to Cedar Rapids, where it pumped for 72 hours at the Quaker Oats plant fire.

Charitonm
   1877   Silsby

Harlan
           Steamer

Manchester: Delaware Historical Museum
           Steamer

Oelwein
           Silsby

KANSAS
Topeka: Topeka Fire Department
   1904   American-LaFrance, 2nd size, No. 2998

Wichita: Cowtown Museum
   1902   American Metropolitan, Extra 1st size, No. 2821

LOUISIANA
Gretna: Louisiana State Fire Museum
   1876   Nichols (Gould patent) 250 gpm
   Note: This engine is hand-drawn, and remained in service until 1928. It is the only steamer of its type still in existence.

New Orleans: New Orleans Fire Department Museum
   1896   Ahrens, 2nd size, No. 2438

MAINE
Bangor: Cole Land Transportation Museum
   1907   Amoskeag

Belfast: Belfast Fire Department
   1888   Amoskeag

An 1899 LaFrance steamer owned by the Phillipsburg Fire Department in Phillipsburg, Pennsylvania.

Boothbay: Boothbay Railway Village
1885   Button, 800 gpm, No. 170
*Note: Originally purchased by Old Town, Maine, for $3,192.
It remained in service for 38 years.*

Camden
1896   Amoskeag 1st size, No. 694

Fairfield: Fairfield Fire Department
1882   Amoskeag #571, 3rd size

Houlton: Houlton Fire Department
1872   Amoskeag, 3rd size, No. 377
*Note: This engine was originally purchased for $2,300. The
frame is of the rare "harp" configuration.*

Ogunquit: Ogunquit Fire Department
1886   Button

Skowhegan: Seal Cove Auto Museum
Amoskeag, 3rd size

Vinahaven: Vinahaven Fire Department
1888   Silsby

An 1873 Silsby steamer at Ye Olde Fire Station Museum in Cicero, New York.

This 1883 steamer was in active service at Sidney Park, Ohio until 1916. After many years in storage, it was restored to like-new condition by the Dayton Fire Department and moved to Carillon Park in Dayton, Ohio.

This 1880 horse-drawn steamer is on display at the Pioneer Village in Minden, Nebraska.

This 1861 harp frame steamer was the first horse-drawn steam-propelled pumper in Oklahoma. It is on display at the Oklahoma Firefighters Museum in Oklahoma City, Oklahoma.

MARYLAND

Baltimore: Baltimore City Fire Museum
1905   LaFrance, Extra 1st size, No. 501
Note: This steamer is displayed with a Christie tractor.

Baltimore: B & O Railroad Museum
1892   LaFrance, No. 246

Cambridge: Rescue Fire Company
1906   LaFrance steamer

Crisfield: Crisfield Fire Department
Clapp & Jones

Easton: Easton Fire Department
Silsby

Elkton: Singerly Engine Company
Steamer
Note: This engine is featured on a print as well as a jigsaw puzzle.

Hebron: Chesapeake Fire Museum
1890   LaFrance

Lutherville: Fire Museum of Maryland
1878   Clapp & Jones, 400 gpm
Note: This engine is on loan from the Smithsonian Institution.
1885   Amoskeag, 4th size, 350 gpm, No. 552
1888   Clapp & Jones, 3rd size 600 gpm, No. 503
Note: This engine fought the Great Baltimore Fire of 1904.
1899   American, 4th size, 500 gpm, No. 2642
1905   LaFrance w/Christie tractor, 1100 gpm, Extra 1st size, No. 510
Note: This museum is one of the largest fire museums in the United States. On the first Sunday of May each year, the steamers are taken outside, fired up and pumped.

Pocomoke City: Pocomoke City Fire Department
Clapp & Jones

Salisbury: Salisbury Fire Department
1879   Silsby No. 616

MASSACHUSETTS

Bedford: New Bedford Fire Museum
1884   Steamer
1890   Amoskeag, 2nd size, No. 662

Boston (South Boston): Boston Fire Museum
1882 Amoskeag w/Christie tractor
1896 Amoskeag w/Christie tractor

Brewster: New England Fire & History Museum
1879 Silsby, 1st size, No. 789
1910 American-LaFrance Metropolitan, No. 3317

Brookline: Larz Anderson Museum
1906 Amoskeag, 1st size, No. 785

Hardwick: Private owner George Anderson
    Amoskeag
    Amoskeag
    LaFrance

Pittsfield: Berkshire County Museum of Firefighting
    Steamer

South Carver: National Fire Museum
1889 Amoskeag, 3rd size, No. 639
1913 Ahrens Continental w/Christie tractor, 2nd size 700 gpm, No. 199

Wakefield: Wakefield Fire Engine Company No. 1
1907 Amoskeag, No. 831, 600 gpm
Note: *Original cost was $5,157. This steamer pumped 20-1/2 hours at the Chelsea, Massachusettes conflagration in 1908. In 1912 it was replaced by a motorized engine, but remained in reserve until 1930.*

Waltham: Charles River Museum of Industry
1871 Amoskeag, 2nd size 700 gpm, No. 364

MICHIGAN
Allendale: Engine House No. 5 Museum
    Silsby

Alpena: in a museum
1871 Clapp & Jones

Dearborn: Henry Ford Museum & Greenfield Village
1884 Button, 5th size, No. 147
1892 Amoskeag, Extra 1st size, No. 686
1906 Amoskeag, 1st size 900 gpm , No. 809
    Cosmopolitan

Flint: Private owner Wesley Trathen
1900 American Metropolitan, 5th size, No. 2722
1899 Clapp & Jones, 4th size, No. 2665

This steamer is on display at The Firehouse Museum in San Diego, California.

An 1881 Silsby on display at the Wirt Park Fire Museum, Hanover, Pennsylvania.

An 1869 3rd size Silsby steamer at the Fire Barn No. 5 Museum in Elgin, Illinois.

Detroit: Box 42 Associates
1908   Ahrens, 1st size 900 gpm, No. 155

Detroit: Detroit Historical Museum
Metropolitan
Note: This engine is stored in the museum basement.

Grand Rapids: City Museum
Steamer

Harrisville: In county building
Cosmopolitan

Hickory Corners: In an automobile museum
1895   American, 3rd size, No. 2338

Homer: Homer Fire Department
Button, 3rd size

An 1891 Silsby steamer on display at the CIGNA Museum and Art Collection in Philadelphia, Pennsylvania.

The Pioneer, an 1857 Reaney & Neafie on display at the CIGNA Museum and Art Collection in Philadelphia, Pennsylvania. This engine is thought to be the oldest steam fire engine in existence in the United States.

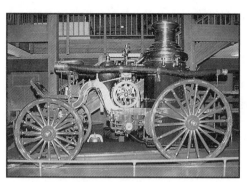

This 1889 Ahrens steamer is refitted with a Nott spiral tube boiler and is on display at the Yakima Valley Museum in Washington.

An 1875 hand-drawn Clapp & Jones on display at the New York State Museum in Albany, New York.

Lansing: Private owner
1876   Clapp & Jones, No. 143

Lansing: Michigan Millers Insurance Co.
1895   American No. 2378

Mackinac
      Button

Traverse City: Traverse City Fire Department
1901   Metropolitan, No. 2806

MINNESOTA
Burnsville: Private owner Ken Peterson
1890   Ahrens, 2nd size, No. 626
1906   American-LaFrance, 1st size, No. 508
1912   Nott, 800 gpm, No. 791

Ellsworth
      Waterous

Ferbus Falls
1882   Silsby, 4th size, No. 714

Jordon
      Waterous

Minneapolis: National Firefighters Memorial Museum
1902   Nott

New Ulm
1888   Silsby

Pine City
      Waterous

St. Paul: Minnesota Historical Society
1895   Waterous, village size

St. Paul: Private owner Ken Freiberg
1863   Amoskeag, No. 78, 2nd size, "harp" frame
1891   Ahrens, 2nd size 700 gpm, No. 648

St. Paul: St. Paul Fire Department
1903   American Metropolitan

Tower: At a pavillion in a park
1892   Ahrens, 3rd class, No. 668

Winona
      American Metropolitan

MISSISSIPPI
Aberdeen: Aberdeen Fire Department
1899   American, 4th size, No. 2695

Columbus: Columbus Fire Department
Steamer

Louisville: The American Heritage "Big Red" Fire Museum
1869   Cole Brothers
1888   Silsby, 5th size, No. 910

Natchez: Natchez Fire Department
Steamer

MISSOURI
St. Louis: Ahrens-Fox Fire Engine Co.
1877 Ahrens, 3rd size, No. 182
Note: This company is owned by firebuffs Ken Menke Sr. and Jr. who purchased the rights to the Ahrens-Fox name. This engine is thought to be the second oldest surviving steamer manufactured in Cincinnati.

St. Louis: Anheuser-Busch "Grants Farm" Museum
1888   Ahrens, 2nd size, No. 564

MONTANA
Virginia City: Bovey Restorations
LaFrance w/tractor

NEBRASKA
Minden: Harold Warp's Pioneer Village
1902   American, 1st size, No. 2859, 950 gpm
Note: This engine fought the Great Chicago Fire, and the famous Iroquois Theater Fire in Chicago.
1909   American-LaFrance w/tractor

Nebraska City: Nebraska City Volunteer Fire Department
1884   Button, 5th size 400 gpm, No. 156
Note: The original cost of this steamer was $2,800.

NEVADA
Reno: Hurrah's Museum
1874   Silsby, 3rd class, No. 441

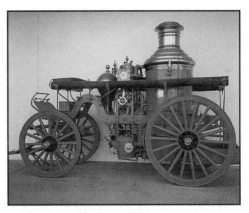

A 1902 American Fire Engine Company Metropolitan, No. 2946, is exhibited at the Museum of Arts & Sciences in Evansville, Indiana.

An 1891 Ahrens steamer, No. 64 is displayed at Belle Plaines' Fire Department Museum in Belle Plaines, Iowa.

169

A 1907 Ahrens Continental on display at the Valdez Heritage Center in Valdez, Alaska. The steamer never left Valdez and was in service until 1935. The photo below shows the condition of the engine before it was fully restored by Andy Swift.

Virginia City: Virginia City Historical Society
Clapp & Jones
Steamer

NEW HAMPSHIRE

Berlin: Berlin Fire Department
1905 Amoskeag, 2nd size, No. 783

East Swanzey: Private owner
1901 Amoskeag, No. 767

Exeter: Exeter Fire Department
1873 Amoskeag, 2nd size, No. 458

Franklin: Franklin Firefighters Museum
1900 American, 500 gpm

Lincoln: White Mountain Central Railroad Fire Station
1909 American & British Mfg. Co., 900 gpm, No. 846
Amoskeag, 550 gpm, No. 796

Manchester: Engine No. 2
1871 Amoskeag

North Woodstock: Clark's Trading Post
1909 Amoskeag, No. 846
Amoskeag
Silsby

Tuftonboro: Private owner Jerome Rooney
Steamer

Wolfeboro: Monitor Firehouse Museum - Clark House Museum Complex
1872 Amoskeag, 2nd size, beautifully restored by Stephen Heaver, Jr.

NEW JERSEY

Belmar: Belmar-Goodwill Hose Fire Company
1869 Button

Belmar: Belmar-Union Fire Co. No. 1
1889 Button, 5th size 250 gpm, No. 213

Boonton: New Jersey Firemen's Museum
1884 Amoskeag #583
1915 American-LaFrance #3437, 750 gpm

Boonton: Boonton Fire Department
Steamer

Reno No. 1, a 1902 American, 2nd size, No. 2823. Privately owned and restored by Dave Hubert, Coto de Caza, California.

Bridgeton: Bridgeton Fire Company
1873 Silsby

Burlington: Burlington-Hope Fire Co. No. 1
1894 LaFrance, No. 343

Dover: Dover Fire Museum
1870's Steamer

Dunellen: Day Museum
1887 Silsby, 5th size, No. 873

Frenchtown: Frenchtown Fire Company
1875 Clapp & Jones

Milltown: Eureka Fire Museum
1870 Silsby

**Mountain View (Wayne Township):
Community Fire Co. No. 1**
1899 American w/Christie tractor, No. 2640

An 1888 Ahrens, 500 gpm, No. 549 on display at the McKinley Museum in Canton, Ohio.

171

An 1873 Clapp & Jones, 3rd size that saw service until 1892. It has been beautifully restored and is owned by the Woodland Fire Department in Woodland, California.

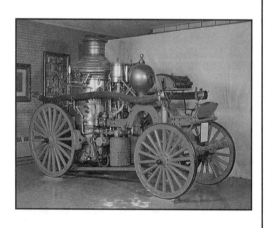

A LaFrance steamer on display at The American Museum of Fire Fighting in Hudson, New York. This steamer was last used at a fire in 1940.

Mt. Holly: Mt. Holly Relief Fire Co., No. 1
1880   Silsby

North Plainfield: North Plainfield Exempt Firemen's Museum
1863   Amoskeag, 2nd size, No. 75

Somerville: Somerville Exempt Firemen's Museum
1873   Steamer

Wayne: Wayne Community Fire Co.
1899   American Metropolitan w/Christie tractor, 2nd size, No. 2640

Woodbury: Museum
1911   Ahrens-Fox Continential, 3rd size 600 gpm, No. 184

Wycoff: Wycoff Exempts
1904   Nott, 1st size, No. 633

NEW MEXICO
Albuquerque: The Firehouse Restaurant
1873   Steamer

Roswell: Private owner M. Glover
1900   American Metropolitan, 4th size, No. 2693

Scandia: Displayed in a restaurant
Silsby

NEW YORK
Albany: New York State Museum
1874   Clapp & Jones, 5th size.
Note: This engine was used as late as 1940 by the Albany Fire Department to thaw frozen hoses.
1901   American, 3rd size 600 gpm, No. 2797

Bloomsbury: Bloomsbury Fire Company
1897   Waterous

Buffalo: Buffalo Fire Historical Society
1907   American-LaFrance, 1st size, 850 gpm, No. 531

Cicero: Ye Olde Fire Station Museum
1873   Silsby, 250 gpm, No. 911

Congers
Cosmopolitan

East Hampton, L.I.: East Hampton Fire Department
1906 Nott w/American-LaFrance tractor

Freeport: Freeport Fire Department
1906 Nott w/American-LaFrance Type 31 tractor

Friendship
1890 Silsby, 5th size, No. 657

Hudson: American Museum of Firefighting
1869 Clapp & Jones, No. 91.
Note: This engine was reported to have fought the Great Chicago Fire in 1871. In 1994 it was featured in the motion picture The Road To Wellsville *about the Kellogg family, starring Anthony Hopkins.*
1870 Clapp & Jones, No. 83
1882 LaFrance, No. 289
Note: This engine fought its last fire in 1940.
1898 American Cosmopolitan
Note: This tiny [by comparison] "sidewalk" size engine is only 6 feet long and 6 feet high.

Ithaca: Ithaca Fire Department Headquarters
1896 LaFrance, No. 349

**Kingston: Volunteer Firemen's Hall and Museum
         of Kingston**
1898 LaFrance

Mechanicsville
1871 Button

Monroe: Museum Village in Orange County
1882 Clapp & Jones
Note: This steamer was originally purchased for $4,000.
1907 American-LaFrance Metropolitan, No. 3208

New York City: The New York Fire Museum
1901 American-LaFrance

Oswego: Oswego Fire Department
        Amoskeag

Prospect: Private owner
        American-LaFrance Metropolitan, 900 gpm,
        No. 3069

Riverhead: Washington Engine Co. No. 2
1903 American Metropolitan, 3rd size 600 gpm,
        No. 2947

This 1889 Button, 5th size, 350 gpm is on display at the Belmar-Union Fire Co. No. 1 in Belmar, New Jersey.

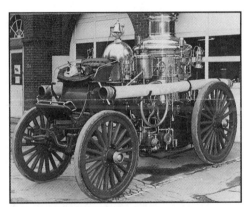

This 1893 Amoskeag steam fire engine, Extra 1st size, 1100 gpm is on display at the Fort Wayne Firefighters Museum, Inc. in Fort Wayne Indiana.

A 1911 American-LaFrance steamer is on display at Portland, Oregon's Jeff Morris Fire Museum. This steamer stayed in service until 1922 or 1923 and has been restored to its exact original condition.

Hugenot No. 1, an 1879 Silsby is on display at the New England Fire & History Museum in Brewster, Massachusetts.

Schuylerville
> Button

Seneca Falls: Historical Society of Seneca Falls
> Silsby, No. 685

Stillwater
> Button, No. 185

Stony Brook, L.I.: The Museum at Stony Brook
> 1874   Amoskeag

Utica: At an insurance company
> American-LaFrance Metropolitan, 1000 gpm, No. 3059

NORTH CAROLINA
Cleveland: American-LaFrance Museum
> 1904   American-LaFrance Cosmopolitan, 5th size, No. 2959
> *Note: Restored by Andy Swift.*
> 1911   American-LaFrance Metropolitan, 600 gpm.
> *Note: Restored by Andy Swift.*
> 1886   Silsby/American/Manning, 1st size

Elizabeth City: Museum of the Albemarle
> 1888   Silsby
> *Note: This steamer originally cost $3,100.*

New Bern: New Bern Firemen's Museum
> 1879   Silsby, 4th size, No. 604
> *Note: In service until 1915 — a period of 36 years.*

Rocky Mount
> 1896   Silsby, 5th size, No. 2471

OHIO
Arcanum: Arcanum Fire Department
> 1885   Ahrens, 4th size, No. 425

Bryan
> 1900   Metropolitan

Bucyrus: Bucyrus Fire Department
> Silsby

Canton: McKinley Museum
> 1888   Ahrens, 3rd size, 500 gpm, No. 549
> *Note: Retired from active service in 1917.*

Cincinnati: Cincinnati Fire Museum
1884   Ahrens, 3rd size, 600 gpm, No. 394
Note: *This engine pumped water from basements during the 1937 Ohio River flood, 53 years after its manufacture.*

Cleveland: Crawford Auto/Aviation Museum
1888   Ahrens, 3rd size, No. 541

Columbus: Ohio State Museum
1861   Silsby #28

Columbus: Columbus Fire Museum
1881   Amoskeag, Extra 1st size, No. 560

Columbus: Historical Society of Columbus
1907   Ahrens Continential #125, 3rd size, 600 gpm

Dayton: Carillon Park
1883   Ahrens, 2nd size, No. 378

An 1872 Amoskeag, 3rd size, No. 377 is at the Houlton Fire Department in Houlton, Maine. This steamer is fully operational.

A 1910 Ahrens Continental, 1st size, 900 gpm, No. 179 is at the Memphis Fire Department Museum in Memphis, Tennessee.

Photo from the collection of Richard Adelman

175

A 1907 Amoskeag steamer located at the Cole Land Transportation Museum in Bangor, Maine.

The Aurora, a restored 1879 Silsby on display at the Marietta Fire Station No. 1 in Marietta, Georgia.

Gahanna: Private owners Jack & Karen Selvey
    1892 Ahrens, 3rd size, No. 2110
    1895 American, 1st size, No. 2339

Galion: Galion Fire Department
    1906 Ahrens Continental, 3rd size 600 gpm, No. 106

Hamilton: Butler County Historical Society
    1873 Ahrens, 2nd size, 700 gpm, No. 32
    Note: This steamer is thought to be the oldest surviving steamer manufactured in Cincinnati.

Hamilton: Private owner: Hugh Holbrock
    1904 American-LaFrance Metropolitan No. 3277

Leipsic: Leipsic Fire Department
    1895 American 5th size, 450 gpm, No. 2364

Lima: Allen County Museum
    1886 Ahrens, 6th size, No. 487

Loveland: Loveland Fire Department
    1894 Ahrens Continental, 3rd size, No. 2252

Maumee: In a car wash
    Steamer of Canadian Manufacture

Montpelier: Williams County Historical Society
    1900 American, 1st size, No. 2723

Morrow: Private owner Lewis Brown
    Ahrens, 5th size, No. 555

Oxford: Oxford Fire Department
    1895 American, 5th size, No. 2386

Oxford: Private owner William Patten Schlott
    1902 Metropolitan, 2nd size, No. 2911

Piqua: Piqua Fire Department
    1904 American-LaFrance Metropolitan, 800 gpm, 2nd size, No. 2997
    Note: The original cost was $4,750.

Ripley: Ripley Fire Department
    1887 Ahrens, 5th size, No. 481

Saint Paris: Johnson-Saint Paris Fire Department
    1885 Ahrens, 5th size, No. 415

Sandusky: Cedar Point
    Amoskeag

Tiffin: In a museum
   1866 Cole Brothers

Toledo: Toledo Firefighters Museum
   1895   Ahrens, 5th size, No. 2364

VanWert: Central's Fire Museum
   1907   Ahrens Continental, 3rd size 600 gpm, No. 139
   Note: Beautifully restored by Ken Soderbeck.
         Merryweather *(Manufactured in England.)*

OKLAHOMA
Oklahoma City: Oklahoma State Firefighters Museum
   1861   Amoskeag, harp frame
   Note: This is one of the earliest steamers still in existence.
   1900   American, 3rd size, No. 2696

OREGON
Albany: Engine Co. No. 1 Muster Team
   1907   American-LaFrance Metropolitan, 2nd size
         700 gpm, No. 3178

Forest Grove: Forest Grove Fire Department
   1907   American-LaFrance

Junction City
         Steamer

Milwaukie: Private owner Al Foglio
   1902   American, Extra 1st size, No. 2824

Portland: Jeff Morris Fire Museum
   1879   Amoskeag, 300 gpm, No. 219
   1911   American-LaFrance, 3rd size, No. 3327

Portland: Private owner Bruce Kegg c/o Engine 17
   1880   Merriweather No. 9515
   Note: Hand drawn on two wheels, manufactured in England.
   1890   Amoskeag
   1914   Merriweather (England)

Portland: Private owner Myron Curtis
   1896   American
   1904   Nott

Salem
         Steamer

PENNSYLVANIA
Allentown: Allentown Fire Department
   1909   Ahrens, 1st size, 900 gpm, No. 170

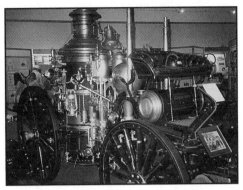

A 1909 American-LaFrance on display at the Edison Museum in Fort Myers, Florida.

A 1906 Ahrens Extra 1st size, 1100 gpm, No. 110 on display at the Old Firehouse & Police Museum in Superior, Wisconsin.

An 1895 American, 5th size is owned by the Leipsic Fire Department in Leipsic, Ohio.

Ambler: Ambler-Wissahickon Fire Co.
1896   American (Silsby), 3rd size, No. 2483

Barto: Private owner Hyde W. Ballard
1900   Metropolitan

**Boyertown: Boyertown-Hafer Museum
              aka Boyertown-Burks County Museum**
1898   Metropolitan

**Chambersburg: Chambersburg Volunteer Fireman's
              Museum**
1903   LaFrance

Clearfield
          LaFrance

Crum Lynne: Crum Lynne Vauclain Fire Co.
1904   American-LaFrance Metropolitan

Everett
1880   Silsby, 4th size, No. 636

Gettysburg
1886   Silsby, 2nd size, No. 841

Shown above are two of the five steamers located at the Fire Museum of Maryland in Lutherville, Maryland.

Glen Mills: Private owner Bud Luckenbach
1892 Silsby

Hanover: Wirt Park Fire Museum
1881 Silsby, 4th size, 550 gpm, No. 688
Note: Original purchase price $3,300.

Harrisburg: Fire Museum of Greater Harrisburg
1877 Silsby, 3rd size, No. 560
Note: On loan from Hamburg Fire Co., Hamburg, PA.

Harrisburg: State Museum of Pennsylvania
1870 Silsby, 3rd size, No. 232

Hazelton: Hazelton Fire Department
1894 LaFrance, 4th size, No. 421

Hershey: Hershey Museum
1884 Button, 6th size, No. 145

Honesdale: Honesdale Protection Fire Co.
1875 Silsby

Lansford: American Fire Co. No. 1
1916 Ahrens, extra first size, No. 205
Note: This engine was in actual service until 1968, and fought its last fire in 1967, making it the final steam fire engine in service in the United States. It has been appraised at $180,000.

Lebanon: Lebanon Union Fire Company
1866 Amoskeag

Minersville: Minersville-Mountaineer Hose Co.
1866 Amoskeag
Note: This steamer may be purchased for $150,000.

Orland: Private owners Harry & Len Supplee
American-LaFrance Metropolitan, No. 3253

Philadelphia: CIGNA Museum & Art Collection
1857 Reaney & Neafie
Note: This engine is thought to be the oldest steam fire engine in existence in the United States.
1891 Silsby, 4th size, No. 1013

Philadelphia: Fireman's Hall Museum
1907 American-LaFrance Metropolitan, 1st size, No. 3203

A Silsby on display at a restaurant in Scandia, New Mexico.

A 1908 American-LaFrance Metropolitan on display at the Orlando Fire Station No. 3 Museum in Orlando, Florida.

An 1888 Silsby resides in New Ulm, Minnesota.

A Silsby steamer resides in Oelwein, Iowa. The two cans on either side of the driver's seat were for horse blankets in winter and horse fly netting in summer.

Phillipsburg: Phillipsburg Fire Department
1899   LaFrance, 4th size, 600 gpm
Steamer #431
Note: *The original cost of this steamer was $3,750.*

Spring City: Spring City-Liberty Fire Company
1882   Silsby, 2nd size, No. 684

Stroudsburg: Stroudsburg Fire Department
1871   Clapp & Jones
Note: *This engine fought the Stroudsburg High School fire in 1927.*

Titusville: Drake Museum
1868   Amoskeag, 1st size, No. 283

Williamsport: Williamsport Fire Department
1886   LaFrance, 3rd size, 600 gpm

York: The Fire Museum of York County
Merryweather *(Manufactured in England.)*

RHODE ISLAND
Jamestown: Jamestown Fire Museum
1885   Steamer
1894   LaFrance, 3rd size, No. 307

Narragansett: Narragansett Fire Department
1907   Amoskeag w/Federal tractor, Extra 1st size, No. 810
Note: *This engine is thought to be the largest surviving steamer in the United States. It is also though to be the only surviving Amoskeag that was built in Providence, Rhode Island.*

Woonsocket: Woonsocket Fire Department
1872   Jeffers
Note: *This is one of only two known surviving steamers manufactured by Jeffers. It is incomplete with the pump missing.*

SOUTH CAROLINA
Aiken
Steamer

Charleston: Charleston Fire Department Museum
1870   Amoskeag, 1st size, No. 329

Columbia: Columbia Fire Department
1903   American Metropolitan #2894

SOUTH DAKOTA
Sioux Falls: Sioux Falls Fire Department
1882   Silsby, 3rd size, No. 718

TENNESSEE
Chattanooga: Chattanooga Fire Department
1892   American, 3rd size, No. 2104

Knoxville: Knoxville Fire Department
Steamer

Memphis: Memphis Fire Department Museum
1910   Ahrens Continental, 1st size, No. 179

Nashville: Tennessee Children's Museum
1900   American, 3rd size, No. 2765

TEXAS
Beaumont: Fire Museum of Texas
1879   Silsby

Dallas: Dallas Firefighters Museum
1884   Ahrens, 3rd size, No. 392

Dallas: Private owner Harvey Carter
1896   Ronald (manufactured in Canada)

El Paso: El Paso Fire Department
1893   American, 900 gpm

Fredericksburg: Frederickburg Fire Department
American-LaFrance Cosmopolitan

Houston: Houston Fire Museum
1892   Ahrens No. 449 or No. 2106

San Antonio: San Antonio Transporation Museum
1892   American, 3rd class, No. 2106

VERMONT
Bellows: Steamtown
1885   Button, 3rd size, No. 170

Middlebury: Middlebury Fire Department
1861   Jeffers
Note: This is the oldest of two Jeffers Steamers known to survive.

A 1902 Amoskeag steamer is on display at the Manchester Historical Society in Manchester, Massachusetts.

This beautifully restored steamer resplendent with chrome plating on the boiler and air chamber, was photographed in Manchester, New Hampshire.

This engine is maintained by American Fire Company of Lansford, Pennsylvania. It is a 1915 White - 1916 Ahrens Fox extra first size pumper. It remained in actual service until 1968, making it the final steamer in service in the United States.

This Waterous is located in Pine City, Minnesota.

VIRGINIA
Charlottesville: Charlottesville Fire Department
1904   Nott

Richmond: Steamer Co. No. 5 Museum
1904   American-LaFrance 1000 gpm
1906   Amoskeag, 750 gpm, No. 798

Roanoke: Private Zoo
1907   Ahrens Continental, 1st size, 900 gpm

WASHINGTON
Aberdeen: Aberdeen Fire Department
1902   American Metropolitan, Extra 1st size, No. 2892

Everett: Everett Fire Dept. Firefighters Assn.
1906   Ahrens Continental, 3rd size 600 gpm, No. 123

LaCenter: Whitefire Antiques
1892   American, 3rd size, No. 2105

McCleary: in a park
1906   Ahrens Continental, 2nd size, No. AAA

Seattle: Museum of Science
1890   Amoskeag, 3rd size, No. 666

Seattle: Seattle Fire Department
1899   American, 1st size

Snomish
Amoskeag

Spokane: Private owner Dan Eagle
1901   American, Extra 1st size, No. 2791

Yakima: Yakima Valley Museum
1889   Ahrens, refitted with a Nott spiral tube boiler,
4th size, No. 577

WEST VIRGINIA
Bluefield: Bluefield Fire Department
1908   Ahrens Continental, 1st size 900 gpm

Wheeling: Wheeling Fire Department
1895   American, 1st size, No. 2339

WISCONSIN

Clintonville: Four Wheel Drive Museum
Steamer

Jefferson: Jefferson Fire Department
Steamer

Manitowoc: Manitowoc Fire Department
Steamer

Racine: Firehouse 3 Museum
1882   Clapp & Jones, 1st size
Note: This engine was in active reserve until the 1940's.

Sheyboygan: Jung Museum
1873   Silsby, 3rd size, No. 405

Slinger: Venerable Fire Collection, Inc.
1876   Silsby, 3rd size 500 gpm, No. 612
Note: This engine was displayed at the Philadelphia Exposition in 1876 celebrating the 100th anniversary of the United States of America.
1900   American Metropolitan, 1st size 900 gpm, No. 2737

Spring Green: The House On The Rock
1893   Amoskeag
Note: This engine is in storage and is not on display.

Superior: Old Firehouse & Police Museum
1906   Ahrens, Extra 1st size, 1100 gpm, No. 110

Wausau: Wausau Fire Department
Nott

WYOMING

Cheyenne
Nott

This 1905 Amoskeag 2nd size resides in Berlin, New Hampshire at the Berlin Fire Department.

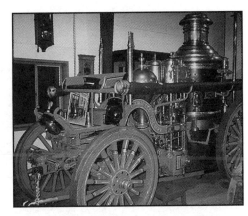

This 1900 American Metropolitan, 1st size can be seen at the Venerable Fire Collection in Slinger, Wisconsin.

Note:
Several additional steamers are known to exist but have not been specifically located.
Also, one owner has requested that his steamer not be included in this list.

A 1906 Nott steamer with a 1912 American-LaFrance tractor is pumping water for the
1905 Hale water tower at the Fire Museum of Maryland's "Steam Sunday Spectacular" on May 5, 1996.

Photo by W. Fred Conway

CHAPTER 9

How to Operate
A Steam Fire Engine

*I*nstructions for engineers (operators) of steam fire engines
were issued by the various manufacturers, and two of them –
Amoskeag and American – are reproduced on the following pages
as well as instructions from the
"Handbook of Modern Steam Fire Engines"
published in 1876.

*John Costa (left) throttles up an 1899 American steamer
at the Fire Museum of Maryland in May, 1996.
Museum curator Stephen Heaver, Jr. is at right.*

This 1868 advertising broadside shows the famous line of Amoskeag fire apparatus.

AMOSKEAG STEAM FIRE ENGINES

Suggestions to Engineers
Running the Amoskeag Engines.

I.

In charging the furnace, use plenty of dry shavings and kindling wood, filling the furnace nearly full, which in most cases will give steam enough to commence work on arrival at a fire, provided the fire is started on leaving the house, which, as a general rule, is advisable.

II.

In the use of coal, be careful to keep *a thin and clear fire.* Be sure that the grate is entirely covered. Do not break up the coal unnecessarily in the furnace. The best coal for this purpose is English Cannel, free from dirt and dust.

III.

As soon as ten pounds of steam has been generated, open gradually the steam blower; this will enliven the fire and cause the steam to rapidly increase in pressure. When the engine is stopped for a time the blower may be advantageously used, but generally when running it should be kept closed.

IV.

Be careful not to let so much fire collect under the boiler as to burn the wheels. There is some danger of this.

V.

Fire may be started in the boiler, with the water midway between the second and third gauge cocks, the first gauge cock being understood to be the lower one. When the engine is running, the water should generally be carried so as to stand to about the third gauge cock, which is placed near the top of the tubes. The engine, however, may be run to its greatest capacity, by carrying the water a little lower than the third gauge cock, which, with care, may be done with safety. Under no circumstances should water be carried lower than the second gauge cock.

AMOSKEAG STEAM FIRE ENGINES

VI.

Avoid using an unnecessary amount of steam. The tendency is to use more than is required. From seventy to ninety pounds is as much as is generally required to do good fire duty.

VII.

One of the feed pumps should be worked nearly all the time when running, in order to keep the water in the boiler at the proper height, and to preserve an even pressure of steam.

VIII.

When foul water is used in the boiler it is likely to produce foaming or priming. When this occurs, and it is not desirable to stop the engine, the trouble may be prevented or diminished by opening the surface blower valve, with which the boiler is provided, and blowing from the surface of the water the scum and oily matter which usually causes the foaming; while doing this the water should be carried as high as the surface blower valve. In this way the difficulty can generally be prevented without any serious interruption of the working of the engine. When the engine can be stopped, the water should be entirely blown out of the boiler through the blow-off cock near the bottom, with a steam pressure of about twenty pounds. Refill the boiler with fresh water and repeat the operation until the boiler becomes clean.

IX.

Always examine the boiler tubes after working and do not let them get clogged up.

X.

Take the engine off the springs before starting and place it on the springs again when done working.

XI.

Take care to have the suction hose and its connections perfectly air-tight.

XII.

Open the discharge gate and cylinder drain cocks before starting.

AMOSKEAG STEAM FIRE ENGINES

XIII.

Always start the engine gradually. With a single long line of hose it may be necessary to open the relief valve a little, but at other times be particular to keep it closed, except when it is desired to feed the boiler without forcing any water through the hose.

XIV.

The inside of the steam cylinders, the steam valves, the link blocks, and all parts of the engine where there is a liability to friction, should be kept thoroughly lubricated.

XV.

The main pumps of the engine should be frequently examined, and care taken that the valves and springs are in perfect order. The valves should have a lift of three-eights of an inch.

XVI.

Every part of the engine liable to disarrangement or accident should be thoroughly examined every time the engine has been out of the house, whether it has been worked at a fire or not.

XVII.

Always keep the engine clean and at all times in perfect order in all its parts, and the superiority of the improved Amoskeag steam fire engine, in the hands of a good engineer, will be manifest to all.

NOTE.–These suggestions are made more particularly for the benefit of engineers who have not had much experience in running steam fire engines.

Supplies.

The following supplies are usually furnished with each steam fire engine:

Two pieces suction hose, each ten feet long, with couplings.

A brass strainer for suction hose.

A brass hydrant connection for suction hose.

Two discharge pipes for leading hose.

Four changeable hose pipe nozzles.

Two firemen's hand lanterns.

A brass oil can.

A jack screw.

A shovel.

A fire poker.

A tool box furnished with a hammer and a set of wrenches.

HAND=BOOK

OF THE

STEAM FIRE ENGINE

WITH

INSTRUCTIONS FOR THE RUNNING, CARE, AND MAN-
AGEMENT OF THE MACHINE

AND

DIRECTIONS FOR OPERATING HEATER,

ALSO

SUGGESTIONS FOR THE CARE OF HOSE, AND OTHER
USEFUL INFORMATION.

COPYRIGHT, 1897, BY

AMERICAN FIRE ENGINE COMPANY,

SENECA FALLS, N. Y., AND CINCINNATI, OHIO.

MODERN FIRE FIGHTING APPARATUS
THE FIRST STEAM ENGINE — PERIOD 1861

Created especially for National Union Insurance Companies.

©N.U.F.I. Co.

In spite of the notation at the bottom of the picture, this was not the first steam fire engine, but was evidently manufactured some eight years after the Uncle Joe Ross, *which was the first successful steamer.*

HANDBOOK OF THE STEAM FIRE ENGINE

PREFACE.

While some engineers of steamers may be of opinion that the greater part of the information contained in this book is needless, being of a very simple nature, it should be borne in mind that most men who run steam fire engines are not practical machinists and have but a superficial knowledge of the uses of steam and of hydraulics.

In view of this, the necessity for such plain and full directions must be apparent: and it cannot be too strongly impressed upon those interested, that the efficiency and durability of such a piece of machinery are considerably enhanced by the care which it receives.

The safety of life and property is very often dependent upon the skill and good judgment of the engineer, and as the maximum effect of such apparatus is generally required at the most critical time and under the most exciting circumstances, it is important that he should realize the responsibility of his position, and endeavor by constant and persistent practice to acquire that confidence and proficiency that will insure both a correct and decisive action in all matters pertaining to the management of the machine.

During this course of self instruction, these directions should be frequently reviewed, as the experience from actual practice insures a more comprehensive understanding of the information herein contained.

A similar book containing instructions specially applicable to engines constructed with the Silsby Rotary Pump, and another for engines with the Ahrens Coil Boiler, are published by us, and will be sent, on application, to those having charge of such engines.

AMERICAN FIRE ENGINE CO.

GENERAL DIRECTIONS.

All things about the house should be kept in good order and neat condition, particularly the engine, which ought always to be clean and bright. Avoid neglect, which tends to waste and decay, as dirt often covers unsuspected faults.

While standing in the house, the engine should at all times be kept ready for immediate service, with plenty of shavings and kindlings, in the fire box, and as much kindlings and coal in the fuel pan as can be conveniently carried.

In winter, if no heater is attached to the engine, the room must be kept warm, to insure against frost.

The joints and connections in the suction must be perfectly tight.

The stuffing boxes of the engine and pump should be well packed.

All of the bearings and journals, as well as the oil cans, should be well supplied with good oil. The best lard oil is recommended for this purpose, and in winter it should be mixed with kerosene, in the proportion of two parts of the former to one of the latter, to prevent its becoming thick.

From three-fourths to one inch of water should be indicated in the glass gauge, except there is a heater attached to the engine, when from four to five inches should be carried. The bottom of the glass tube being on a line with the crown-sheet, when one inch of water shows in the tube the water-line in the boiler is then one inch above the crown-sheet.

Every engine house should be provided with a force pump, for filling the boiler with water, as well as for washing and other purposes, fitted for one-inch hose, together with at least 25 feet of the latter.

It is advisable occasionally – say once a month – in towns where fires are not frequent, to take the engine out for practice and drill, and to make sure that it is in proper working order, after which the boiler should be blown off and refilled with fresh water, as hereinafter directed.

HANDBOOK OF THE STEAM FIRE ENGINE

LAYING OF FIRE.

Before laying the fire, see that the grate and fire box are clean, also that the grate bars are fast, so they will not be liable to jar out, and that all the steam outlets of the boiler are tightly closed.

Lay on the grate some dry pine shavings – not too many – spread evenly over the grate, with a few hanging down between the bars; on the shavings put some finely-split pine or hemlock wood, then some a little coarser, and finally a quantity coarser still. It is well to put on the top some finely-split hard wood. These kindlings must all be dry and split – not sawed – and should be put in loosely, in layers, the layers being crossed, so that there will be a free circulation of air between them.

Never start a fire unless a full gauge cock of water is in the boiler.

Always keep a good torch in the fuel pan, ready for use. This can be made by taking a stick about two feet long and trying some cotton waste on one end, and saturating the waste with kerosene.

STARTING AND MAINTAINING THE FIRE.

To light the fire: Apply torch, already described, below the grate, never in the door; and while doing so move the torch around to insure thoroughly igniting the shavings.

Be particular not to open the fire door oftener than necessary, especially when getting up steam.

In addition to the wood in the furnace, an extra supply is carried in the fuel pan. For convenience this is put up in bundles; their size should not exceed four or five inches in diameter, nor much over a foot in length. If these dimensions are exceeded they become cumbersome and cannot be readily passed into the furnace.

The kindling should be carefully prepared, and the quantity carried sufficient to generate a working pressure in the boiler before coal is added to the fire.

When there is a pressure to 40 to 60 pounds of steam, begin throwing in coal, a little at a time, broken up in pieces about the size of a man's fist. Bituminous coal should be used, the same as that from which illu-

minating gas is made. It should be of the very best quality, entirely free from slate or sulphur.

The mistake is frequently made of allowing most of the wood to burn out before putting in any coal. This should be avoided, as the kindlings must be burning nicely in order to start the coal. If the supply of wood should become exhausted, always begin throwing in coal while there is still enough wood in the fire box to ignite it, even if the gauge does not indicate any steam whatever.

Do not put the wood or coal all close to the fire door, but scatter it about and spread it evenly over the grate.

As soon as the engine is started, coal should be put in often, a little at a time, and the grate should be kept nicely covered, but not thickly – say to a depth of three or four inches. Be particular to fire evenly and regularly, taking care that there are no air holes through the fire, and to open the fire door only when necessary.

The grate bars should be kept well raked out from below, and the fire and coal occasionally stirred off the grate bars inside the fire box, using the flat side of the poker for the later operation. But do not "clean" oftener than necessary; keep the fire door open as short a time as possible, and use no more coal than is required.

OPERATING THE ENGINE.

The engineer should start up the machine gradually, but before doing so he ought to satisfy himself that the joints and connections in the suction hose are air tight, that the discharge gate is open and the churn valve closed, and that the fire has been properly attended to. Let the cylinder cocks be open and the exhaust nearly closed, and all the bearings and journals well oiled. The wheels should be properly blocked, especially if standing on a grade. When starting, the throttle valve should be opened slowly at first, or condensed steam will be thrown out of the stack on the dome, and is liable to stain it.

The automatic air cocks on the upper pump heads must be opened immediately after starting. They serve to promptly relieve the upper pump chambers of air, and may be closed as soon as water is ejected from their orifices.

HANDBOOK OF THE STEAM FIRE ENGINE

When condensation has ceased, the engine being warm, the drain cocks should be closed and the machine speeded up gradually until a good pressure of steam is obtained.

After the engine is fairly started, do not stand too close, but let your position be a step back; and, with your face towards the machine, endeavor to train your eyes and hands to command the entire situation. While it is perfectly proper to be near the throttle, in order to promptly close it in case of bursting hose or failure of the water supply, do not acquire the habit of constantly clinging to the same, for there are other duties equally as important that require your attention.

In the general hurry and rush, avoid all excitement, and let your duties be attended to in a calm and collected manner.

Until the engineer has had some experience with the machine, and is thoroughly familiar with its workings, it is not advisable for him to use more than 90 or 100 pounds of steam, which is all that is required for ordinary fire duty, and the necessity for more than 120 pounds will never arise.

The water in the boiler should be carried as high as six or eight inches in the glass tube as soon as the engine is fairly at work and a good pressure of steam is obtained. The gauges will indicate more water in the boiler when the machine is running than it will with the same quantity of water if it is not at work. For this reason, the boiler should be kept well supplied with water; and the feed tank (when there is one) should be kept always full.

In case the glass tubes get broken, the height of the waterline in the boiler can be ascertained by means of the gauge-cocks, opening them but a trifle. If opened wide the tendency would be to draw up the water. A little experimenting will enable one to use them properly.

But sole reliance should not be placed on the glass tube at any time, and the gauge-cocks ought to be used frequently. Both the gauge-cocks and the glass water gauge should be kept clean, and water from the glass gauge should be blown out occasionally.

The uniformity of the boiler's action is materially aided by maintaining an even fire and a steady feed.

If there is a tendency to foam, the feed should be increased and the surface blower opened quite frequently to relieve the boiler of the scum and surplus water. If the foaming is unusually violent, it may be subdued by stopping the engine for a few moments and permitting the water to settle.

During temporary stops the fire should be cleaned, the clinkers removed, and the moving parts of the machinery examined and oiled.

When the engine is not running, the fire may be replenished if necessary; and it can be kept bright by slightly opening the blower valve, by means of which a steam jet is blown into the smoke-stack for the purpose of improving the draught.

BOILER FEED.

The boiler is usually fed by force pumps, the plungers of which are secured directly to the yokes of the main engines. Both pumps are arranged to work in unison; and the supply is generally taken from the discharging chamber of the main pumps, and is controlled by an ordinary globe valve.

Should the water being delivered by the main pumps be unsuitable for feeding the boiler, this valve must remain closed, and a supply from some other source introduced through the opening provided for that purpose.

Every engine required to pump salt water, or other water unfit for the boiler supply, should be provided with a freshwater feed tank.

The purpose of the automatic air cock (if there is one) is to prevent the rattling of the check valves when the pumps are being only partially filled; if the supply is to be draughted from a barrel or tank, the entrance of air through this cock must be prevented.

In any engine, to feed the boiler directly from the main pump the water pressure gauge must indicate a greater pressure than the steam gauges; and it may be necessary, in order to obtain the desired water pressure, to partially close the discharge gates of the pump if a large nozzle or two or more streams are being used.

When feeding the boiler, it is a good plan to occasionally feel the pipe leading from check to boiler with the hand, as one can tell by this means whether

HANDBOOK OF THE STEAM FIRE ENGINE

the pump is feeding properly. If feeding all right, the pipe will be cool. If the pipe is hot, the pump is not feeding properly, and it should be attended to.

In case of low water, and it is found impossible to feed the boiler in any of the different ways provided, the fire must be drawn instantly. Don't turn on the feed, start or stop the engine, nor open the safety valve; let the steam outlets remain as they are, and allow the boiler to cool down.

RELIEF VALVE.

This is a device attached to the discharge main of the pump, and connecting with the suction chamber, its purpose being to relieve the hose of undue pressure. It is used in connection with a shut-off nozzle. When such nozzle is either partially or fully closed the valve is operated automatically, like a safety valve, and the surplus water not required for the duty being performed is diverted from the hose into the suction chamber of the pump, without any cessation to the machinery. Its operation is similar to that of a churn valve, the difference being that the relief valve works automatically while the churn valve does not.

If your engine is supplied with a relief valve you should familiarize yourself with its construction and working. It is not practicable for us to give directions here that will apply to all the several different types of relief valves now in use, most of which are no longer made. Care should be taken, however, whatever the style of valve, to see that all connections are kept tight, in order to prevent any leakage of air into the suction chamber of the pump.

There ought always to be a valve between the relief valve and the suction chamber of pump, so as to cut out the relief valve in case same should from any cause become disabled.

PRIMING VALVES.

The priming valves, in cases where such valves are attached to a fire engine, control small passages leading from the discharging side of the main pumps to the upper receiving chambers of the same. If the air cocks fail to show water promptly, flood the upper

pump ends by opening these valves for a moment — provided, of course, that the lower ends of the same have already taken suction.

THE VARIABLE EXHAUST.

In connection with good coal and good firing on the part of the stoker, the engineer must make proper use of the exhaust level, to maintain an ample working pressure of steam. When there is plenty of steam the exhaust should be kept wide open; if more steam is required push in the lever. This will diminish the opening, and the velocity of the exhaust will be increased, improving the draught, but creating a back pressure on the engine.

The variable exhaust is particularly useful when fire starting, but as the boiler steams more freely open it to the fullest extent.

THE CHURN VALVE.

The principal object of the churn valve is to permit the operation of the pumps without discharging any water through the natural channels; it controls a passage by which the discharging side of the pumps is connected with the suction chamber.

In draughting water, when the pumps are first started, this valve must remain closed until the pumps are filled with water, thereby excluding the air which would find its way into the suction chamber if the same were open.

It should also be closed when the pumps are at rest, to prevent the dropping of the water in the suction pipe.

It may be opened slightly with good effect when pumping through long lines of hose, or when first starting against a heavy resistance, thereby increasing the piston speed of the machinery without actually delivering a greater quantity of water.

It also permits the force pumps to be kept in motion, for the purpose of supplying the boiler at times when it is undesirable to deliver water through the hose lines.

When the engine is put to suction, acquire the habit of feeling this valve to assure its complete closure.

HANDBOOK OF THE STEAM FIRE ENGINE

WATER SUPPLY.

Owing to the contracted diameter of ordinary fire hose, as well as the roughness of its interior surfaces when under pressure, the flow of the water is resisted; the loss of power due to friction increases directly with the length of the line and nearly as the square of velocity. In other words, if the loss due to a given flow be 12 pounds for 100 feet of hose, then 24 pounds will be required to maintain the same rate through an additional 100 feet. To double the velocity will require four times the pressure, or 48 pounds for 100 feet and 96 pounds for 200 feet. In addition to the pressure required to overcome the resistance due to friction, a margin is required to deliver the water from the nozzle with suitable velocity.

From this brief explanation, it must be plain that the capacity of any engine is diminished as the length of the line is increased; and although the source of supply may be abundant, the amount of water actually available at the nozzle is greatly reduced. Since it is necessary to keep within the limits of the strength of the hose, it is essential that the velocity of flow be diminished; to accomplish this end, and also retain the discharging pressure necessary at the pipe, a nozzle of smaller bore is demanded.

The cause and effect of the different conditions met in actual practice should be carefully observed and studied. The evils of many unalterable obstacles may be frequently modified, if not entirely overcome, by an intelligent disposition of the factors in the case.

The suction basket or strainer should always be attached when draughting water, and every precaution taken to insure tight connections in the suction. The basket must be kept well under the surface, and kept from clogging if the water be foul. Additional strainers should be provided, placed just inside of the suction inlets of the pump when the suction is carried disconnected; when the suction is permanently connected to the pump, the strainer is set in the end of the suction. These strainers must always be examined and cleaned before the engine is returned to quarters, and at all other times when there is any reason to suspect that they are obstructed.

When the supply is taken from a hydrant, satisfy yourself that the same has been fully turned on; if opened before water is wanted through the hose the discharge gates on the engine must be closed. Unless the pressure is excessive, the hydrant is usually permitted to remain open while the steamer is attached, the discharge during temporary stops being controlled by the engine gates.

Frequently the first water taken from a hydrant is stagnated; hence, if necessary to feed the boiler before any considerable quantity has passed, it is advisable to permit it to waste by opening an idle gate.

The apparatus should always be halted, or placed at a proper point, with reference to the source of the water supply. Good judgment on the part of the driver will often obviate short and awkward bends in the suction hose, and also facilitate the work of making the necessary connections. The suction hose should always receive considerable attention; oil is very injurious to the rubber, and when allowed to remain long in contact with its surfaces it will cause decay. Ordinary precaution will be sufficient to prevent injury by chafing on sharp stones or rough surfaces when the pumps are in operation.

When attached to a hydrant or plug, do not run the engine faster than you can get water to supply the pump, and if the pressure is not sufficient to allow the pump to work to its full capacity, avoid using too large nozzles.

If it is suspected that one of the joints in the suction is loose, the speed of the engine may be slackened without stopping entirely, until water is thrown eight or ten feet from the nozzle, when if the pump is taking air the stream will crack and snap instead of flowing out smoothly. If it is found that the pump is taking air through the suction, and the leak cannot be located in any other way, it may be found nozzle should be used; if 20 feet, 1-inch; and if 25 feet, 7/8-inch.

Care should be taken not to use too large nozzles if two or more streams are being thrown.

HANDBOOK OF THE STEAM FIRE ENGINE

NOZZLES.

The sizes of nozzles named below will give the most satisfactory results, those in *italics* being the ones best adapted for fire duty.

EXTRA FIRST SIZE ENGINE.–1,100 to 1,150 gallons capacity. Through short lines of hose: *One 1 1/2-inch smooth-bore nozzle for one stream;* one 1 3/4-inch ring nozzle, or one 2-inch ring nozzle; *1 5/16-inch ring nozzles for two streams.* With 1,000 feet of hose, one 1 5/16-inch ring nozzle.

FIRST SIZE ENGINE.–900 to 1,000 gallons capacity. Through short lines of hose: *One 1 3/8-inch smooth-bore nozzle for one stream;* one 1 1/2-inch ring nozzle, or one 1 5/8-inch ring nozzle; *1 1/4-inch ring nozzles for two streams.* With 1,000 feet of hose, one 1 1/4-inch ring nozzle.

SECOND SIZE ENGINE.-700 to 800 gallons capacity. Through short lines of hose: *One 1 1/4-inch smooth-bore nozzle for one stream;* one 1 3/8-inch ring nozzle, or one 1 1/2-inch ring nozzle; *1 1/8-inch ring nozzles for two streams.* With 1,000 feet of hose, one 1 1/8-inch ring nozzle.

THIRD SIZE ENGINE.– 600 to 650 gallons capacity. Through short lines of hose: *One 1 1/8-inch smooth-bore nozzle for one stream;* one 1 1/4-inch ring nozzle, or one 1 3/8-inch ring nozzle; *1-inch ring nozzles for two streams.* With 1,000 feet of hose, one 1-inch ring nozzle.

FOURTH SIZE ENGINE. – 500 to 550 gallons capacity. Through short lines of hose: *One 1 1/16-inch smooth-bore nozzle for one stream;* one 1 1/8-inch ring nozzle, or one 1 1/4-inch ring nozzle; *7/8-inch ring nozzles for two streams.* With 1,000 feet of hose, one 1-inch ring nozzle.

FIFTH AND SIXTH SIZE ENGINES. – 300 to 450 gallons capacity. Through short lines of hose: *One 1-inch smooth-bore nozzle for one stream;* one 1-inch ring nozzle, or one 1 1/8-inch ring nozzle; *7/8-inch ring nozzles for two streams.* With 1,000 feet of hose, one 7/8-inch ring nozzle.

SHUTTING DOWN.

In extremely cold weather, if it is desired to stop doing duty for any reason, it is a good plan to keep the main pump constantly but slowly revolving, even if it is just barely moving, and to keep a light feed on the force pumps, to prevent freezing. This should be done, also, when necessary to change positions at fires, while the engine is being transferred. In small towns it is well to have a good supply of water in the boiler, and sufficient steam to revolve the engine and pump slowly while returning to the house.

Preparatory to the final shutting down of the apparatus, with a view of returning to quarters, permit the steam pressure to rise to the point of blowing off; also let the fire be burned clear and bright before the withdrawing the same from the furnace, which may be readily done by closing the fire door and opening the blower valve. This will burn off most of the soot adhering to the heating surfaces. Allow water to drop down to the first gauge cock, which will insure your obtaining dry steam; when the blower is opened with a high water line, water is apt to rush through the blower, and wet steam is not so effective in blowing off the soot.

There should be a steam pressure of about 30 pounds when the grate is dumped, after which all remaining soot and ashes should be blown with steam from the top of the smoke-stack down through the smoke flues into the fire box, using for this purpose the small cleaning hose. Then the soot should be blown from the fire box and water tubes, and the ashes from around them, using the cleaning hose and steam through the fire door; the grate may then be replaced.

Not less than once a month, after dumping the grate, with from 15 to 20 pounds of steam, all of the water and steam should be blown out of the boiler through the blow-off cock, in the water-leg of the boiler.

RETURNING TO QUARTERS.

Promptly refill the lubricators and all other oil cups, and thoroughly examine the mechanism, and also the running gear, as soon as the apparatus is returned to its quarters.

HANDBOOK OF THE STEAM FIRE ENGINE

If, however, the work has been of long duration or the water bad, the boiler should be thoroughly washed out before again placing the machine in service.

To do this properly, a one-inch hose with suitable nozzle must be provided, and if there be no hydrant connection or pressure, a force pump may be substituted. Remove all the plugs at the bottom of the boiler, and with the hose and scrapers free the shell of the sediment lodged therein.

While the water is out of the boiler, examine the stop cocks on the ends of the glass water gauge, and see that their openings are clear; always coat their surfaces with cylinder oil when replacing, and adjust them to be easily closed should the glass be broken.

After pumping dirty or salt water, the pumps should be emptied and well rinsed, and then refilled or primed.

After every working, and while the parts are still warm, pour a small cup of good cylinder oil into each of the oil cups on the top heads of the engines; have the pistons at a point preventing the oil from entering the ports, and after allowing sufficient time for the same to distribute itself over the piston head, give the engines several turns by hand, thereby coating the sides of the cylinders with a film of oil and effectually preserving them against rust.

No oil should be allowed to come in contact with the suction hose, which must be kept free from oil, both inside and outside, to insure its preservation.

The engine should at all times be kept scrupulously clean and well polished.

WHILE STANDING IN THE HOUSE.

The boiler should be kept safe, clean, and perfectly tight. See that no water comes in contact with the exterior of the boiler, and if a leak is discovered it should be repaired as soon as possible. Such a defect as a small leak, unimportant in itself, if allowed to continue is liable in a short time to corrode and weaken a boiler.

It is a matter of the greatest importance that all of the joints and connections in the suction should be kept tight at all times. Every little while the engineer ought to take the wrench furnished for that purpose, and see that every joint in the suction is provided with a piece of good packing and that is perfectly tight. From standing in the house unused, the packing is liable to get dry and the joints become loose, and they should be attended to frequently.

The steam gauges should stand at zero when pressure is off, and should agree with each other while the machine is working, as well as show the same pressure as the safety-valve when that is blowing off. If a gauge is found to be wrong at any time, it should be sent to the engine builder or to the manufacturer for repairs.

If necessary to clean the glass tube in the water gauge, close the cocks on top and bottom, fill the tube with benzine, and allow it to stand an hour or two. Then draw the benzine out, open the cocks, and let water in again. Never pass a stick, cotton waste, or anything of that sort through the tube. If touched on the inside with a stick it would be liable to break the first time water is let into it.

If there is anything about the engine that is not fully understood, or if it fails to do its work properly from any cause, the maker should be communicated with at once. In our own case, inquires will be promptly answered, and required information or suggestions will be cheerfully furnished.

GENERAL SUGGESTIONS.

The fire engine is essentially an apparatus adapted to emergencies, and owing to the intermittent nature of the duty performed, it is quite likely, unless the proper precautions are observed, that its several parts, more especially its interior mechanism, will suffer more deterioration while standing idle than from actual service. It is necessary that these interior parts, as well as those more readily apparent, be cared for with a view of keeping them constantly in condition to endure the most severe and protracted strains at the shortest notice.

The engineer should aim to keep all joints tight, the piston rods and valves well packed, and all working parts thoroughly oiled.

If the journals or other working parts require taking up, remember that a little play is preferable to an adjustment liable to cripple the engine at a critical mo-

HANDBOOK OF THE STEAM FIRE ENGINE

ment. To insure perfect safety, always thoroughly test the apparatus after making such repairs, by subjecting the parts effected to the strains usually encountered in actual service.

The principal requirement of the steam cylinders is proper and constant lubrication. Let this one item be attended to, and its mechanism will practically take care of itself for many years.

As in the course of years the working parts of steam fire engines – like those of other machines – will wear out. We build such parts of our machines in duplicate; we can, therefore, promptly ship any part of one of our engines. In sending orders, the number on the builder's plate of the machine should be given, as a complete mechanical record is kept by us of each engine shipped from our works.

THE ENGINE HEATER.

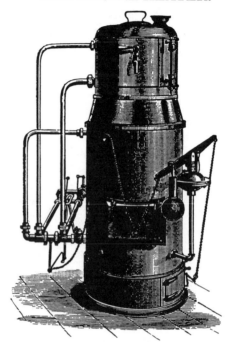

A stationary heater for the fire engine consists of a small boiler, placed at some convenient point near the same when in quarters. It is connected with the engine boiler by means of automatic couplings and suitable circulating pipes, the entire arrangement being adapted to maintain the water contained therein at any temperature desired.

Although the best types of fire engines boilers require but a few minutes time to generate a working pressure from cold water, the general adoption of the many modern improvements for facilitating the movements of the men and apparatus has made the stationary heater an essential part of a complete equipment.

A very reliable and satisfactory heater for this duty is built by the American Fire Engine Company. It is fully shown in the accompanying illustrations, and explicit directions for operating the same are appended.

Experience proves that the life of the boiler is prolonged by being kept constantly in a state of activity, and the elevated temperature of the water insures prompt and efficient work by the steamer at the very time when a few moments delay may breed disaster.

HANDBOOK OF THE STEAM FIRE ENGINE

HEATER ATTACHED.

HEATER DETACHED.

Decorated as a parade float, this steamer is awaiting its turn to enter the procession at Portland, Oregon.

Photo by Ken Lauderbeck. Courtesy of Matt Lee

HAND-BOOK

OF MODERN

STEAM FIRE-ENGINES,

INCLUDING

THE RUNNING, CARE, AND MANAGEMENT OF STEAM FIRE-ENGINES AND FIRE-PUMPS.

BY

STEPHEN ROPER, ENGINEER,

Author of
" Roper's Catechism of High Pressure or Non-Condensing Steam-Engines,"
" Roper's Hand-Book of the Locomotive," " Roper's Hand-
Book of Land and Marine Engines," etc.

PHILADELPHIA:
CLAXTON, REMSEN & HAFFELFINGER,
624, 626 & 628 MARKET STREET.
1876.

*This street scene in Franklin, New Hampshire, near the turn of the century shows the
steamer, ladder wagon, and hose tender returning to quarters after a fire run.*

ROPER'S HANDBOOK OF THE MODERN STEAM FIRE ENGINES

INSTRUCTIONS FOR THE CARE AND MANAGEMENT OF STEAM FIRE-ENGINES AND BOILERS.

The careful maintenance in working order of steam fire-engines, and their judicious management when in service, are of the utmost importance, as they are essential to the development of the power so absolutely necessary to produce important and satisfactory results. Though steam fire-engines embrace quite a variety of designs and forms, yet the circumstances under which they operate are very similar; consequently, it may be possible to give some instructions for their care and management that will be beneficial to all those having them in charge.

When laying the fire, be sure and place plenty of shavings on the grate; then cover with dry kindling-wood and fill the furnace full with the ordinary blocks of wood used for that purpose. This will generally be sufficient to raise steam as soon as the fire is reached, that is, if the fire is lighted as soon as the alarm is given.

If coal be the fuel used, keep the fire thin, in order to prevent clogging in the furnace, and use as large lumps as possible; the best coal for steam fire-engines is clean cannel.

The water in the boiler when the engine is working, should stand at the third gauge-cock, and should never be allowed to be lower than between the first and second.

Never carry a higher pressure of steam than that actually necessary to work the engine, as extraordinary high-pressures are both dangerous and injurious to the boiler and its connections.

Use one pump continually for supplying the feed-water to the boiler, and regulate the supply so as to keep the water at the proper level, which will be of great assistance in maintaining a uniform pressure of steam.

If the steam does not generate sufficiently fast to work the engine, the variable-exhaust should be used; in fact, it should always be closed when the engine is started, and allowed to remain so until the pressure is sufficient, after which it should be opened.

If the steam generates faster than is necessary to work the engine, opening the furnace-door and increasing the feed-water supply will have a tendency to check it.

Avoid loud blowing off at the safety-valve or wasting steam as much as possible, as all such things are evidences of carelessness.

If it becomes necessary to stop the engine with a heavy fire in the furnace, open the furnace-door and uncover a part of the grate, in order to allow the cool air to pass up; then throw some lumps of fresh coal on the fire, and start the injector, if there be one attached to the engine.

Before starting the engine, open the discharge-gate and the drip-cocks of the steam-cylinder, and bring the engine moderately up to speed; all steam fire-engines perform better work when started slowly, besides being less liable to accident.

If the line of hose be very long, the throttle must be opened gradually, as if it is opened too suddenly, there is a liability to burst the hose.

ROPER'S HANDBOOK OF THE MODERN STEAM FIRE ENGINES

The steam-cylinders and slide-valves of fire-engines should always be oiled when the engine returns from a fire, then it will be ready for service when required again. Good lard oil or melted tallow is the best lubricant for steam-cylinders.

All the moving parts should be thoroughly oiled before the engine is cleaned, so that the extra oil that escapes from the boxes or rubbing surfaces may be wiped up during the process of cleaning.

Never let waste fire collect under or near the engine, as the wheels and woodwork would be liable to be burned.

All the revolving parts of the Silsby Rotary Engine should be kept thoroughly oiled when in use, and each time, after being used, a small quantity of good oil should be poured into the water-cylinder, and the engine turned round a few times, for the purpose of distributing the oil over the inner surface of the pump to prevent it from rusting.

The pump-valves should be frequently examined, at least once a month, for the purpose of seeing if they are all intact, or if the springs are of the proper tension to admit of the right lift. The lift of the valves of the pumps of steam fire-engines generally ranges from three-eights to a half inch.

Be sure and take the engine off the springs before starting, and place it on them again when done working.

On returning from a fire thoroughly examine every part of the engine, whether it has been worked or not, as many of the parts that are exposed to a great strain are liable to be cracked or sprung by being run over rough streets.

When adjusting or repairing the engine or pump, if it becomes necessary to drive any of the parts together, a hammer or monkey-wrench never should be used unless a piece of sheet-copper or brass is interposed between the hammer and the parts to be driven. Any engineer can make a soft hammer for this purpose by filling a short piece of copper or brass tube with Babbit metal or lead.

The piston-and valve-rod stuffing-boxes should be frequently packed with some of the patent braided packing in use for that purpose. The fact is, steam fire-engines, or any other class of engines, are not packed nearly as often as they ought to be, as, when the packing loses its elasticity, it is completely worthless, and by becoming dry and hard, it has a tendency to make the engine thump, and also to cut or flute the rods.

Before packing the glands, all the old packing should be carefully removed and the dust blown out; every engineer should provide himself with special tools for this purpose. A small steel bar about one-quarter inch in diameter and twelve inches long, drawn to a point at one end and having a loop or eye at the other, will effectually remove the old packing from the boxes; no rough instrument should ever be used for this purpose, as it will abrade or scratch the rod, which will in turn destroy the packing.

The packing for piston- and valve-rods should be a little larger in diameter than the gland is thick, in order to admit of being slightly flattened before being inserted in the box; it should be cut in lengths sufficient to encircle the rod, but the ends should not quite touch, as the packing ought to be allowed room to expand. It should be driven into the boxes with drifts made of hard wood about the thickness of the gland, slightly convex on one side and concave on the other; the rings should be inserted so as to break joints, and the stuffing-box screwed up so as to force the packing home to the bottom of the box, after which the gland may be slacked up for the purpose of allowing the packing to expand.

To find the right size of the packing for any stuffing-box, measure the diameter of the steam of the stuffing-box and the rod with the calipers; the diameter of the size of the packing will be half the difference between the diameter of the rod and the diameter of the box.

The very best description of packing may be rendered worthless by being ignorantly or injudiciously used.

If the leakage around the rods becomes excessive after the engine is newly packed, and the glands screwed up as tight as they ought to be, if circumstances will permit, it is always better to stop and remove one or two of the rings and replace them in opposite directions, which will in a majority of cases stop the leaking.

Continual screwing up on the glands produces friction on the rods, which causes them to heat and destroy the elasticity of the packing; if it becomes necessary to frequently tighten the stuffing-boxes, it is always better to do it when the engine is standing still.

Pistons and valve-rod packing should always be kept in a clean place secure from dust, ashes, or sand.

The object of the safety-valve is to relieve the boiler from extraordinary pressure, and when the proper limit is attained, it speaks in a warning voice to the boiler attendant to "stop." The safety-valve is only a means of safety when well proportioned and well cared for after being put in use; it should never be weighed or screwed down for the purpose of carrying extraordinary pressure, as that is not necessary when the boiler and engine are in good order, and well proportioned for their work.

Safety-valves should be frequently and carefully ground on their seats. Pulverized glass, or the mud from a grinding-stone trough dried on a piece of sheet-iron or tin, is better for this purpose than emery.

The steam-gauge is another means of indicating approaching danger from over-pressure; and though it does not speak like the safety-valve, it is a silent and impressive monitor. Its steady moving hand on the face of the dial points with unerring aim to the danger.

The steam- and water-gauges of fire-engines should be tested at least twice a year by the direct application of a column of mercury, and no reliance whatever should be placed in so-called standard gauges, unless they are known to be made by manufacturers of undoubted reputation.

The glass water-gauge is one of the simplest as well as one of the most useful attachments of the steam-boiler; no other means of determining the height of water in steam-boilers can be so reliable.

Glass water-gauges should be frequently cleaned; this can be done by blowing out through

ROPER'S HANDBOOK OF THE MODERN STEAM FIRE ENGINES

the lower valve; but it may become necessary sometimes to use a swab, and in such cases the wood to which the swab is attached should be covered with cloth, as even wood touching the inside of the glass will produce an abrasion and cause the tube to break.

Before cleaning the engine, all the bolts, nuts, screws, and keys should be examined, in order to see that they are all tight and in good order, so as to prevent the necessity of handling them after the engine is cleaned.

To clean the bright work of the engine, whether iron or steel, use double or triple 0 crocus or emery cloth, which always should be rubbed in one direction, for any variation from the same direction will scratch the work. If the emery cloth be backed by a piece of an old felt hat or collar of a coat, it will last longer and do the work better.

Bright or finished work of engines should never be touched with the hand after being cleaned, especially in warm weather, as the acid in the perspiration will rust either iron or steel and dull the lustre of brass.

Receipts for cleaning brass and copper will be found in another part of this book.

It is not only the parts of the engine exposed to view that ought to be cleaned, but every part should show on examination that it was cared for. A handsomely kept engine, with all its parts clean and in good order, furnishes stronger evidence of an engineer's capabilities than a volume of written recommendations.

Every engineer in charge of a steam fire-engine should keep an extra set of pump-piston packing on hand, and, in fact, duplicates of all the different parts that he would be likely to need in an emergency. He should also have either in his possession, or in some accessible place, a monkey-wrench and wrenches to fit the different nuts of the engine and pump, a hammer, cold chisels, calipers, cut-nippers, tin shears, dividers, spanners, monkey-jack, ratchet-drill, files, jack-knife, pinch-bars, etc, or any tool that would be likely to be needed in case of a break-down, or if it becomes necessary to adjust any part of the machine, which should be kept in conspicuous and accessible places, clean, and in good order; as all tools and appliances thrown aside or stowed away in obscure places are liable to be eaten up with rust and difficult to be found when wanted.

ENGINEERS.

Steam fire-engines should be in charge of practical engineers, not necessarily machinists, but men having a thorough knowledge of steam and steam machinery, and capable of adjusting all the different parts of their engines, and telling whether they are out of order or not. They should fully understand the causes of deterioration in the boilers of this class of machines, and the best means of protecting them from the evils which endanger their safety and limit their usefulness. They should have, if not a thorough, a tolerably good knowledge of hydraulics and hydraulic machines, and be capable of determining their capacity, and understanding the strains to which they are subjected when in use; these qualifications have been heretofore overlooked, though it seems rather strange that this should be so.

ROPER'S HANDBOOK OF THE MODERN STEAM FIRE ENGINES

That the duties which this class of men is expected to perform are of a very important character, all will admit; and it would be difficult to assign any reasonable cause why they should not be encouraged to qualify themselves for their faithful and intelligent performance; and while it is a fact, that many of the men in charge of steam fire-engines are capable and intelligent engineers, yet, unfortunately, they are not all so; nor will they ever be so, as a body, until they receive their appointments on real merit, instead of through political influence, and are retained in the service during good behavior, and encouraged to improve themselves. Every city should furnish the men in charge of steam fire-engines with a library of scientific books, and given them an opportunity to assist in repairing their engines and boilers, so that they may become efficient, if not expert, in their care and management; such an arrangement would incur a small expenditure of money at first, but this outlay would soon be amply returned by the increased intelligence and efficiency of the engineers, and the saving in the wear and tear of machinery, which would necessarily result from the more intelligent interest which they would take in their duties.

ROUTINE OF BUSINESS IN PAID FIRE DEPARTMENTS.

The following is the order of business in the Paid Fire Departments in all the principal cities in the United States:

The Foreman of each company musters his men in quarters and calls the roll at 8 o'clock A.M. All members present are required to show or account for all property or devices belonging to the department in their care or possession. All being found correct, the company break ranks and proceed to duty.

The Foreman makes out his morning report and forwards it to head-quarters. The engineers proceed to clean their engine, the drivers to clean and care for the horses, the remaining members to clean quarters, such as scrubbing floors, white-washing, splitting wood, etc.

At meal hours, one-half of the members proceed to their meals, although in some instances they go by twos.

There is always on the first floor in quarters one man in full uniform, for the purpose of giving information to visitors and sounding the alarm-going to call the members to duty in case of a fire. It is also his duty to open the doors leading to the stables and allow the horses to proceed to their proper places to be hitched, they being always in harness except when the drivers are cleaning them; and even then the harness is only taken off one at a time, in order to cause as little delay as possible in case an alarm should be sounded.

The horses being hitched, the driver takes his seat, and each member has his position by numbers, the engineer standing on the platform with torch in hand, ready to apply it to the shavings in the furnace as soon as the engine passes out of the door. One hoseman rides on the engine to assist the engineer in making his connections with the plug. The remaining members take their positions on the tender, which follows in the wake of the steamer about twenty or thirty yards.

ROPER'S HANDBOOK OF THE MODERN STEAM FIRE ENGINES

When they arrive at the fire, the foreman, or officer in command, proceeds to the premises on fire, the driver stops his engine at the nearest fire-plug, unhitches his horses and leads them to a place of safety, remaining with them. The engineer takes the suction-hose and makes the connection between the fire-plug, and its then ready for service.

The tender-driver stops at the engine and allows the men to dismount, when they take a turn on the hose round one of the spokes of the forward wheel of the engine, while the tender-driver proceeds in the direction of the fire, allowing the hose to unwheel as he goes; when a sufficient quantity is unwheeled, the members detach it, put on the pipe and stand waiting orders; in the meantime the driver finds a place of safety for his horse and tender, in the rear of the engine, in order that the engineer and stoker may see what equipments are borrowed from the tender by other companies.

The fire being extinguished and the company's service no longer needed, the officer in command issues orders to "take up;" the engineer stops the engine, draws the fire, disconnects the suction-hose, closes the fire-plug, disconnects the discharge-hose, and puts all tools in their proper places; in the meantime the driver leads his horses back to the engine.

The tender is next sent for, the men disconnect the hose and commence to reel them up, the tender moving towards the engine. When all the hose are reeled up, the officer in command gives orders to proceed to quarters, no member riding except the drivers. When they arrive at quarters, the engine-driver stops in front of the door, unhitches his horses, and leads them to the stable.

All the members assist in putting the engine into quarters, after which the firemen and engineers clean the furnace, recharge it with shavings and wood, attach the heater-pipe, and make everything ready in case of an alarm. The hosemen unreel the hose, replace them with dry hose, and proceed to wash those that were in use at the fire.

The member or officer having charge of the house, enters on the blotter the name of the street and number of the house where the fire occurred, whether insured or not, cause of fire, etc.

In every six days each member is allowed twenty-four hours leave of absence. No two officers are off at one time.

CHAPTER 10

Commemorative First Day Covers

*S*team fire engines are recognized as
an integral part of our national heritage
as evidenced by these First Day Covers issued by
the United States Postal Service.

Fire Engine
Self-propelled steamers came
into use at the turn of the century.

Fire Pumper
The Fire Pumper brought greater fire safety
to nineteenth century America.

THE FIRST TO THE LAST —
A SPAN OF 63 YEARS

Manufactured in 1853, the Uncle Joe Ross, *built in Cincinnati by Abel Shawk and the Latta brothers, was America's first successful steam fire engine.*

The final steam fire engine manufactured in the United States was a 1917 Metropolitan pulled by a CTC tractor, and delivered to Trenton, New Jersey. Although no picture is known to exist, it is similar in all respects to the Metropolitan shown above.

CHAPTER 11

Conclusion

Although Cincinnati paved the way, closely followed by St. Louis and Louisville, in converting their fire departments from volunteers with hand engines to paid men with steamers, America's largest fire department - that of New York City - held out the longest. Not until thirteen years after the Uncle Joe Ross and her crew of paid firemen ousted the Cincinnati volunteers did New York finally give in and accept steamers with paid firefighters to man them.

New York's volunteer firemen were so politically entrenched that they were able to influence elections and decisions coming from City Hall. They bitterly opposed steam fire engines. In his annual report for 1859, New York Fire Chief Harry Howard wrote:

"It cannot be denied that steam fire engines possess power not possessed by hand apparatus, but the necessity of their use alone in this city is a question which time alone can determine. The steam fire engines now owned by the city, if permitted to discharge water at every fire, would entail more damage by that element than the one it is sought to subdue. The City of New York is protected by a volunteer fire department unequalled in the world. The introduction of steam fire engines would embarrass seriously the volunteer system."

The following year, Chief Howard was succeeded by Chief John Decker, who wrote, in his own annual report, the following:

"There is no doubt but that these engines, at large fires, are of service as an auxiliary to the hand engines, but, in my judgement, they can never take the place of the hand apparatus."

New York City Fire Chief Harry Howard opposed steamers.

215

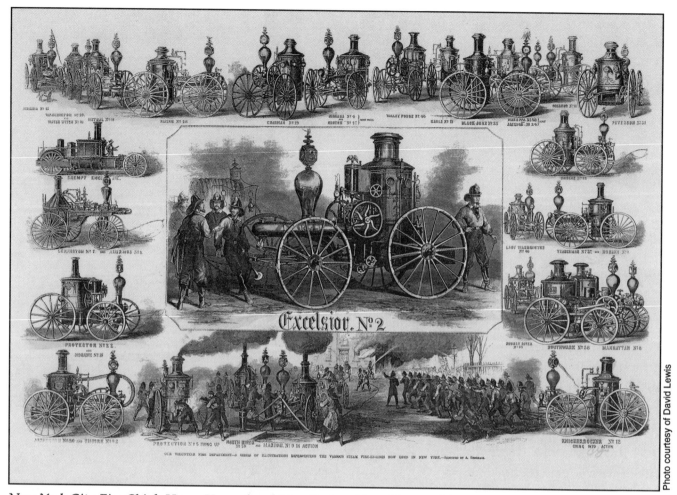

New York City Fire Chiefs Harry Howard and John Decker delayed but could not stop that city's conversion from hand engines to steamers. This illustration depicts many of New York City's early steam fire engines.

But, finally, in 1865, progress prevailed, and the paid Metropolitan Fire Department with fifteen Amoskeag steamers took over the task of protecting New York City from fire. For half a century the steamers did yeoman service until they, too, were begrudgingly replaced by still more progressive methods of firefighting - motorized fire engines.

The half century during which steamers served as the backbone of America's firefighting arsenal is often referred to as the most romantic era of firefighting history. It is sad that we might never see a horse-drawn steamer coming down the street with smoke and sparks spewing from its stack, while more sparks fly from the shod horses' hooves as they strike the cobblestones on their race to a fire. With the passing of the steamers, part of the glamor of the fire service disappeared forever.

Again, imagine the general scene at a fire a century ago - excited, prancing horses, shouting firemen and engineers, hose carts weaving around chugging steamers with sparks and heavy coal smoke chuffing from their polished stacks, which often produced more smoke than the burning building itself; steam whistles frantically shrieking for more coal and thousands of gallons of water being pumped by the noble and faithful steamers to subdue the fire demon. What a sight our forefathers beheld!

But perhaps you *can* see it after all. The publishers of this book plan to produce a video of not only restored steamers in action but of archival motion picture footage of actual fire scenes from a century ago, once again showing, in all of their glory, those magnificent old steam fire engines.

APPENDIX

Steamer Shipping Records

$\mathcal{T}$he shipping records of more than 4,000 of the
approximately 5,000 steam fire engines manufactured in the United States
are contained in these lists, which include the manufacturer,
year of manufacture, size of engine, serial number,
and the city to which it was destined.
Those historians who compiled and supplied this information
are listed at the beginning of each section.

Nine American-LaFrance steamers have been loaded onto railroad flat cars at Elmira, New York, for shipment to Philadelphia. Nearly all steam fire engines were shipped to their destinations via rail.

217

The 3-wheeled engine manufactured by Ahrens in 1869 was Ahrens No. 1 and was named A.B. Latta in honor of the celebrated co-inventor of steam fire engines. Shown in front of its quarters in Cincinnati, this engine was shipped by railroad to fight the Great Chicago fire in 1871.

$\mathscr{A}$hrens Steam $\mathscr{F}$ire Engines
Cincinnati, Ohio

1. A. B. & E. Latta 1852-1862
    (The Buckeye Works)

2. Lane & Bodley 1863-1868

3. C. Ahrens & Co. 1869-1875
    (Incorporated as Ahrens Manufacturing Co. 1875)

4. Ahrens Manufacturing Co. 1875-1891

Consolidated with the Button Fire Engine Co., Clapp & Jones and Silsby Co.
to form the American Fire Engine Co. with plants in Cincinnati and Seneca Falls, New York.

(A few Ahrens engines were built after the consolidation
but by 1894 the original Ahrens engines had been replaced
by the new "American" engine.)

Information compiled by:

Harold S. Walker, P. E.
Edward R. Tufts
John M. Peckham

A. B. & E. Latta
(1852 - 1862)

City	Date	Size	Serial #
Boston, Massachusetts	1855		
Cincinnati, Ohio	1852		
Cincinnati, Ohio	1853		
Cincinnati, Ohio	1854		
Cincinnati, Ohio	1854		
Cincinnati, Ohio	1854		
Cincinnati, Ohio	1854		
Cincinnati, Ohio	1854		
Cincinnati, Ohio	1854		
Cincinnati, Ohio	1856		
Cincinnati, Ohio	1856		
Cincinnati, Ohio	1856		
Columbus, Ohio	1857		
Harrisburg, Pennsylvania	1854		

City	Date	Size	Serial #
Louisville, Kentucky	1857		
Louisville, Kentucky	1858		
Louisville, Kentucky	1858		
Louisville, Kentucky	1859		
Louisville, Kentucky	1860		
Memphis, Tennessee	1861		
New Orleans, Louisiana	1855		
St. Louis, Missouri	1857		
St. Louis, Missouri	1857		
St. Louis, Missouri	1857		
St. Louis, Missouri	1858		
St. Louis, Missouri	1858		
St. Louis, Missouri	1858		

Lane & Bodley
(1863 - 1868)

City	Date	Size	Serial #
Akron, Ohio	1866		
Battle Creek, Michigan	1863		
Cincinnati, Ohio	1865		
Cincinnati, Ohio	1867		
Cincinnati, Ohio	1867		
Cincinnati, Ohio	1867		
Cincinnati, Ohio	1867		
Cleveland, Ohio	1863		
Dayton, Ohio	1863		
Evansville, Indiana	1866		
Galveston, Texas	1866		
Grand Rapids, Michigan	1865		

City	Date	Size	Serial #
Hamilton, Ohio	1864		
Leavenworth, Kansas	1866		
Louisville, Kentucky	1865		
Memphis, Tennessee	1866		
Newark, Ohio	1866		
Omaha, Nebraska	1866		
Oshkosh, Wisconsin	1866		
Quincy, Illinois	1866		
Racine, Wisconsin	1866		
St. Louis, Missouri	1865		
St. Paul, Minnesota	1866		

C. Ahrens & Co.
(1869 - 1875)

City	Date	Size	Serial #	City	Date	Size	Serial #
Alton, Illinois	1871	2nd	9	Louisville, Kentucky	1872	2nd	20
Chicago, Illinois	1873	2nd	31 (C)	Louisville, Kentucky	1872	2nd	22 (C)
Cincinnati, Ohio (Latta Type)	1869	1st	3 (C)	Louisville, Kentucky	1872	2nd	24 (C)
Cincinnati, Ohio (Latta Type)	1869	2nd	1 (C)	Louisville, Kentucky	1874	2nd	33 (C)
Cincinnati, Ohio (Latta Type)	1870	1st	4 (C)	Madison, Indiana	1870	2nd	5
Cincinnati, Ohio	1870	2nd	6	Madison, Indiana	1871	2nd	12
Cincinnati, Ohio	1870	2nd	7	Memphis, Tennessee	1874	2nd	40
Cincinnati, Ohio	1871	2nd	10	Nashville, Tennessee	1874	2nd	38
Cincinnati, Ohio	1871	2nd	11	Owensboro, Kentucky	1873	2nd	26 (C)
Cincinnati, Ohio	1871	2nd	13	Oxford, Ohio	1875	3rd	45
Cincinnati, Ohio	1871	2nd	14	Quincy, Illinois	1874	2nd	35
Cincinnati, Ohio	1871	2nd	17	Shelbyville, Indiana	1875	2nd	42
Cincinnati, Ohio	1873	2nd	27 (C)	St. Louis, Missouri	1870	2nd	8
Cincinnati, Ohio	1874	2nd	34 (C)	St. Louis, Missouri	1871	2nd	15
Cincinnati, Ohio	1874	2nd	36	St. Louis, Missouri	1871	2nd	16
Cincinnati, Ohio	1875	2nd	43	St. Louis, Missouri	1872	2nd	19
Eaton, Ohio	1872	2nd	18	St. Louis, Missouri	1872	2nd	21 (C)
Galion, Ohio	1873	2nd	25 (C)	St. Louis, Missouri	1872	2nd	23 (C)
Greensburg, Indiana	1874	2nd	39	St. Louis, Missouri	1873	2nd	28 (C)
Hamilton, Ohio	1869	2nd	2 (C)	St. Louis, Missouri	1873	2nd	29 (C)
Hamilton, Ohio	1873	2nd	32 (C)	St. Louis, Missouri	1873	2nd	30 (C)
Indianapolis, Indiana	1874	1st	41	St. Louis, Missouri	1875	1st	44
Indianapolis, Indiana	1874	2nd	37				

Ahrens Manufacturing Co.
(1875 - 1891)

City	Date	Size	Serial #	City	Date	Size	Serial #
		4th	218	Chicago, Illinois	1885	4th	427
	1877	3rd	173	Chicago, Illinois	1885	4th	429
	1884	3rd	403	Chicago, Illinois	1885	4th	439
Akron, Ohio	1886		465	Chicago, Illinois	1885	4th	440
Arcanum, Ohio	1885		425	Chicago, Illinois	1885	4th	441
Ashtabula, Ohio	1886		455	Chicago, Illinois	1886	4th	491
Auburn, Indiana	1884		416	Chicago, Illinois	1886	4th	501
Aurora, Indiana	1876	3rd	166	Chicago, Illinois	1887	4th	521
Bardstown, Kentucky	1886		453	Chicago, Illinois	1887	4th	523
Battle Creek, Michigan	1881	3rd	290	Chicago, Illinois	1887	4th	524
Belle Plaine, Iowa	1888		556	Chicago, Illinois	1888		567
Belle Plaine, Iowa	1890		641	Chicago, Illinois	1888		568
Birmingham, Alabama	1886		459	Chicago, Illinois	1888		576
Birmingham, Alabama	1886		461	Chicago, Illinois	1889	2nd	601
Birmingham, Alabama	1887	4th	520	Chicago, Illinois	1890	1st	634
Cambridge City, Indiana	1876	3rd	163	Chicago, Illinois	1890	4th	603
Canton, Ohio	1888		549	Chicago, Illinois	1890	4th	618
Catletsburg, Kentucky	1884		417	Chicago, Illinois	1890	4th	619
Centralia, Washington	1887		512	Chicago, Illinois	1891	4th	655
Centralia, Washington	1890		625	Chicago, Illinois	1891	4th	656
Chattanooga, Tennessee	1875	3rd	146	Chicago, Illinois	1891	4th	657
Chattanooga, Tennessee	1884		418	Chicago, Illinois	1891	4th	658
Chattanooga, Tennessee	1888		558	Chicago, Illinois	1891		649
Chicago, Illinois	1880	2nd	248	Chicago, Illinois	1891		666
Chicago, Illinois	1880	2nd	254	Chillicothe, Ohio	1880	3rd	232
Chicago, Illinois	1880	3rd	260	Cincinnati, Ohio	1877	3rd	172
Chicago, Illinois	1880	3rd	262	Cincinnati, Ohio	1877	3rd	186
Chicago, Illinois	1880	3rd	264	Cincinnati, Ohio	1878	2nd	198
Chicago, Illinois	1881	1st	268	Cincinnati, Ohio	1879	3rd	228
Chicago, Illinois	1881	1st	296	Cincinnati, Ohio	1881	1st	280
Chicago, Illinois	1881	1st	306	Cincinnati, Ohio	1882	1st	314
Chicago, Illinois	1881	2nd	298	Cincinnati, Ohio	1882	1st	316
Chicago, Illinois	1881	2nd	300	Cincinnati, Ohio	1883	2nd	322
Chicago, Illinois	1881	2nd	308	Cincinnati, Ohio	1884	1st	410
Chicago, Illinois	1882	3rd	334	Cincinnati, Ohio	1885		443
Chicago, Illinois	1882	3rd	336	Cincinnati, Ohio	1887		503
Chicago, Illinois	1882	3rd	342	Cincinnati, Ohio	1888	3rd	534
Chicago, Illinois	1883	2nd	374	Cincinnati, Ohio	1888		550
Chicago, Illinois	1883	3th	366	Cincinnati, Ohio	1888		552
Chicago, Illinois	1883	4th	368	Cincinnati, Ohio	1888		553
Chicago, Illinois	1884	4th	407	Cincinnati, Ohio	1888		571
Chicago, Illinois	1884	4th	408	Cincinnati, Ohio	1888		573
Chicago, Illinois	1884	4th	409	Cincinnati, Ohio	1890		604

Ahrens Manufacturing Co.

City	Date	Size	Serial #
Cincinnati, Ohio	1890		620
Cincinnati, Ohio	1891	2nd	672
Cincinnati, Ohio	1891	2nd	674
Cleveland, Ohio	1877	3rd	168
Cleveland, Ohio	1878	3rd	200
Columbia, Tennessee	1878	4th	190
Columbus, Ohio	1888	3rd	574
Columbus, Ohio	1889	3rd	596
Columbus, Ohio	1890	2nd	607
Columbus, Ohio	1890	2nd	608
Columbus, Ohio	1890	3rd	610
Columbus, Ohio	1890	3rd	611
Columbus, Ohio	1890	3rd	613
Council Bluffs, Iowa	1880	3rd	212
Covington, Kentucky	1876	3rd	169
Covington, Kentucky	1877	2nd	171
Covington, Kentucky	1877	3rd	167
Covington, Kentucky	1882	1st	346
Cynthiana, Kentucky	1876	3rd	159
Dallas, Texas	1884	2nd	392
Dallas, Texas	1890	2nd	643
Dallas, Texas	1890	2nd	644
Dayton, Ohio	1885		445
Dayton, Ohio	1889		589
Decatur, Illinois	1890		647
Delphos, Ohio	1881	3rd	272
Delphos, Ohio	1883	4th	376
Denver, Colorado	1890	2nd	628
Deshler, Ohio	1886		487
Detroit, Michigan	1887	1st	518
Detroit, Michigan	1888	3rd	538
Detroit, Michigan	1890	1st	623
Dubuque, Iowa	1890	3rd	640
Duluth, Minnesota	1890		626
Frankfort, Kentucky	1881	3rd	292
Franklin, Ohio	1877	4th	178
Fresno, California	1887		526
Gallipolis, Ohio	1877	3rd	184
Galveston, Texas	1877	3rd	174
Georgetown, Kentucky	1877	4th	170
Germantown, Ohio	1886		475
Grand Rapids, Michigan	1890		632
Greencastle, Indiana	1882	3rd	302

City	Date	Size	Serial #
Harrison, Ohio	1883		388
Hillsboro, Ohio	1875	2nd	151
Hot Springs, Arkansas	1880	3rd	256
Huntington, West Virginia	1882	3rd	328
Indianapolis, Indiana	1876	1st	155
Indianapolis, Indiana	1876	2nd	160
Indianapolis, Indiana	1876	3rd	164
Indianapolis, Indiana	1888		530
Indianapolis, Indiana	1891		669
Indianapolis, Indiana	1891		670
Indianapolis, Indiana	1891		671
Jefferson, Missouri	1884		393
Lake Province, Louisiana	1879	4th	204
Lake View, Illinois	1887		527
Lake, Illinois	1882	2nd	312
Lawrenceburg, Indiana	1883	3rd	340
Lawrenceburg, Indiana	1883	3rd	348
Lawrenceburg, Kansas	1886		458
Leavenworth, Kansas	1875	3rd	157
Lebanon, Ohio	1885		423
Lima, Illinois	1881	4th	244
Los Angeles, California	1886		493
Los Angeles, California	1888	3rd	543
Los Angeles, California	1888	3rd	544
Los Angeles, California	1888		537
Louisville, Kentucky	1876	1st	165
Louisville, Kentucky	1879	3rd	220
Louisville, Kentucky	1880	2nd	252
Louisville, Kentucky	1880	3rd	270
Louisville, Kentucky	1881	2nd	276
Louisville, Kentucky	1881	2nd	278
Louisville, Kentucky	1882	3rd	344
Louisville, Kentucky	1883	1st	384
Louisville, Kentucky	1884		400
Louisville, Kentucky	1888	3rd	535
Louisville, Kentucky	1890		629
Louisville, Kentucky	1890		646
Madison, Indiana	1891		660
Memphis, Tennessee	1882	2nd	318
Memphis, Tennessee	1882	2nd	320
Memphis, Tennessee	1884	3rd	414
Memphis, Tennessee	1884	5th	395
Memphis, Tennessee	1884	5th	406

Ahrens Manufacturing Co.

City	Date	Size	Serial #
Miamisburg, Ohio	1886		470
Milwaukee, Wisconsin	1879	2nd	224
Milwaukee, Wisconsin	1880	2nd	246
Milwaukee, Wisconsin	1883	1st	372
Milwaukee, Wisconsin	1884	3rd	401
Milwaukee, Wisconsin	1884		396
Milwaukee, Wisconsin	1886		451
Milwaukee, Wisconsin	1887		505
Milwaukee, Wisconsin	1888		546
Milwaukee, Wisconsin	1888		547
Milwaukee, Wisconsin	1889		587
Milwaukee, Wisconsin	1889		591
Milwaukee, Wisconsin	1890		617
Milwaukee, Wisconsin	1890		635
Minneapolis, Minnesota	1883	3rd	352
Minneapolis, Minnesota	1885		437
Minneapolis, Minnesota	1886		499
Minneapolis, Minnesota	1886		500
Minneapolis, Minnesota	1890		637
Minneapolis, Minnesota	1890		638
Montgomery, Alabama	1879	3rd	226
Montreal, Canada	1877	4th	180
Montreal, Canada	1877		196
Morrow, Ohio	1888	5th	555
Mt. Sterling, Kentucky	1889		580
N. Amherst, Ohio	1888	3rd	541
Nashville, Tennessee	1875	3rd	158
Nashville, Tennessee	1883	2nd	380
Nashville, Tennessee	1883	2nd	382
New Orleans, Louisiana	1878	4th	192
New Orleans, Louisiana	1879	3rd	214
New Orleans, Louisiana	1879	3rd	222
New Orleans, Louisiana	1879	4th	206
New Orleans, Louisiana	1880	3rd	230
New Orleans, Louisiana	1880	4th	238
New Orleans, Louisiana	1880	4th	240
New Orleans, Louisiana	1880	4th	258
New Orleans, Louisiana	1881	3rd	294
New Orleans, Louisiana	1881		288
New Orleans, Louisiana	1882	3rd	324
New Orleans, Louisiana	1882	5th	326
New Orleans, Louisiana	1883	4th	370
New Orleans, Louisiana	1883	5th	338

City	Date	Size	Serial #
New Orleans, Louisiana	1884		413
New Orleans, Louisiana.	1885		431
New York, New York	1880	2nd	250
New York, New York	1883	3rd	358
New York, New York	1883	3rd	360
New York, New York	1883	4th	354
New York, New York	1883	4th	356
Newark, Ohio	1879	2nd	216
North Vernon, Indiana	1886		477
Oakland, California	1884	2nd	411
Omaha, Nebraska	1878	3rd	210
Oshkosh, Wisconsin	1881	2nd	274
Ottawa, Kansas	1883	3rd	386
Paducah, Kentucky	1881	4th	284
Paris, Kentucky	1878	1st	188
Pekin, Illinois	1884	3rd	405
Pendleton, Oregon	1885		432
Pensacola, Florida	1881	4th	310
Peoria, Illinois	1883	3rd	364
Phoenix, Arizona	1887		506
Portland, Indiana	1886		479
Portsmouth, Ohio	1883	3rd	362
Pueblo, Colorado	1889		583
Quincy, Illinois	1890	2nd	616
Racine, Wisconsin	1884	3rd	412
Ripley, Ohio	1886		481
Rushville, Indiana	1881	4th	282
San Antonio, Texas	1886		449
San Diego, California	1888	3rd	561
Seattle, Washington	1889		597
Seattle, Washington	1889		598
Seymour, Indiana	1885		433
Sheboyan, Wisconsin	1883	3rd	350
Sidney, Ohio	1883	3rd	378
Springfield, Illinois	1890		622
St. Louis, Missouri	1875	1st	148
St. Louis, Missouri	1875	1st	149
St. Louis, Missouri	1875	1st	150
St. Louis, Missouri	1875	1st	152
St. Louis, Missouri	1875	1st	154
St. Louis, Missouri	1875	3rd	147
St. Louis, Missouri	1876	1st	156
St. Louis, Missouri	1876	3rd	162

Ahrens Manufacturing Co.

City	Date	Size	Serial #	City	Date	Size	Serial #
St. Louis, Missouri	1878	3rd	208	St. Paul, Minnesota	1887		511
St. Louis, Missouri	1880	3rd	236	St. Paul, Minnesota	1887		529
St. Louis, Missouri	1882	1st	330	Sullivan, Indiana	1885		435
St. Louis, Missouri	1884	3rd	390	Superior, Wisconsin	1890		648
St. Louis, Missouri	1884	3rd	394	Tacoma, Washington	1888		577
St. Louis, Missouri	1884	3rd	398	Toledo, Ohio	1889		593
St. Louis, Missouri	1884	3rd	399	Toledo, Ohio	1889		594
St. Louis, Missouri	1884	3rd	402	Topeka, Kansas	1877	2nd	194
St. Louis, Missouri	1885	3rd	419	Tower, Minnesota	1891		668
St. Louis, Missouri	1885	3rd	420	Uniontown, Pennsylvania	1877	4th	176
St. Louis, Missouri	1886	3rd	467	USQC Fort Duchesne, Utah	1880	4th	242
St. Louis, Missouri	1887	3rd	502	Versailles, Kentucky	1888	5th	540
St. Louis, Missouri	1887	3rd	508	Vicksburg, Mississippi	1882	3rd	332
St. Louis, Missouri	1887	3rd	532	Vicksburg, Mississippi	1885		422
St. Louis, Missouri	1888	2nd	564	Vincennes, Indiana	1880	3rd	234
St. Louis, Missouri	1888	2nd	565	Washington, Indiana	1878	4th	202
St. Louis, Missouri	1888	3rd	562	Watertown, Wisconsin	1876	2nd	161
St. Louis, Missouri	1889	2nd	600	Waukesha, Wisconsin	1882	4th	286
St. Louis, Missouri	1889	3rd	599	Wausaw, Wisconsin	1880	3rd	266
St. Louis, Missouri	1891	2nd	651	Waverly, Ohio	1875	3rd	153
St. Louis, Missouri	1891	2nd	653	Waynesville, Ohio	1886	2nd	457
St. Marys, Canada	1877	3rd	182	West Bellville, Illinois	1881	5th	304
St. Paris, Ohio	1884		415	Westwood, Ohio	1887		514
St. Paul Minnasota	1884		391	Westwood, Ohio	1891		661
St. Paul, Minnesota	1886		448	Wichita, Kansas	1889		602
St. Paul, Minnesota	1886		483	Wilkes-Barre, Pennsylvania	1889		582
St. Paul, Minnesota	1887		509	Wilmington, Ohio	1890	4th	605

American (Ahrens Division)
(1892-1903)

Information compiled by:

Ed Hass

City	Date	Size	Serial #	City	Date	Size	Serial #
Aberdeen, Mississippi	1899	4th	2695	Chicago, Illinois	1895	3rd	2413
Aberdeen, Washington	1902	X1st	2892	Chicago, Illinois	1895	4th	2208
Akron, Ohio	1900	2nd	2766	Chicago, Illinois	1895	4th	2384
Anacortes, Washington	1892	3rd	2103	Chicago, Illinois	1896	3rd	2466
Ardimore, Oklahoma	1900	3rd	2696	Chicago, Illinois	1896	3rd	2467
Atchinson, Kansas	1900	3rd	2739	Chicago, Illinois	1896	4th	2447
Babahoyo, Ecuador	1901	4th	2809	Chicago, Illinois	1896	4th	2468
Bakersfield, California	1900	2nd	2767	Chicago, Illinois	1896	4th	2469
Battle Creek, Michigan	1902	X1st	2838	Chicago, Illinois	1897	1st	2545
Birmingham, Alabama	1894	2nd	2260	Chicago, Illinois	1897	1st	2546
Birmingham, Alabama	1900	1st	2785	Chicago, Illinois	1897	1st	2547
Birmingham, Alabama	1902	2nd	2908	Chicago, Illinois	1897		2528
Bloomingham, Illinois	1902	4th	2909	Chicago, Illinois	1898	1st	2612
Bloomington, Illinois	1900	1st	2753	Chicago, Illinois	1898	2nd	2589
Boise, Idaho	1902	3rd	2910	Chicago, Illinois	1898	2nd	2610
Cavite, Philippines	1902	4th	2890	Chicago, Illinois	1898	2nd	2611
Chattanooga, Tennessee	1892	3rd	2104	Chicago, Illinois	1899	2nd	2667
Chattanooga, Tennessee	1896	2nd	2446	Chicago, Illinois	1899	2nd	2668
Chicago, Illinois	1892	3rd	2109	Chicago, Illinois	1899	2nd	2670
Chicago, Illinois	1892	3rd	2128	Chicago, Illinois	1899	2nd	2672
Chicago, Illinois	1892	3rd	2129	Chicago, Illinois	1899	DX1st	2592
Chicago, Illinois	1892	4th	2147	Chicago, Illinois	1899	DX1st	2593
Chicago, Illinois	1893	3rd	2143	Chicago, Illinois	1899	DX1st	2594
Chicago, Illinois	1893	3rd	2144	Chicago, Illinois	1900	1st	2756
Chicago, Illinois	1893	3rd	2145	Chicago, Illinois	1900	2nd	2754
Chicago, Illinois	1893	3rd	2224	Chicago, Illinois	1900	2nd	2755
Chicago, Illinois	1893	4th	2148	Chicago, Illinois	1902	1st	2835
Chicago, Illinois	1893	4th	2149	Chicago, Illinois	1902	1st	2857
Chicago, Illinois	1893	4th	2150	Chicago, Illinois	1902	1st	2858
Chicago, Illinois	1893	4th	2175	Chicago, Illinois	1902	1st	2859
Chicago, Illinois	1893	4th	2176	Cincinnati, Ohio	1893	2nd	2248
Chicago, Illinois	1893	4th	2222	Cincinnati, Ohio	1897	1st	2516
Chicago, Illinois	1893	4th	2225	Cincinnati, Ohio	1897	1st	2517
Chicago, Illinois	1893	4th	2226	Cincinnati, Ohio	1900	2nd	2713
Chicago, Illinois	1893	4th	2227	Cincinnati, Ohio	1902	2nd	2816
Chicago, Illinois	1893	4th	2234	Cincinnati, Ohio	1902	2nd	2817
Chicago, Illinois	1894	4th	2277	Cincinnati, Ohio	1902	2nd	2818
Chicago, Illinois	1894	4th	2279	Clarksville, Tennessee	1893	3rd	2146
Chicago, Illinois	1894	4th	2286	Clarksville, Tennessee	1894	3rd	2235
Chicago, Illinois	1894	4th	2288	Colorado Springs, Colorado	1898	2nd	2606

American

City	Date	Size	Serial #	City	Date	Size	Serial #
Columbus, Ohio	1894	1st	2258	Kewaunee, Wisconsin	1897	4th	2510
Columbus, Ohio	1896	3rd	2460	Leipsic, Ohio	1895	5th	2364
Columbus, Ohio	1897	2nd	2490	Los Angeles, California	1899	1st	2639
Columbus, Ohio	1897	2nd	2491	Los Angeles, California	1899	2nd	2640
Columbus, Ohio	1897	3rd	2527	Los Angeles, California	1899	3rd	2638
Coney Island, New York	1903	5th	2937	Louisville, Kentucky	1892	1st	2124
Dallas, Texas	1893	1st	2274	Louisville, Kentucky	1895	3rd	2405
Dallas, Texas	1902	2nd	2903	Louisville, Kentucky	1895	3rd	2406
Dallas, Texas	1902	X1st	2904	Louisville, Kentucky	1896	1st	2414
Dayton, Ohio	1900	2nd	2746	Louisville, Kentucky	1902	1st	2819
Decatur, Illinois	1900	1st	2723	Louisville, Kentucky	1902	1st	2820
Denver, Colorado	1900	X1st	2706	Loveland, Ohio	1894	3rd	2252
Denver, Colorado	1902	X1st	2883	Madison, Indiana	1899	2nd	2658
Denver, Colorado	1902	X1st	2893	Manila, Philippines	1894	X1st	2258
Denver, Colorado	1902	X1st	2914	Manila, Philippines	1894	X1st	2259
Detroit, Michigan	1896	2nd	2362	Manila, Philippines	1902	2nd	2828
Duluth, Minnesota	1900	X1st	2705	Manila, Philippines	1902	2nd	2829
Durban, South Africa	1903	5th	2939	Manila, Philippines	1903	4th	2931
El Paso, Texas	1901	1st	2789	Manila, Philippines	1903	4th	2932
Erie, Pennsylvania	1894	2nd	2261	Manila, Philippines	1903	4th	2933
Evanston, Illinois	1893	3rd	2249	Matanzas, Cuba	1901	2nd	2807
Evansville, Indiana	1892	3rd	2101	McKinney, Texas	1895	4th	2383
Evansville, Indiana	1892	3rd	2102	McKinney, Texas	1895	4th	2385
Evansville, Indiana	1903	1st	2946	Michigamme, Michigan	1900	5th	2722
Fort Smith, Arkansas	1900	3rd	2741	Millersburg, Kentucky	1903	5th	2944
Fort Thomas, Kentucky	1903	5th	2943	Milwaukee, Wisconsin	1892	X1st	2123
Fort Worth, Texas	1895	1st	2368	Milwaukee, Wisconsin	1893	2nd	2173
Fountain City, Wisconsin	1893	6th	2172	Milwaukee, Wisconsin	1893	2nd	2214
Glenville, Ohio	1900	4th	2768	Milwaukee, Wisconsin	1893	4th	2171
Grand Rapids, Michigan	1896	1st	2438	Milwaukee, Wisconsin	1893	4th	2177
Grand Rapids, Michigan	1896	X1st	2458	Milwaukee, Wisconsin	1893	4th	2228
Guayaquil, Ecuador	1899	X1st	2659	Milwaukee, Wisconsin	1894	2nd	2280
Hammond, Indiana	1899	2nd	2687	Milwaukee, Wisconsin	1898	2nd	2445
Honolulu, Hawaii	1900	1st	2780	Milwaukee, Wisconsin	1900	1st	2737
Houston, Texas	1901	4th	2798	Milwaukee, Wisconsin	1900	1st	2738
Indianapolis, Indiana	1896	1st	2420	Milwaukee, Wisconsin	1902	1st	2905
Indianapolis, Indiana	1901	X1st	2782	Milwaukee, Wisconsin	1902	1st	2906
Indianapolis, Indiana	1901	X1st	2783	Milwaukee, Wisconsin	1902	1st	2907
Indianapolis, Indiana	1903	3rd	2925	Milwaukee, Wisconsin	1902		2861
Jackson, Michigan	1900	2nd	2773	Milwaukee, Wisconsin	1902		2862
Jackson, Mississippi	1900	3rd	2762	Milwaukee, Wisconsin	1902		2863
Kalamazoo, Michigan	1895	3rd	2338	Morgan City, Louisiana	1900	3rd	2770
Kalamazoo, Michigan	1902	X1st	2882	Nashville, Tennessee	1892	DX1st	2108

American

City	Date	Size	Serial #	City	Date	Size	Serial #
Nashville, Tennessee	1897	2nd	2511	San Antonio, Texas	1892	3rd	2107
Nashville, Tennessee	1900	3rd	2765	San Antonio, Texas	1892	3rd	2130
New London, Wisconsin	1894	4th	2287	San Diego, California	1902	3rd	2896
New Orleans, Louisiana	1896	2nd	2423	San Francisco, California	1895	1st	2399
New Orleans, Louisiana	1896	2nd	2428	San Francisco, California	1895	1st	2404
New Orleans, Louisiana	1896	3rd	2430	San Francisco, California	1899	1st	2652
New Orleans, Louisiana	1897	2nd	2555	San Francisco, California	1899	1st	2653
New Orleans, Louisiana	1897	2nd	2561	San Francisco, California	1899	2nd	2675
New Orleans, Louisiana	1897	3rd	2493	San Francisco, California	1899	2nd	2676
New Orleans, Louisiana	1897	4th	2502	San Francisco, California	1899	3rd	2623
New Orleans, Louisiana	1897	4th	2503	San Francisco, California	1899	3rd	2624
New Orleans, Louisiana	1897	4th	2504	San Francisco, California	1901	2nd	2786
New Orleans, Louisiana	1897	4th	2519	San Jose, California	1901	2nd	2804
New Orleans, Louisiana	1897	4th	2554	San Salvador, El Salvador	1903	5th	2938
New Orleans, Louisiana	1897	5th	2520	Seattle, Washington	1899	1st	2686
New Orleans, Louisiana	1897	5th	2522	Seattle, Washington	1902	3rd	2854
New Orleans, Louisiana	1897	5th	2523	Seattle, Washington	1902	3rd	2856
New Orleans, Louisiana	1897	5th	2524	Spencerville, Ohio	1895	6th	2387
New Orleans, Louisiana	1897	5th	2526	Spokane, Washington	1900	1st	2777
New Orleans, Louisiana	1898	2nd	2569	Springfield, Illinois	1894	2nd	2316
New Orleans, Louisiana	1898	2nd	2570	Springfield, Missouri	1902	2nd	2911
New Orleans, Louisiana	1898	2nd	2577	Springfield, Missouri	1902	2nd	2912
New Orleans, Louisiana	1898	4th	2578	Springfield, Ohio	1903	2nd	2839
Niles Center, Ohio	1902	6th	2869	Springfield, Ohio	1903	2nd	2841
North Lewisburg, Ohio	1903	5th	2942	St. Joseph, Missouri	1894	2nd	2262
Oakland, California	1900	3rd	2715	St. Louis, Missouri	1892	2nd	2121
Ottawa, Illinois	1894	3rd	2209	St. Louis, Missouri	1892	3rd	2125
Oxford, Ohio	1895	5th	2386	St. Louis, Missouri	1892	3rd	2126
Piqua, Ohio	1892	3rd	2142	St. Louis, Missouri	1893	2nd	2174
Portland, Oregon	1901	X1st	2791	St. Louis, Missouri	1893	2nd	2246
Portland, Oregon	1902	X1st	2824	St. Louis, Missouri	1893	3rd	2181
Portsmouth, Ohio	1903	2nd	2948	St. Louis, Missouri	1893	3rd	2247
Quincy, Illinois	1902	3rd	2842	St. Louis, Missouri	1894	2nd	2285
Reading, Pennsylvania	1893	1st	2203	St. Louis, Missouri	1894	3rd	2253
Reading, Pennsylvania	1893	2nd	2121	St. Louis, Missouri	1895	1st	2381
Reno, Nevada	1902	2nd	2823	St. Louis, Missouri	1895	2nd	2337
Rockford, Illinois	1892	3rd	2105	St. Louis, Missouri	1895	2nd	2360
Rockford, Illinois	1894	2nd	2319	St. Louis, Missouri	1895	4th	2320
Rockford, Illinois	1899	2nd	2656	St. Louis, Missouri	1895	4th	2321
Rushville, Indiana	1893	3rd	2250	St. Louis, Missouri	1896	2nd	2417
Sacramento, California	1903	X1st	2928	St. Louis, Missouri	1896	2nd	2492
Salt Lake City, Utah	1902	1st	2844	St. Louis, Missouri	1896	4th	2421
San Antonio, Texas	1892	3rd	2106	St. Louis, Missouri	1898	1st	2563

American

City	Date	Size	Serial #
St. Louis, Missouri	1898	1st	2584
St. Louis, Missouri	1898	1st	2585
St. Louis, Missouri	1898	3rd	2562
St. Louis, Missouri	1900	1st	2747
St. Louis, Missouri	1900	4th	2693
St. Louis, Missouri	1900	4th	2694
St. Louis, Missouri	1901	1st	2799
St. Louis, Missouri	1902	1st	2880
St. Louis, Missouri	1902	1st	2881
St. Louis, Missouri	1902	X1st	2867
St. Louis, Missouri	1902	X1st	2868
St. Louis, Missouri	1902	X1st	2902
Stock	1893	2nd	2179
Stock	1893	2nd	2180
Tacoma, Washington	1902	1st	2913

City	Date	Size	Serial #
Traverse City, Michigan	1895	3rd	2378
Traverse City, Michigan	1901	2nd	2806
Unknown	1893	5th	2178
Unknown	1893		2182
Unknown	1893		2183
Unknown	1893		2184
Unknown	1893		2185
Unknown	1893		2186
West Bend, Wisconsin	1902	3rd	2870
Wheeling, West Virginia	1892	2nd	2141
Wheeling, West Virginia	1892	3rd	2110
Wheeling, West Virginia	1895	1st	2339
Wheeling, West Virginia	1903	3rd	2945
Wichita, Kansas	1902	X1st	2821
Xenia, Illinois	1902	6th	2866

Ahrens Fire Engine Company
(1904-1910)

Ahrens-Fox Fire Engine Company
(1910-)

Sizes:	
X1st	1100 GPM
1st	900 GPM
2nd	700 GPM
3rd	600 GPM
4th	500 GPM

Information compiled by:

Harold S. Walker, P. E.
Edward R. Tufts

City	Date	Size	Serial #
Allentown, Pennsylvania	1909	1st	170
Atlanta, Georgia	1909	1st	
Atlanta, Georgia	1910	1st	
Aurora, Indiana	1911	1st	194
Baltimore, Maryland	1908	1st	
Baltimore, Maryland	1909	1st	
Baltimore, Maryland	1909	1st	
Baltimore, Maryland	1909	1st	
Berkeley, California	1908	2nd	155
Berkley, California	1906	2nd	
Buffalo, New York	1906	2nd	
Canal Dover, Ohio	1907	3rd	125
Charleston, West Virginia	1906		
Charleston, West Virginia	1908	3rd	
Chicago, Illinois	1907	2nd	120
Chicago, Illinois	1907	2nd	121
Chicago, Illinois	1907	2nd	133
Chicago, Illinois	1907	2nd	134
Chicago, Illinois	1907	2nd	135
Chicago, Illinois	1907	2nd	136
Chicago, Illinois	1911	2nd	185
Chicago, Illinois	1912	2nd	190
Chicago, Illinois	1912	2nd	191
Chicago, Illinois	1912	2nd	192
Chicago, Illinois	1912	2nd	193

City	Date	Size	Serial #
Cincinnati, Ohio	1906	2nd	
Clarksburg, West Virginia	1910		
Cleveland, Ohio	1904	4th	100
Columbus, Ohio	1906	3rd	
Columbus, Ohio	1909	2nd	
Covington, Kentucky	1908	1st	
Dallas, Texas	1906	2nd	
Dayton, Ohio	1908	2nd	154
Denver, Colorado	1906	1st	
Denver, Colorado	1909	1st	
Denver, Colorado	1910	1st	
Denver, Colorado	1912	1st	
Detroit, Michigan	1908	1st	155
Detroit, Michigan	1908	1st	156
East St. Louis, Missouri	1905	3rd	102
East St. Louis, Missouri	1909	3rd	
Everett, Washington	1907	3rd	
Galion, Ohio	1907	3rd	
Grand Rapids, Michigan	1906	1st	
Greenville, Texas	1910		
Houston, Texas	1908	1st	
Indianapolis, Indiana	1905	4th	101
Janesville, Wisconsin	1909	1st	
Kansas City, Missouri	1907	X1st	
Lansford, Pennsylvania	1914	X1st	205

Ahrens Fire Engine Co.
Ahrens-Fox Fire Engine Co.

City	Date	Size	Serial #
Los Angeles, California	1907	4th	
Los Angeles, California	1909	4th	
Louisville, Kentucky	1906	1st	
Louisville, Kentucky	1907	2nd	144
Louisville, Kentucky	1907	2nd	145
Louisville, Kentucky	1908	2nd	
Memphis, Tennessee	1909	2nd	178
Memphis, Tennessee	1909	2nd	179
Montgomery, Alabama	1906	3rd	
New Orleans, Louisiana	1909	2nd	
New Orleans, Louisiana	1909	2nd	
Omaha, Nebraska	1908	1st	
Orlando, Florida	1908	1st	
Paterson, New Jersey	1914	1st	
Philadelphia, Pennsylvania	1914	4th	200
Philadelphia, Pennsylvania	1914	4th	201
Philadelphia, Pennsylvania	1914	4th	202
Philadelphia, Pennsylvania	1914	4th	203
Roanoke, Virginia	1907	2nd	146
Rochester, New York	1914	1st	204
San Diego, California	1906	2nd	
San Francisco, California	1906	3rd	109
San Jose, California	1906	1st	
Seattle, Washington	1906	3rd	

City	Date	Size	Serial #
Seattle, Washington	1907	3rd	147
Somerville, Massachusetts	1914	1st	199
Springfield, Missouri	1910		
St. Louis, Missouri	1907		148
St. Louis, Missouri	1907		149
St. Paul, Minnesota	1907	1st	142
St. Paul, Minnesota	1907	1st	143
St. Paul, Minnesota	1909	2nd	
St. Paul, Minnesota	1909	2nd	
St. Paul, Minnesota	1910		
Superior, Wisconsin	1908	X1st	
Taunton, Massachusetts	1912	2nd	
Terre Haute, Indiana	1906	3rd	
Terre Haute, Indiana	1906	3rd	
Toledo, Ohio	1906	1st	
Toledo, Ohio	1907	2nd	150
Toledo, Ohio	1907	2nd	151
Valdez, Alaska	1907	2nd	152
Van Wert, Ohio	1908	3rd	
Washington, D. C.	1911	2nd	188
Wheeling, West Virginia	1914		
Wheeling, West Virginia	1914		
Woodbury, New Jersey	1911	2nd	184

Ahrens-Continental Steam Fire Engines
(1875 - 1891)

City	Date	Size	Serial #	City	Date	Size	Serial #
Allentown, Pennsylvania	1909	1st	170	Galion, Ohio	1907	3rd	
Atlanta, Georgia	1909	1st		Grand Rapids, Michigan	1906	1st	
Atlanta, Georgia	1910	1st		Greenville, Texas	1910		
Aurora, Indiana	1911	1st	194	Houston, Texas	1908	1st	
Baltimore, Maryland	1908	1st		Indianapolis, Indiana	1905	3rd	101
Baltimore, Maryland	1909	1st		Janesville, Wisconsin	1909	1st	
Baltimore, Maryland	1909	1st		Kansas City, Missouri	1907	X1st	
Baltimore, Maryland	1909	1st		Lansford, Pennsylvania	1914	X1st	205
Berkeley, California	1906	2nd		Los Angeles, California	1907	4th	
Berkeley, California	1908	2nd		Los Angeles, California	1909	4th	
Buffalo, New York	1906	2nd		Louisville, Kentucky	1906	1st	
Canal Dover, Ohio	1906	3rd	125	Louisville, Kentucky	1907	2nd	
Charleston, West Virginia	1906	1st		Louisville, Kentucky	1907	2nd	
Charleston, West Virginia	1908	3rd		Louisville, Kentucky	1908	2nd	
Chicago Heights, Illinois				Memphis, Tennessee	1910	1st	179
Chicago, Illinois	1907	2nd	120	Memphis, Tennessee	1910	2nd	178
Chicago, Illinois	1907	2nd	121	Merced, California	1909	3rd	
Chicago, Illinois	1907	2nd	133	Montgomery, Alabama	1906	3rd	
Chicago, Illinois	1907	2nd	134	New Orleans, Louisiana	1909	2nd	
Chicago, Illinois	1907	2nd	135	New Orleans, Louisiana	1909	2nd	
Chicago, Illinois	1907	2nd	136	Omaha, Nebraska	1908	1st	
Chicago, Illinois	1911	2nd	185	Oreland, Pennsylvania			
Chicago, Illinois	1912	2nd	190	Orlando, Florida	1908	1st	
Chicago, Illinois	1912	2nd	191	Paterson, New Jersey		1st	
Chicago, Illinois	1912	2nd	192	Philadelphia, Pennsylvania	1914	4th	200
Chicago, Illinois	1912	2nd	193	Philadelphia, Pennsylvania	1914	4th	201
Cincinnati, Ohio	1906	2nd		Philadelphia, Pennsylvania	1914	4th	202
Clarksburg, West Virginia	1910			Philadelphia, Pennsylvania	1914	4th	203
Cleveland, Ohio	1904	4th	100	Roanoke, Virginia	1907	1st	
Columbus, Ohio	1906	3rd		Rochester, New York	1914	1st	204
Columbus, Ohio	1909	2nd		San Diego, California	1906	2nd	
Covington, Kentucky	1908	1st		San Francisco, California			
Dallas, Texas	1906	2nd		San Jose, California	1906	1st	
Dayton, Ohio	1908	2nd		Seattle, Washington	1906	2nd	
Denver, Colorado	1906	1st		Seattle, Washington	1907	3rd	
Denver, Colorado	1909	1st		Somerville, Massachusetts		1st	199
Denver, Colorado	1910	1st		Springfield, Missouri	1910		
Denver, Colorado	1912	1st		Springfield, Missouri	1910		
Detroit, Michigan		1st		St. Louis, Missouri	1907		
Detroit, Michigan	1908	1st	155	St. Louis, Missouri	1907		
East St. Louis, Illinois	1905	3rd	102	St. Paul, Minnesota	1908	1st	142
East. St. Louis, Illinois	1909	3rd		St. Paul, Minnesota	1908	1st	143
Everett, Washington	1907	3rd		St. Paul, Minnesota	1909	2nd	

Ahrens-Continental Steam Fire Engine

City	Date	Size	Serial #
St. Paul, Minnesota	1909	2nd	
St. Paul, Minnesota	1910		
Superior, Wisconsin	1908	X1st	
Taunton, Massachusetts	1912	2nd	
Terre Haute, Indiana	1906	3rd	
Terre Haute, Indiana	1906	3rd	
Toledo, Ohio	1906	1st	
Toledo, Ohio	1907	2nd	

City	Date	Size	Serial #
Toledo, Ohio	1907	2nd	
Valdez, Alaska	1907	2nd	
Van Wert, Ohio	1908	3rd	
Washington, D. C.	1911	2nd	188
Wheeling, West Virginia	1914		
Wheeling, West Virginia	1914		
Woodbury, New Jersey	1911	2nd	184

A steamer and accompanying hose wagon are posed in front of their quarters on Franklin Street in Chicago.

Button Steam Fire Engines
Waterford, New York

1862-1865	Button & Blake Successors to L. Button hand engine builder 1834-1862 of Waterford, New York
1865-1882	Button Engine Works and/or L. Button & Son Successors to Button & Blake
1882-1891	Holroyd & Co. (under the name of Button Fire Engine Company
After 1891	American Fire Engine Co., Seneca Falls, New York (A consolidation of Silsby Mfg. Co., Ahrens Mfg. Co., Clapp & Jones Mfg. Co., and the Button Fire Engine Works.

Number of Engines Built: 229

Information compiled by:

Harold S. Walker, P. E.
Edward R. Tufts
John M. Peckham
John J. Robrecht

Note:
Registered Numbers above 229 are for apparatus
that were rebuilt and sometimes sold to a different community.

Button Steam Fire Engines

City	Date	Size	Serial #
Aiken, South Carolina	1880	5th	115
Akron, Ohio	1886	3rd	191
Albany, New York	1864	2nd	11
Almonte, Ontario	1884	4th	150
Amsterdam, New York	1871	4th	70
Ann Arbor, Michigan	1880	6th	116
Arnprior, Ontario	1888	4th	207
Athens, Georgia	1876	5th	99
Augusta, Georgia (U.S. Arsenal)	1883	3rd	134
Augusta, Georgia	1866	3rd	30
Augusta, Georgia	1868		46
Augusta, Georgia	1876	1st	103
Augusta, Georgia	1876		106
Augusta, Georgia	1884	2nd	143
Aurora, Illinois	1875	4th	89
Avoca, Iowa	1883	5th	139
Barre, Massachusetts	1885	5th	166
Baton Rouge, Louisiana (U.S. Arsenal)	1867		36
Battle Creek, Michigan	1863		3
Bayonne, New Jersey	1885	5th	163
Bayonne, New Jersey	1893		
Bellville, Ontario	1866	2nd	27
Belmar, New Jersey	1889	5th	213
Belmar, New Jersey	1910	3rd	
Brewer, Maine	1883	4th	137
Buffalo, New York	1892	2nd	247
Burlington, Vermont	1892	4th	230
Calais, Maine	1872	4th	76
Camden, New Jersey	1890	2nd	218
Canajoharie, New York	1872		77
Canajoharie, New York	1886	3rd	192
Canandaigua, New York	1875		90
Carlisle, Pennsylvania	1871		59
Carlisle, Pennsylvania	1886	3rd	179
Catasauqua, Pennsylvania (Manuf. Co.)	1891	2nd	223
Catasauqua, Pennsylvania	1886	2nd	31
Chambersburg, Pennsylvania	1884	3rd	157
Charleston, South Carolina (U.S. Arsen.)	1866	3rd	23
Charleston, South Carolina	1869		47
Charleston, West Virginia	1885	4th	169
Chicago, Illinois	1869		55
Cohoes, New York (Harmony Mills)	1867	2nd	40
Cohoes, New York	1867	2nd	37

City	Date	Size	Serial #
Cottage City, Massachusetts	1884	5th	144
Coxsackie, New York	1871	4th	67
Danville, Virginia	1883	3rd	142
Davenport, Iowa	1866	2nd	22
Dowagiac, Michigan	1886	2nd	187
Dowagiac, Michigan	1886		178
Eatontown, New Jersey	1864		
Elizabeth, New Jersey	1868		42
Elizabeth, New Jersey	1869		49
Elizabeth, New Jersey	1884		158
Elizabeth, New Jersey	1888	2nd	211
Forepaugh & Sells Bros. Circus	1887		200
Freehold, New Jersey	1887	3rd	194
Fulton, New York	1866	3rd	32
Fulton, New York	1871		64
Garnersville, New York			
Geneva, New York	1864	3rd	5
Geneva, New York	1867	3rd	35
Geneva, New York	1870		56
Gladstone, Michigan	1888	5th	204
Grand Rapids, Michigan	1882	2nd	133
Grand Rapids, Michigan	1887	X1st	206
Great Barrington, Massachusetts	1882	3rd	129
Great Bend, Pennsylvania	1868		
Green Bay, Wisconsin (Fort Howard)	1872	5th	75
Green Island, New York	1884	3rd	151
Hackensack, New Jersey	1893	5th	231
Hamilton, New York	1887	3rd	198
Harmar, Ohio	1875	4th	88
Harrisburg, Pennsylvania	1865	2nd	12
Harrisburg, Pennsylvania	1865	2nd	25
Harrisburg, Pennsylvania	1869	2nd	48
Harrisburg, Pennsylvania	1882	2nd	130
Harrisburg, Pennsylvania	1883	2nd	141
Harrisburg, Pennsylvania	1886	2nd	189
Haverstraw, New York Print Works	1876	4th	96
Herkimer, New York	1875	4th	92
Hightstown, New Jersey	1887	5th	195
Hollidaysburg, Pennsylvania	1871		68
Hollidaysburg, Pennsylvania	1882	3rd	125
Holyoke, Massachusetts	1885	3rd	165
Hoosic Falls, New York	1871	4th	69
Jackson, Mississippi	1868		38

Button Steam Fire Engines

City	Date	Size	Serial #
Jackson, Mississippi	1887	5th	196
Janesville, Wisconsin	1868	2nd	45
Janesville, Wisconsin	1885	2nd	160
Jefferson, Texas	1871	3rd	65
Johnstown, Pennsylvania	1890	5th	222
Jordan, New York	1869	2nd	240
Kaukauna, Wisconsin	1885	4th	168
Keene, New Hampshire	1890	3rd	216
Key West, Florida	1873	2nd	81
Key West, Florida	1880		114
Key West, Florida	1886	5th	183
Key West, Florida	1886	5th	188
Key West, Florida	1887	3rd	203
Kingston, New York	1867		58
La Porte City, Iowa	1881	6th	124
Lambertville, New Jersey	1869		54
Lancaster, Pennsylvania	1865	3rd	17
Lansing, Kansas (State Prison)	1879	3rd	101
Lansingburgh, New York	1864	3rd	7
Lansingburgh, New York	1865	3rd	16
Lansingburgh, New York	1881	2nd	121
Lansingburgh, New York	1881	3rd	120
Leavenworth, Kansas	1867	3rd	34
Lebanon, Pennsylvania	1868	3rd	26
Lebanon, Pennsylvania	1873	2nd	82
Lebanon, Pennsylvania	1884	3rd	149
Leicester, Massachusetts	1869	3rd	51
Leicester, Massachusetts	1889	3rd	186
Little Falls, New York	1871	4th	71
Little Rock, Arkansas	1872	3rd	74
Little Rock, Arkansas	1891	2nd	229
Lock Haven, Pennsylvania	1863	3rd	2
Lynn, Massachusetts	1891	2nd	224
Lyons, New York	1885	2nd	172
Mackinac, Michigan	1887		197
Marshall, Illinois	1890	5th	219
Mechanicville, New York	1891		251
Michigan City, Indiana	1883	5th	131
Mohawk, New York	1875	4th	93
Mt. Sterling, Kentucky	1876	6th	105
Nassau, Bahama Islands	1889	6th	214
Natchez, Mississippi	1871		62
Nebraska City, Nebraska	1884	5th	156

City	Date	Size	Serial #
New Bern, North Carolina	1884	4th	155
New Brighton, New York (L.I.)	1893	4th	
New Brunswick, New Jersey	1867	3rd	39
New Brunswick, New Jersey	1884	3rd	154
New Castle, Pennsylvania	1873	4th	84
New Rochelle, New York	1876	3rd	97
New Rochelle, New York	1885	6th	173
Newark, New Jersey	1889	3rd	217
Newtown, New York	1890	5th	220
Norristown, Pennsylvania	1881		118
Norristown, Pennsylvania	1887		202
Nyack, New York	1884	4th	146
Oil City, Pennsylvania	1870	2nd	60
Old Town, Maine	1885	3rd	170
Oneonta, New York	1875	4th	94
Orrville, Ohio	1888	5th	205
Osage, Iowa	1882	5th	128
Oswego, New York	1886	2nd	182
Paterson, New Jersey	1885	3rd	176
Patterson, Pennsylvania	1886	3rd	180
Peabody, Massachusetts	1865	3rd	14
Peabody, Massachusetts	1874		86
Peabody, Massachusetts	1877	3rd	109
Peoria, Illinois	1888	2nd	209
Piermont, New York	1891	5th	225
Pittsburgh, Pennsylvania	1865	2nd	21
Pittston, Pennsylvania	1888	3rd	210
Plymouth, Massachusetts	1874	4th	87
Port Richmond, New York	1884	6th	145
Potsdam, New York	1888	3rd	208
Pottstown, Pennsylvania	1876	3rd	98
Pottstown, Pennsylvania	1891	3rd	227
Pottstown, Pennsylvania Iron Co.	1876	3rd	111
Quitman, Georgia	1884	5th	159
Reading, Massachusetts	1883	3rd	138
Rhinebeck, New York	1871	4th	72
Richmond, Virginia	1887	3rd	201
Rondout, New York	1867	3rd	33
Roxbury, Massachusetts	1864		9
Royersford, Pennsylvania	1883	3rd	164
Royersford, Pennsylvania	1889	2nd	212
Salem, North Carolina	1886	5th	190
San Francisco, California	1864	3rd	4

Button Steam Fire Engines

City	Date	Size	Serial #
San Juan, Puerto Rico	1893	6th	236
Sandy Hill, New York	1881	6th	119
Saratoga Springs, New York	1866		24
Saratoga Springs, New York	1866		29
Schenectady, New York	1869	2nd	53
Scranton, Pennsylvania	1868	3rd	41
Scranton, Pennsylvania	1891	3rd	226
Seabright, New Jersey	1883	4th	135
Seymour, Connecticut	1884	4th	152
Shelby, Michigan	1886	6th	184
Shenandoah, Pennsylvania	1878	5th	112
Shenandoah, Pennsylvania	1878		102
Shenandoah, Pennsylvania	1885	2nd	174
Springfield, Illinois	1865	3rd	18
Springfield, Illinois	1881	4th	122
St. Louis, Missouri	1866	3rd	19
Stamford, Connecticut	1883	3rd	132
Steelton, Pennsylvania	1886	4th	181
Steubenville, Ohio	1870	3rd	57
Steubenville, Ohio	1871	3rd	66
Stillwater, New York	1886	4th	185
Sydney, New South Wales	1885	5th	175
Thomaston, Maine	1873		83
Tomkinsville, New York (St. Isle)	1880	6th	117
Tomkinsville, New York	1885	5th	167
Trenton, New Jersey	1864	3rd	8
Trenton, New Jersey	1866	2nd	20
Trenton, New Jersey	1872		78
Trenton, New Jersey	1876	3rd	107
Trenton, New Jersey	1881	3rd	123
Troy, New York	1864	3rd	6
Troy, New York	1871	3rd	63
Troy, New York	1882	2nd	126
Troy, New York	1882	2nd	127
Troy, New York	1883	2nd	140
Troy, New York	1885	3rd	171
Troy, New York	1891	2nd	228
Union City, Michigan	1887	4th	199
Utica, New York	1892	2nd	246
Victoria, British Columbia	1868		44
Virginia City, Nevada	1873	3rd	80
Walden, New York	1872		79
Walden, New York	1887	4th	193
Wallingford, Connecticut	1880	5th	104
Wappingers Falls, New York	1869		52
Waterford, New York	1864	2nd	13
Waterford, New York	1873	2nd	81
Waterford, New York	1877	3rd	110
Waterloo, Iowa	1881	6th	124
Waterville, Maine	1884	3rd	148
Watervliet, New York	1865	3rd	15
West Chester, Pennsylvania	1875	4th	100
West Liberty, Ohio	1890	5th	215
West Newbury, Massachusetts	1884	5th	147
West Troy, New York	1864	2nd	10
West Troy, New York	1866	3rd	28
West Troy, New York	1873	4th	85
Weymouth, Massachusetts	1880	4th	113
Whitehall, New York	1869	2nd	50
Whitehall, New York	1877	3rd	108
Wilkes Barre, Pennsylvania	1866	3rd	177
Wilmington, North Carolina	1873		61
Wilmington, North Carolina	1885	3rd	161
Worcester, Massachusetts	1891	2nd	221
Wyandotte, Michigan	1876	3rd	95
York, Pennsylvania	1868	3rd	43
York, Pennsylvania	1885	3rd	162

LaFrance Steam Fire Engines
Elmira, New York

1. LaFrance Manufacturing Co. 1875-1880

2. LaFrance Fire Engine Co. 1880-1902

3. International Fire Engine Co. 1902-1904

4. American LaFrance Fire Engine Co. 1904-1910

Types Built:

Rotary Pump 90
Piston Pump ....<u>449</u>
Total   539

Information compiled by:

Harold S. Walker, P. E.
Edward R. Tufts
John M. Peckham
John J. Robrecht

LaFrance Steam Fire Engines
(1880 - 1907)

City	Date	Size	Serial #	City	Date	Size	Serial #
Aberdeen, Michigan	1882	4th	40	Baltimore, Maryland	1905	2nd	511
Akron, Ohio	1887	2nd	128	Baltimore, Maryland	1906	1st	522
Albany, Georgia	1882	5th	47	Baltimore, Maryland	1906	1st	523
Albia, Iowa	1883	5th	62	Baltimore, Maryland	1907	1st	527
Algiers, Louisiana	1887	6th	129	Baltimore, Maryland	1907	1st	533
Allegheny City, Pennsylvania	1894	2nd	279	Baltimore, Maryland	1907	1st	534
Americus, Georgia	1881	4th	18	Baltimore, Maryland	1907	1st	536
Anaconda, Montana	1896	3rd	367	Baltimore, Maryland	1907	1st	537
Asbury Park, New Jersey	1883	2nd	56	Baltimore, Maryland	1907	1st	538
Ashley, Pennsylvania	1891	4th	198	Barnesville, Ohio	1894	3rd	306
Ashley, Pennsylvania	1907	3rd	539	Bayonne, New Jersey	1893	4th	238
Atlanta, Georgia	1894	1st	305	Bayonne, New Jersey	1895	3rd	345
Atlantic City, New Jersey	1888	2nd	143	Berlin, New Hampshire	1890	2nd	181
Atlantic City, New Jersey	1899	4th	409	Beverly, Massachusetts	1886	3rd	114
Augusta, Georgia	1900	2nd	442	Beverly, Massachusetts	1895	2nd	344
Baltimore County, Maryland	1893	4th	260	Binghampton, New York	1899	2nd	406
Baltimore County, Maryland	1893	4th	261	Binghampton, New York	1901	4th	469
Baltimore, Maryland	1884	4th	73	Bordentown, New Jersey	1893	5th	242
Baltimore, Maryland	1886	3rd	113	Boston, Massachusetts	1895	1st	325
Baltimore, Maryland	1888	3rd	148	Bradford, Pennsylvania	1881	4th	6
Baltimore, Maryland	1889	1st	157	Bridgeport, Connecticut	1890	2nd	192
Baltimore, Maryland	1889	2nd	158	Bridgeport, Connecticut	1892	3rd	226
Baltimore, Maryland	1890	2nd	194	Bridgeport, Connecticut	1894	3rd	294
Baltimore, Maryland	1891	3rd	214	Bridgeton, New Jersey	1880	3rd	182
Baltimore, Maryland	1892	1st	229	Bristol, Connecticut	1881	6th	19
Baltimore, Maryland	1893	2nd	259	Bristol, Connecticut	1881	6th	20
Baltimore, Maryland	1893	3rd	267	Brockton, Massachusetts	1894	X1st	312
Baltimore, Maryland	1894	2nd	204	Brookfield, Massachusetts	1892	5th	209
Baltimore, Maryland	1895	2nd	326	Brooklyn, New York	1876	3rd	363
Baltimore, Maryland	1895	3rd	327	Brooklyn, New York	1886	2nd	110
Baltimore, Maryland	1897	3rd	380	Brooklyn, New York	1887	2nd	134
Baltimore, Maryland	1898	1st	401	Brooklyn, New York	1888	2nd	154
Baltimore, Maryland	1898	2nd	396	Brooklyn, New York	1895	3rd	322
Baltimore, Maryland	1899	1st	423	Brooklyn, New York	1895	3rd	323
Baltimore, Maryland	1901	1st	464	Brooklyn, New York	1895	4th	329
Baltimore, Maryland	1901	1st	470	Brooklyn, New York	1895	4th	330
Baltimore, Maryland	1903	1st	485	Brooklyn, New York	1895	4th	331
Baltimore, Maryland	1903	1st	488	Brooklyn, New York	1895	4th	332
Baltimore, Maryland	1903	1st	489	Brooklyn, New York	1895	4th	333
Baltimore, Maryland	1904	1st	501	Brooklyn, New York	1895	4th	334
Baltimore, Maryland	1905	1st	508	Brooklyn, New York	1896	3rd	358
Baltimore, Maryland	1905	1st	510	Brooklyn, New York	1896	3rd	359
Baltimore, Maryland	1905	2nd	509	Brooklyn, New York	1896	3rd	360

LaFrance Steam Fire Engines

City	Date	Size	Serial #
Brooklyn, New York	1896	3rd	361
Brooklyn, New York	1896	3rd	362
Brooklyn, New York	1896	4th	356
Brooklyn, New York	1896	4th	357
Brooklyn, New York	1897	3rd	384
Brooklyn, New York	1897	4th	385
Brooklyn, New York	1897	4th	390
Brooklyn, New York	1897	4th	391
Brooklyn, New York	1898	4th	408
Brooklyn, New York	1899	4th	412
Brooklyn, New York	1899	4th	413
Brooklyn, New York	1899	4th	414
Brunswick, Georgia	1881	4th	11
Brunswick, Georgia	1886	5th	116
Bryan, Texas	1881	5th	15
Buffalo, New York	1882	3rd	41
Buffalo, New York	1882	4th	49
Buffalo, New York	1883	4th	65
Buffalo, New York	1883	4th	66
Buffalo, New York	1883	4th	67
Buffalo, New York	1884	1st	100
Buffalo, New York	1885	1st	104
Buffalo, New York	1886	X1st	107
Buffalo, New York	1888	2nd	150
Buffalo, New York	1888	2nd	153
Buffalo, New York	1888	X1st	137
Buffalo, New York	1888	X1st	139
Buffalo, New York	1892	2nd	225
Buffalo, New York	1894	1st	288
Buffalo, New York	1894	1st	289
Buffalo, New York	1905	1st	497
Buffalo, New York	1907	1st	531
Buffalo, New York	1907	1st	532
Burlington, New Jersey	1895	3rd	343
Canton, Mississippi	1880	5th	7
Cape Nome, Alaska	1900	3rd	445
Centerville, Iowa	1883	3rd	68
Chambersburg, Pennsylvania	1893	3rd	243
Chambersburg, Pennsylvania	1903	3rd	492
Chester, Pennsylvania	1887	2nd	132
Chicago, Illinois	1887	4th	124
Chico, California	1884	4th	70
Clearfield, Pennsylvania	1904	3rd	451

City	Date	Size	Serial #
Cleveland, Ohio	1892	3rd	222
Cleveland, Ohio	1901	1st	455
Cochran, Georgia			
Columbia, Pennsylvania	1887	3rd	123
Columbus, Ohio	1900	1st	440
Conshohocken, Pennsylvania	1882	2nd	38
Cooperstown, New York	1892	3rd	218
Corsicana, Texas	1897	4th	375
Cumberland, Maryland	1893	3rd	246
Cuthbert, Georgia	1862	6th	139
Cuthbert, Pennsylvania	1882	5th	37
Danbury, Connecticut	1889	3rd	162
Danville, Virginia	1902	3rd	479
Dayton, Ohio	1900	2nd	450
Dayton, Ohio	1900	X1st	448
Dayton, Ohio	1900	X1st	449
Dayton, Ohio	1906	1st	525
Denton, Texas	1882	4th	42
Denver, Colorado	1890	2nd	193
Detroit, Michigan	1896	2nd	347
Detroit, Michigan	1901	3rd	471
Detroit, Michigan	1903	1st	490
Detroit, Michigan	1904	1st	502
Detroit, Michigan	1904	1st	503
Detroit, Michigan	1904	1st	504
Detroit, Michigan	1904	1st	505
Detroit, Michigan	1904	1st	506
Detroit, Michigan	1905	1st	517
Detroit, Michigan	1905	1st	518
Dexter, New York	1905	1st	497
Elizabeth, New Jersey	1892	3rd	235
Elizabeth, New Jersey	1896	3rd	350
Elizabeth, New Jersey	1904	3rd	491
Elmira, New York	1882	5th	51
Elmira, New York	1892	4th	237
Elmira, New York	1893	4th	240
Elmira, New York	1895	4th	338
Elmira, New York	1907	1st	530
Eric, Pennsylvania	1892	3rd	217
Eufaula, Alabama	1882	6th	52
Evansville, Indiana	1888	5th	102
Fall River, Massachusetts	1890	X1st	195
Fall River, Massachusetts	1892	2nd	228

LaFrance Steam Fire Engines

City	Date	Size	Serial #
Fall River, Massachusetts	1895	1st	340
Findlay, Ohio	1902	2nd	478
Flemington, New Jersey	1900	4th	444
Fort Wayne, Indiana	1893	3rd	284
Fort Wayne, Indiana	1893	3rd	285
Fort Wayne, Indiana	1893	3rd	286
Fort Wayne, Indiana	1897	3rd	379
Fort Wayne, Indiana	1898	3rd	397
Fort Wayne, Indiana	1898	3rd	398
Franklin, Pennsylvania	1881	5th	22
Frederick, Maryland	1881	5th	9
Fresno, California	1893	3rd	253
Gloucester, Massachusetts	1899	4th	428
Gouveneur, New York	1880	4th	1
Grand Rapids, Michigan	1890	2nd	180
Grand Rapids, Michigan	1892	2nd	236
Grand Rapids, Michigan	1894	2nd	278
Grand Rapids, Michigan	1899	1st	410
Gravesend, New York	1894	3rd	277
Greely, Colorado	1883	5th	59
Greensboro, North Carolina	1886	6th	117
Greensboro, North Carolina	1904	3rd	496
Greenville, Texas	1883	5th	60
Greenwich, Connecticut	1900	3rd	446
Guayaquil, Ecuador	1884	4th	71
Guayaquil, Ecuador	1901	4th	466
Guayaquil, Ecuador	1901	X1st	460
Hackensack, New Jersey	1895	4th	337
Hampton, Virginia	1891	3rd	200
Harrisburg, Pennsylvania	1889	2nd	160
Harrisburg, Pennsylvania	1897	2nd	392
Haverhill, Massachusetts	1889	2nd	176
Hawkinsville, Georgia	1881	4th	4
Hazelton, Pennsylvania	1894	4th	421
Hoboken, New Jersey	1893	2nd	239
Holyoke, Massachusetts	1881	1st	12
Holyoke, Massachusetts	1883	3rd	142
Holyoke, Massachusetts	1893	2nd	263
Houston, Texas	1893	3rd	271
Houston, Texas	1895	2nd	339
Houston, Texas	1899	5th	408
Houston, Texas	1901	4th	467
Houston, Texas	1901	4th	468

City	Date	Size	Serial #
Hudson, Massachusetts	1871	3rd	212
Huntington, Pennsylvania	1880	3rd	3
Indianapolis, Indiana	1896	2nd	365
Ipswich, Massachusetts	1894	3rd	310
Ithaca, New York	1896	3rd	349
Jackson, Mississippi	1885	4th	76
Jacksonville, Florida	1885	2nd	103
Jacksonville, Florida	1902	2nd	476
Jamestown, New York	1900	4th	441
Jamestown, Rhode Island	1894	3rd	307
Jersey City, New Jersey	1890	2nd	197
Jersey City, New Jersey	1891	3rd	213
Jersey City, New Jersey	1892	3rd	219
Jersey City, New Jersey	1892	3rd	220
Jersey City, New Jersey	1894	2nd	280
Jordan, Eben D. (Farm), Massachusetts	1902	4th	440
Kansas City, Missouri	1893	3rd	254
Kansas City, Missouri	1893	3rd	255
Key West, Florida	1903	3rd	483
Knoxville, Tennessee	1899	4th	422
Knoxville, Tennessee	1904	3rd	500
Kokomo, Indiana	1883	4th	55
Kokomo, Indiana	1884	3rd	72
Lake, Illinois	1888	1st	145
Lake, Illinois	1888	4th	144
Lestershire, New York	1899	3rd	381
Lewistown, Pennsylvania	1896	4th	361
Logan, Ohio	1882	5th	46
Long Branch, New Jersey	1892	2nd	221
Long Branch, New Jersey	1892	2nd	221
Long Island City, New York	1894	3rd	295
Long Island City, New York	1894	3rd	296
Los Angeles, California	1899	2nd	416
Los Angeles, California	1899	2nd	417
Louisville, Kentucky	1899	4th	419
Louisville, Kentucky	1902	1st	473
Lowville, New York	1883	5th	64
Lynn, Massachusetts	1890	2nd	196
Macon, Georgia	1889	5th	169
Macon, Georgia	1890	3rd	183
Mahoney City, Pennsylvania	1885	5th	78
Marchfield, Oregon	1891	5th	206
Mecosta, Michigan	1885	6th	79

LaFrance Steam Fire Engines

City	Date	Size	Serial #	City	Date	Size	Serial #
Media, Pennsylvania	1892	4th	216	New York, New York	1893	3rd	256
Memphis, Tennessee	1902	1st	481	New York, New York	1894	1st	298
Memphis, Tennessee	1903	1st	491	New York, New York	1894	1st	299
Minneapolis, Minnesota	1887	1st	138	New York, New York	1894	3rd	277
Minneapolis, Minnesota	1888	2nd	140	New York, New York	1895	1st	321
Minneapolis, Minnesota	1892	1st	234	New York, New York	1895	3rd	335
Missoula, Montana	1890	3rd	184	New York, New York	1895	3rd	336
Monroe, Wisconsin	1883	4th	53	New York, New York	1895	3rd	381
Montgomery, Alabama	1881	5th	14	New York, New York	1896	1st	348
Montreal, Quebec	1898	X1st	392	New York, New York	1896	1st	367
Morristown, New Jersey	1893	3rd	266	New York, New York	1897	1st	377
Mt. Carmel, Pennsylvania	1882	3rd	44	New York, New York	1897	1st	378
Mt. Vernon, New York	1898	4th	407	New York, New York	1898	1st	395
Mt. Vernon, New York	1901	4th	465	New York, New York	1898	4th	399
Mt. Vernon, New York	1907	2nd	535	New York, New York	1898	4th	400
Mt. Vernon, Washington	1891	4th	199	New York, New York	1899	1st	411
Murphysboro, Illinois	1887	6th	136	New York, New York	1899	1st	424
Nashville, Illinois	1883	6th	54	New York, New York	1899	2nd	420
Nashville, Tennessee	1901	4th	459	New York, New York	1899	4th	415
New Bedford, Massachusetts	1894	3rd	282	New York, New York	1899		S.L.-1
New Bedford, Massachusetts	1894	3rd	315	New York, New York	1900	1st	434
New Britain, Connecticut	1896	2nd	351	New York, New York	1900	1st	435
New Brunswick, New Jersey	1888	3rd	149	New York, New York	1900	2nd	432
New Brunswick, New Jersey	1905	3rd	520	New York, New York	1900	3rd	433
New Haven, Connecticut	1897	2nd	376	New York, New York	1900	3rd	436
New Haven, Connecticut	1905	1st	519	New York, New York	1900	3rd	437
New Haven, Connecticut	1907	1st	526	New York, New York	1900	3rd	438
New Hope, Pennsylvania	1896	3rd	354	New York, New York	1900	3rd	439
New William, Minnesota	1888	6th	141	New York, New York	1900		S.L.-2
New York, New York	1886	1st	108	New York, New York	1900		S.L.-3
New York, New York	1888	1st	146	New York, New York	1901	3rd	461
New York, New York	1888	2nd	147	New York, New York	1901	3rd	462
New York, New York	1889	3rd	163	New York, New York	1901	3rd	463
New York, New York	1889	3rd	164	New York, New York	1906	3rd	3123
New York, New York	1889	3rd	165	Newark, New Jersey	1889	3rd	159
New York, New York	1890	3rd	186	Newark, New Jersey	1894	3rd	289
New York, New York	1890	3rd	187	Newark, New Jersey	1894	3rd	300
New York, New York	1891	3rd	202	Newark, New Jersey	1894	3rd	318
New York, New York	1892	2nd	224	Newark, New Jersey	1895	1st	346
New York, New York	1892	2nd	232	Newark, New Jersey	1901	2nd	474
New York, New York	1892	3rd	233	Newberry, South Carolina	1883	6th	51
New York, New York	1893	2nd	257	Newburgh, New York	1882	4th	48
New York, New York	1893	2nd	258	Newburgh, New York	1896	3rd	368

LaFrance Steam Fire Engines

City	Date	Size	Serial #
Newport News, Virginia	1891	3rd	211
Newport News, Virginia	1901	3rd	457
Niagara Falls, New York	1904	2nd	507
Oakland, California	1889	2nd	173
Oakland, California	1889	2nd	174
Oakland, California	1894	4th	270
Ogden, Utah	1890	4th	179
Omaha, Nebraska	1893	2nd	262
Omaha, Nebraska	1894	2nd	281
Orange, Texas	1883	6th	58
Orange, Texas	1896	4th	364
Oswego, New York	1896	4th	352
Ottawa, Ontario	1897	2nd	389
Passaic, New Jersey	1885	5th	75
Passaic, New Jersey	1895	3rd	342
Peabody, Massachusetts	1887	3rd	131
Petersburg, Virginia	1887	3rd	115
Petersburg, Virginia	1902	2nd	475
Philadelphia, Pennsylvania	1886	2nd	105
Philadelphia, Pennsylvania	1887	2nd	133
Philadelphia, Pennsylvania	1887	6th	122
Phillipsburg, Pennsylvania	1891	4th	204
Phillipsburg, Pennsylvania	1899	4th	431
Pittsburgh, Pennsylvania	1894	2nd	313
Pittsburgh, Pennsylvania	1894	2nd	314
Pittsburgh, Pennsylvania	1899	2nd	475
Port Huron, Michigan	1904	2nd	498
Port Jervis, New York	1894	3rd	309
Port Townsend, Washington	1891	1st	205
Portsmouth, Virginia	1886	3rd	109
Pottsville, Pennsylvania	1893	4th	272
Poughkeepsie, New York	1884	3rd	301
Providence, Rhode Island	1893	3rd	251
Providence, Rhode Island	1894	2nd	190
Providence, Rhode Island	1905	1st	514
Providence, Rhode Island	1905	1st	518
Provo, Utah	1890	5th	185
Reading, Pennsylvania	1887	2nd	135
Reading, Pennsylvania	1889	3rd	175
Red Lion, Pennsylvania	1900	4th	447
Renova, Pennsylvania	1887	3rd	121
Richmond, Virginia	1887	3rd	119
Richmond, Virginia	1891	3rd	207
Richmond, Virginia	1891	3rd	215
Richmond, Virginia	1892	3rd	223
Richmond, Virginia	1897	2nd	383
Richmond, Virginia	1901	1st	480
Richmond, Virginia	1901	2nd	456
Richmond, Virginia	1901	3rd	454
Richmond, Virginia	1905	1st	515
Roanoke, Virginia	1891	4th	210
Roanoke, Virginia	1908	1st	499
Rockaway Beach, New York	1893	4th	249
Rockaway Beach, New York	1893	4th	250
Rockland, Massachusetts	1894	3rd	283
Salem, California	1886	3rd	112
Salem, North Carolina	1905	4th	512
Salinas, California	1893	5th	273
San Bernadino, California	1884	5th	43
San Diego, California	1887	6th	130
San Francisco, California	1883	5th	69
San Francisco, California	1885	5th	101
San Francisco, California	1888	2nd	151
San Francisco, California	1888	4th	152
San Francisco, California	1890	3rd	177
San Francisco, California	1890	3rd	178
San Francisco, California	1893	4th	269
San Francisco, California	1893	4th	270
San Francisco, California	1893	4th	274
San Francisco, California	1893	4th	275
San Francisco, California	1894	4th	276
San Francisco, California	1894	4th	302
San Francisco, California	1895	1st	341
San Francisco, California	1897	1st	373
San Francisco, California	1897	1st	374
San Francisco, California	1897	1st	388
San Francisco, California	1897	3rd	371
San Francisco, California	1897	3rd	372
San Francisco, California	1897	3rd	386
San Francisco, California	1897	3rd	387
Sanford, Florida	1886	5th	106
Santa Rosa, California	1886	6th	111
Savannah, Georgia	1886	6th	50
Savannah, Georgia	1887	3rd	125
Savannah, Georgia	1889	5th	170
Savannah, Georgia	1894	2nd	303

LaFrance Steam Fire Engines

City	Date	Size	Serial #
Savannah, Georgia	1898	1st	402
Savannah, Georgia	1900	1st	443
Savannah, Georgia	1904	X1st	495
Schenectady, New York	1890	X1st	188
Scranton, Pennsylvania	1883	4th	63
Seattle, Washington	1899	1st	429
Seattle, Washington	1906	1st	524
Shelbyville, Kentucky	1889	3rd	166
South Bend, Washington	1891	4th	208
Spencer, Massachusetts	1895	4th	328
Springfield, Massachusetts	1896	2nd	370
Springfield, Ohio	1902	1st	472
Springfield, Ohio	1902	2nd	482
St. Boniface, Manitoba	1882	5th	50
St. Clair, Pennsylvania	1889	5th	171
St. Paul, Minnesota	1885	1st	
Stamford, Connecticut	1892	3rd	231
Stockton, California	1890	3rd	189
Suffolk, Virginia	1883	5th	155
Superior, Wisconsin	1894	1st	293
Syracuse, New York	1899	1st	426
Syracuse, New York	1901	1st	452
Tampa, Florida	1894	5th	316
Tampa, Florida	1894	5th	317
Toledo, Ohio	1893	1st	247
Toledo, Ohio	1893	1st	248
Toledo, Ohio	1899	1st	404
Toledo, Ohio	1899	1st	405
Toledo, Ohio	1904	X1st	493
Toledo, Ohio	1907	2nd	527
Toledo, Ohio	1907	2nd	528
Trenton, New Jersey	1889	3rd	167

City	Date	Size	Serial #
Utica, New York	1894	2nd	291
Utica, New York	1894	2nd	292
Vicksburg, Michigan	1881	4th	17
Waco, Texas	1892	2nd	263
Warren, Massachusetts	1893	4th	244
Warren, Massachusetts	1893	4th	245
Washington, D. C.	1894	3rd	320
Washington, D. C.	1898	3rd	394
Washington, New Jersey	1894	4th	308
Waterloo, Iowa	1899		420
Waukegan, Wisconsin	1882	3rd	48
Waxahachie, Texas	1901	3rd	453
West Pittston, Pennsylvania	1896	3rd	385
Westborough, Massachusetts	1892	3rd	230
Williamsport, Pennsylvania	1888	1st	156
Williamsport, Pennsylvania	1903	3rd	486
Wilmington, Delaware	1887	3rd	120
Wilmington, Delaware	1889	2nd	172
Wilmington, Delaware	1891	3rd	201
Windbar, Pennsylvania	1901	4th	458
Winsboro, South Carolina	1882	5th	36
Winston, North Carolina	1882	4th	39
Winston, North Carolina	1893	3rd	252
Winston, North Carolina	1903	3rd	487
Worcester, Massachusetts	1891	2nd	191
Worcester, Massachusetts	1894	3rd	319
Worcester, Massachusetts	1897	2nd	382
Worcester, Massachusetts	1902	4th	477
Worcester, Massachusetts	1905	X1st	516
Yazoo, Michigan	1880	4th	5
York, Pennsylvania	1888	2nd	168
York, Pennsylvania	1889	2nd	161

LaFrance Steam Fire Engines
Steam Fire Engines Rebuilt 1881 - 1907

City	Original	Date	Size	Serial #
Aiken, South Carolina	Button	1880	5th	115
Albany, Georgia	LaFrance	1882	5th	47
Albany, New York	Amoskeag	1867	2nd	244
Albany, New York	Amoskeag	1867	2nd	258
Altoona, Pennsylvania	Amoskeag	1867	2nd	239
Altoona, Pennsylvania	Amoskeag	1868	2nd	285
Ambler, Pennsylvania	Jeffers			
Americus, Georgia	Jeffers		4th	
Asbury Park, New Jersey	LaFrance	1883	2nd	56
Asbury Park, New Jersey	Silsby	1876	3rd	
Ashley, Pennsylvania	LaFrance	1891	4th	198
Atlantic City, New Jersey	LaFrance	1888	2nd	143
Baltimore, Maryland	Clapp & Jones	1886	2nd	472
Baltimore, Maryland	Clapp & Jones	1888	3rd	503
Baltimore, Maryland	Clapp & Jones	1890	1st	553
Baltimore, Maryland	Ives Bros.		1st	
Baltimore, Maryland	Ives Bros.		1st	
Baltimore, Maryland	Ives Bros.		1st	
Baltimore, Maryland	Ives Bros.		1st	
Baltimore, Maryland	LaFrance	1888	1st	157
Baltimore, Maryland	LaFrance	1888	3rd	113
Baltimore, Maryland	LaFrance	1888	3rd	148
Baltimore, Maryland	LaFrance	1892	1st	229
Baltimore, Maryland	Wm. Ives			
Bethlehem, Pennsylvania	Clapp & Jones	1869	3rd	
Bethlehem, Pennsylvania	Clapp & Jones	1874	4th	510
Beverly, Massachusetts	Hunneman	1881	2nd	744
Biddeford, Maine	Amoskeag	1868	2nd	292
Biloxi, Mississippi	Dennison		4th	
Bridgeport, Connecticut	Amoskeag	1865	2nd	125
Bridgeport, Connecticut	LaFrance	1890	2nd	192
Bridgeton, New Jersey	Silsby	1877	3rd	562
Bristol, Rhode Island	Cole Bros.		2nd	
Brockton, Massachusetts	LaFrance	1894	X-1st	312
Brooklyn, New York	Amoskeag	1871		381
Brooklyn, New York	Amoskeag	1873	2nd	428
Brooklyn, New York	Amoskeag	1873	2nd	429
Brooklyn, New York	Amoskeag	1873		427
Brooklyn, New York	Amoskeag	1885	2nd	598
Brooklyn, New York	Amoskeag	1885	2nd	600
Brooklyn, New York	LaFrance	1887	2nd	134
Brooklyn, New York	LaFrance	1887	2nd	154
Brooklyn, New York	LaFrance	1887	3rd	323

City	Original	Date	Size	Serial #
Brunswick, Georgia	LaFrance	1886	5th	116
Bryan, Ohio	Harrell & Hayes		2nd	
Buffalo, New York	Amoskeag	1875	2nd	498
Buffalo, New York	Button		2nd	
Buffalo, New York	LaFrance			
Buffalo, New York	LaFrance			
Buffalo, New York	LaFrance	1882	4th	49
Buffalo, New York	Silsby		3rd	669
Buffalo, New York	Silsby	1872	1st	392
Buffalo, New York	Silsby	1872	1st	393
Buffalo, New York	Silsby	1872	1st	395
Buffalo, New York	Silsby	1872	1st	397
Buffalo, New York	Silsby	1882	3rd	678
Buffalo, New York	Silsby	1882	3rd	699
Burlington, New Jersey	LaFrance	1880	3rd	343
Camden, New Jersey	Amoskeag	1868	2nd	287
Camden, New Jersey	Amoskeag	1869	2nd	318
Canisteo, New York	LaFrance			
Cape May, New Jersey	Silsby	1879	4th	601
Charleston, South Carolina	Clapp & Jones	1883	4th	
Chester, Pennsylvania	LaFrance	1887	2nd	132
Cleveland, Ohio	Amoskeag	1874		497
Cleveland, Ohio	Amoskeag	1879		544
Cohoes, New York	Silsby	1879	4th	605
Danbury, Connecticut	LaFrance	1889	3rd	162
Dayton, Ohio	Amoskeag	1867		38
Detroit, Michigan	Amoskeag	1873		447
Elizabeth, New Jersey	Button	1884		158
Elizabeth, New Jersey	Button	1888	2nd	211
Elmira, New York	Amoskeag	1864	3rd	91
Elmira, New York	Amoskeag	1868	1st	300
Elmira, New York	LaFrance		2nd	133
Elmira, New York	LaFrance	1882		51
Frederick, Maryland	LaFrance	1881	5th	9
Giddings, Texas	Clapp & Jones		4th	
Hagerstown, Maryland	Jas. Smith		3rd	
Hampton, Virginia	Amoskeag	1886	2nd	620
Hampton, Virginia	LaFrance		3rd	200
Hanover, Pennsylvania	Silsby	1882	4th	688
Harrisburg Pennsylvania	Amoskeag	1867	1st	225
Harrisburg Pennsylvania	Amoskeag	1867	1st	225
Harrisburg Pennsylvania	LaFrance		2nd	160
Harrisburg Pennsylvania	Silsby	1887	3rd	883

LaFrance Steam Fire Engines
Steam Fire Engines Rebuilt 1881 - 1907

City	Original	Date	Size	Serial #
Hoboken, New Jersey	LaFrance		2nd	239
Honesdale, Pennsylvania	Silsby	1870	3rd	249
Honesdale, Pennsylvania	Silsby	1874	3rd	483
Huntington Pennsylvania	LaFrance		3rd	3
Ithaca, New York	Clapp & Jones	1874	4th	6
Jackson, Mississippi	LaFrance		4th	76
Jacksonville, Florida	Jeffers		3rd	
Jacksonville, Florida	LaFrance		2nd	103
Jersey City, New Jersey	LaFrance		3rd	219
Jersey City, New Jersey	LaFrance		3rd	220
Jersey City, New Jersey	LaFrance		4th	250
Knoxville, Tennessee	Silsby	1878	4th	599
Long Island City, New York	Silsby		2nd	6
Louisville, Kentucky	Amoskeag			
Lowville, New York	LaFrance	1883	5th	64
Lynn, Massachusetts	Portland Co.		2nd	
Macon, Georgia	Clapp & Jones	1873	4th	
Memphis, Tennessee	Ahrens	1866		155
Mt. Vernon, New York	LaFrance	1898	4th	407
Muskegan, Wisconsin	LaFrance	1882	3rd	45
New Brighton, New York	Amoskeag		3rd	
New Brunswick, New Jersey	LaFrance	1888	3rd	149
New Haven, Connecticut	Silsby	1894	2nd	2255
New Orleans, Louisiana	Jeffers		3rd	
New York, New York	Ahrens	1883	2nd	358
New York, New York	Ahrens	1883	2nd	360
New York, New York	Amoskeag	1861	3rd	36
New York, New York	Amoskeag	1865	3rd	158
New York, New York	Amoskeag	1866	3rd	159
New York, New York	Amoskeag	1866	3rd	160
New York, New York	Amoskeag	1866	3rd	164
New York, New York	Amoskeag	1871	2nd	363
New York, New York	Amoskeag	1871	2nd	364
New York, New York	Amoskeag	1873	2nd	437
New York, New York	Amoskeag	1877	3rd	517
New York, New York	Amoskeag	1877	3rd	517
New York, New York	Amoskeag	1877	3rd	520
New York, New York	Clapp & Jones		1st	15
New York, New York	Clapp & Jones		1st	19
New York, New York	Clapp & Jones	1881	4th	359
New York, New York	Clapp & Jones	1881	4th	365
New York, New York	Clapp & Jones	1881	4th	368
New York, New York	Clapp & Jones	1881	4th	370

City	Original	Date	Size	Serial #
New York, New York	Clapp & Jones	1883	4th	417
New York, New York	Clapp & Jones	1884	4th	432
New York, New York	Clapp & Jones	1884	4th	434
New York, New York	Clapp & Jones	1884	4th	436
New York, New York	Clapp & Jones	1884	4th	438
New York, New York	Clapp & Jones	1886	2nd	473
New York, New York	LaFrance	1894	3rd	295
New York, New York	LaFrance	1894	3rd	297
New York, New York	LaFrance	1886	2nd	108
New York, New York	LaFrance	1888	1st	146
New York, New York	LaFrance	1888	2nd	147
New York, New York	LaFrance	1890	3rd	186
New York, New York	LaFrance	1900	1st	434
Newark, New Jersey	Amoskeag	1862	2nd	58
Newark, New Jersey	Cole Bros.		3rd	
Newark, New Jersey	Dennison		4th	
Newark, New Jersey	Gould		2nd	
Newark, New Jersey	LaFrance	1901	2nd	474
Newport News, Virginia	LaFrance	1891	3rd	211
Newport, Rhode Island	Jeffers		4th	
Niagara Falls, Ontario	Amoskeag		2nd	185
Orange, New Jersey	Amoskeag			
Orange, Texas	LaFrance	1896	6th	58
Oshkosh, Wisconsin	Silsby	1874	2nd	443
Peabody, Massachusetts	LaFrance	1887	3rd	131
Philadelphia, Pennsylvania	Amoskeag		1st	
Philadelphia, Pennsylvania	Reaney & Neafie		1st	
Phillipsburg, Pennsylvania	LaFrance	1883	5th	64
Pittsburgh, Pennsylvania	Amoskeag	1867	2nd	262
Pittsburgh, Pennsylvania	LaFrance	1886	3rd	114
Pittsburgh, Pennsylvania	LaFrance	1894	2nd	313
Portsmouth, New Hampshire	Gould		2nd	
Portsmouth, Virginia	LaFrance	1886	3rd	109
Reading, Pennsylvania	Amoskeag	1867	2nd	234
Renova, Pennsylvania	LaFrance	1887	3rd	121
Richmond, Virginia	Clapp & Jones	1888	3rd	502
Richmond, Virginia	Clapp & Jones	1893	3rd	2161
Richmond, Virginia	Silsby	1881	3rd	667
Roanoke, Virginia	LaFrance	1891	4th	210
Rockland, Massachusetts	Amoskeag	1866	2nd	201
Rockland, Massachusetts	LaFrance	1894	3rd	283
Rome, New York	Silsby	1884	4th	778
Roswell, New Mexico	Amoskeag			

LaFrance Steam Fire Engines
Steam Fire Engines Rebuilt 1881 - 1907

City	Original	Date	Size	Serial #
Salem, Massachusetts	Amoskeag	1873	2nd	434
Savannah, Georgia	Amoskeag	1865	2nd	133
Savannah, Georgia	Jeffers		3rd	
Scranton, Pennsylvania	LaFrance	1883	4th	63
Seattle, Washington	Waterous			
Shamakin, Pennsylvania	Silsby	1881	4th	661
Stamford, Connecticut	Button	1883	4th	132
Stamford, Connecticut	LaFrance	1892	3rd	231
Suffolk, Virginia	LaFrance	1883	5th	155
Syracuse, New York	Amoskeag	1871	2nd	384
Titusville, Pennsylvania	Amoskeag	1868	1st	283
Toledo, Ohio	Ahrens	1889	2nd	593
Toledo, Ohio	Ahrens	1889	2nd	594
Toledo, Ohio	LaFrance	1893	1st	247
Toledo, Ohio	LaFrance	1893	1st	248
Toledo, Ohio	LaFrance	1899	1st	404
Toledo, Ohio	LaFrance	1899	1st	405
Townsend, Massachusetts	Amoskeag	1875	3rd	479
Trenton, New Jersey	Amoskeag	1880	2nd	549
Troy, New Hampshire	Silsby	1873	3rd	407
Utica, New York	LaFrance	1894	2nd	292
Warren, Ohio	Silsby	1868	2nd	168
Washington, D.C.	Clapp & Jones	1884	4th	7
Washington, D.C.	Clapp & Jones	1885	4th	10
Waterloo, Iowa	LaFrance	1899		420
Waterloo, New York	Silsby	1872	3rd	372
Waverly, Iowa	Arlington Works			
Williamsport, Pennsylvania	Amoskeag	1867	2nd	240
Williamsport, Pennsylvania	Amoskeag	1867	2nd	269
Williamsport, Pennsylvania	LaFrance	1889	2nd	172
Wilmington, Delaware	Amoskeag	1889	2nd	641
Wilmington, Delaware	LaFrance	1887	3rd	120
Wilmington, Delaware	LaFrance	1891	3rd	201
Winchester, Virginia	Gould		2nd	
Winston, North Carolina	LaFrance	1882	4th	39
Worcester, Massachusetts	Button	1891	2nd	221
Worcester, Massachusetts	Gould		2nd	
Worcester, Massachusetts	LaFrance		3rd	223
Yazoo, Michigan	LaFrance	1880	4th	5
York, Pennsylvania	LaFrance	1889	2nd	161
York, Pennsylvania	LaFrance	1889	2nd	168
Youngstown, Ohio	Silsby	1868	2nd	169

Silsby Steam Fire Engines
Seneca, New York

Information compiled by:

Harold S. Walker, P. E.
Edward R. Tufts
John M. Peckham
John J. Robrecht

Silsby Steam Fire Engines
(1858 - 1900)

City	Date	Size	Serial #	City	Date	Size	Serial #
Abbeville, Louisiana	1891	5th	1006	Astoria, Organ	1877	3rd	575
Ada, Ohio	1874		439	Atchinson, Kansas	1887	5th	552
Adrian, Michigan	1865	2nd	85	Athol, Massachusetts	1892		
Adrian, Michigan	1873	2nd	430	Atlanta, Georgia	1871	3rd	295
Akron, Ohio	1866	2nd	103	Atlanta, Georgia	1876	2nd	540
Akron, Ohio	1873	3rd	366	Atlantic City, New Jersey	1887	2nd	851
Akron, Ohio	1890	3rd	867	Auburn, New York	1889	1st	956
Albany, Georgia	1870	3rd	261	Augusta, Georgia	1872	4th	307
Albion, Michigan	1878	4th	596	Augusta, Georgia	1872	4th	357
Alexandria Bay, New York	1887	5th	902	Augusta, Georgia	1879	2nd	617
Alexandria Bay, New York	1899	5th	2689	Augusta, Georgia	1882	3rd	718
Alexandria, Louisiana	1881	5th	662	Augusta, Georgia	1884	2nd	772
Algiers, Louisiana	1885	5th	823	Austin, Texas	1871	3rd	271
Allegheny, Pennsylvania	1874	1st		Austin, Texas	1875	4th	488
Allegheny, Pennsylvania	1884	3rd	781	Avon, Massachusetts	1880	3rd	646
Allegheny, Pennsylvania	1886	2nd	861	Aylmer, Ontario			
Allegheny, Pennsylvania	1890	1st	952	Bakersfield, California	1872	3rd	341
Allentown, Pennsylvania	1865	2nd	90	Baldwinsville, Massachusetts	(See Templeton, Massachusetts)		
Allentown, Pennsylvania	1866	2nd	116	Baldwinsville, New York	1875	4th	480
Allentown, Pennsylvania	1872	3rd	363	Baltimore, Maryland	1887	3rd	892
Allentown, Pennsylvania	1876	2nd	551	Barrie, Ontario	1871	3rd	298
Allentown, Pennsylvania	1900	2nd	2702	Bath, New York	1872		355
Alliance, Ohio	1873	3rd	406	Battlecreek, Michigan	1874	1st	463
Alma, Colorado	1882	6th	686	Bay City, Michigan	1865	2nd	88
Alma, Wisconsin	1888	5th	919	Bayonne, New Jersey	1892	3rd	1017
Alpena, Michigan	1875	4th	489	Bayside, Long Island, New York	1893	4th	2231
Altoona, Pennsylvania	1893	3rd	2219	Beaufort, South Carolina	1871	3rd	302
Ambler, Pennsylvania	1896	3rd	2483	Beaufort, South Carolina	1874	4th	465
Amboy, Illinois	1871	3rd	300	Beaver Falls, Pennsylvania	1875	4th	490
Amoskeag, Georgia	1876			Bedford, Pennsylvania	1872	3rd	343
Anaconda, Montana	1887	3rd	596	Belle Plains, Mississippi	1874	3rd	370
Anderson, Indiana	1874	3rd	432	Bellefontaine, Pennsylvania	1875	4th	506
Andover, Massachusetts	1886	5th	847	Bellefonte, Pennsylvania	1890	5th	988
Andover, Ohio	1875	3rd	511	Bellevue, Ohio	1875	3rd	513
Annapolis, Maryland	1884	4th	795	Bellows Falls, Vermont	1886	3rd	867
Anoka, Minnesota	1878	3rd	597	Bennington, Vermont	1871	2nd	303
Antigo, Wisconsin	1873	1st	387	Benton Harbor, Michigan	1876	3rd	536
Appleton, Wisconsin	1873	1st	387	Berlin, Ontario	1873	1st	422
Asbury Park, New Jersey	1870	3rd	235	Berlin, Wisconsin	1886	3rd	863
Asbury Park, New Jersey	1876	3rd		Billerica, Massachusetts	1891	4th	1007
Asbury Park, New Jersey	1898	2nd		Binghamton, New York	1862		
Ashland, Ohio	1867	1st	105	Blassburg, Pennsylvania	1877	3rd	551
Ashland, Ohio	1877	2nd	580	Bloomington, Indiana	1871	2nd	290

Silsby Steam Fire Engines

City	Date	Size	Serial #
Bloomington, Indiana	1892	3rd	2132
Bloomsburg, Pennsylvania	1890	4th	985
Boise, Idaho	1879	4th	613
Bonnville, New York	1882	5th	685
Boston, Massachusetts	1859		
Boston, Massachusetts	1859		
Boston, Massachusetts	1860		
Boston, Massachusetts	1880	1st	647
Boston, Massachusetts	1883	3rd	757
Boston, Massachusetts	1884	3rd	782
Boston, Massachusetts	1885	2nd	813
Boston, Massachusetts	1886	2nd	850
Boston, Massachusetts	1888	2nd	963
Boston, Massachusetts	1888	2nd	964
Boston, Massachusetts	1890	2nd	976
Boston, Massachusetts	1890	2nd	977
Boston, Massachusetts	1890	2nd	998
Boston, Massachusetts	1890	2nd	999
Boston, Massachusetts	1892	3rd	2159
Boyertown, Pennsylvania	1873	3rd	401
Bozeman, Montana	1888	4th	933
Bradford, Massachusetts	1882	3rd	692
Bradford, Pennsylvania	1880	4th	637
Bradford, Pennsylvania	1881	4th	654
Brenham, Texas	1879	3rd	607
Brewster, New York	1886	6th	858
Bridgeton, Maine	1887	4th	891
Bridgeton, New Jersey	1877	3rd	562
Bridgewater, Massachusetts	1883	6th	752
Bristol, Pennsylvania	1872	3rd	374
Brockport, New York	1877	3rd	557
Brockton, Massachusetts	1881	2nd	664
Brockton, Massachusetts	1883	3rd	716
Brockton, Massachusetts	1887	2nd	871
Brooklyn, Iowa	1874		451
Brooklyn, New York	1859		
Buchanan, Michigan	1876	4th	541
Buchanan, Michigan	1885	4th	805
Bucyrus, Ohio	1869	3rd	208
Buffalo, New York	1860		12
Buffalo, New York	1861		
Buffalo, New York	1861		
Buffalo, New York	1869	2nd	244

City	Date	Size	Serial #
Buffalo, New York	1870	1st	260
Buffalo, New York	1872	1st	392
Buffalo, New York	1872	1st	393
Buffalo, New York	1872	1st	395
Buffalo, New York	1872	1st	397
Buffalo, New York	1875	1st	516
Buffalo, New York	1882	3rd	678
Buffalo, New York	1882	3rd	699
Burlington, Iowa	1867	3rd	127
Burlington, Iowa	1869	2nd	223
Burlington, Vermont	1867	2nd	145
Cadiz, Ohio	1872	3rd	320
Callao, Peru	1884	5th	747
Callao, Peru	1894	4th	2263
Cambridge, Maryland	1882	4th	719
Cambridge, Ohio	1873	4th	400
Camden, South Carolina	1871		
Camden, South Carolina	1871	2nd	277
Camden, South Carolina	1874	3rd	449
Campello, Massachusetts			
Canal Dover, Ohio	1874	3rd	449
Canal Fulton, Ohio	1874		438
Canandaiquz, New York	1870	2nd	216
Canandaiquz, New York	1882	5th	726
Canton, Illinois	1874	3rd	435
Canton, Massachusetts	1885	5th	827
Canton, Missouri	1874	4th	466
Canton, New York	1882	5th	710
Cape May, New Jersey	1879	2nd	601
Cape May, New Jersey	1882	5th	687
Cardenas, Cuba	1889		944
Cardenas, Cuba	1904	3rd	3014
Cardington, Ohio	1874	4th	482
Cario, Illinois	1865	3rd	82
Carlisle, Pennsylvania	1870	3rd	238
Carlisle, Pennsylvania	1894	3rd	2453
Carrollton, Louisiana	1887	4th	881
Carson City, Nevada	1873	5th	409
Carthage, New York	1875	3rd	475
Casz De Moneda, Mexico	1878	3rd	603
Catasaugua, Pennsylvania	1866		
Catasaugua, Pennsylvania	1890	2nd	982
Catskill, New York	1871	3rd	316

Silsby Steam Fire Engines

City	Date	Size	Serial #
Cedar Falls, Iowa	1871	3rd	273
Cedar Falls, Iowa	1871	3rd	302
Cedar Rapids, Iowa	1869	3rd	187
Cedarville, Ohio	1888	5th	907
Cenfuegos, Cuba	1882		
Centerville, Indiana	1875	4th	501
Central Islip, New York	1883	5th	724
Chariton, Iowa	1877	4th	578
Chariton, Iowa	1883	3rd	758
Charitonm, Iowa	1877		
Charleston, South Carolina	1871	2nd	277
Charleston, South Carolina	1871	3rd	278
Charleston, South Carolina	1888	1st	903
Charleston, South Carolina	1890	1st	968
Charleston, South Carolina	1895	3rd	2348
Charleston, West Virginia	1871	3rd	293
Charlevoix, Michigan	1877		
Charlotte, Michigan	1872	3rd	330
Charlotte, New York	1889	5th	949
Charlottetown, PEI	1875	2nd	501
Chaska, Minnesota	1870		
Chattanooga, Tennessee	1867	3rd	147
Chelsea, Massachusetts	1882	1st	695
Chelsea, Massachusetts	1887	2nd	890
Chester, Pennsylvania	1874	4th	473
Chester, Pennsylvania	1885	2nd	815
Chester, Pennsylvania	1894	2nd	2300
Cheyenne, Wyoming	1868	3rd	188
Chicago, Illinois	1858		
Chicago, Illinois	1858		
Chicago, Illinois	1858		
Chicago, Illinois	1859		
Chicago, Illinois	1868	2nd	182
Chicago, Illinois	1868	2nd	190
Chicago, Illinois	1868	2nd	215
Chicago, Illinois	1869	2nd	224
Chicago, Illinois	1869	3rd	221
Chicago, Illinois	1870	2nd	254
Chicago, Illinois	1871		
Chicago, Illinois	1872	2nd	318
Chicago, Illinois	1872	3rd	319
Chicago, Illinois	1872	3rd	375
Chicago, Illinois	1872	3rd	376
Chicago, Illinois	1872	3rd	377
Chicago, Illinois	1873	1st	472
Chicago, Illinois	1873	2nd	410
Chicago, Illinois	1873	2nd	411
Chicago, Illinois	1873	2nd	417
Chicago, Illinois	1873	2nd	425
Chicago, Illinois	1874	1st	467
Chicago, Illinois	1875	1st	500
Chicago, Illinois	1875	2nd	485
Chicago, Illinois	1878	2nd	594
Chicago, Illinois	1878	2nd	595
Chicago, Illinois	1884	3rd	768
Chico, California	1883		
Chillicothe, Ohio	1867	2nd	142
Chippewa Falls, Washington	1882	2nd	721
Chippewa Falls, Wisconsin	1870	5th	256
Circleville, Ohio	1867	2nd	148
Claremont, New Hampshire	1884	4th	789
Clarksville, Tennessee	1872	5th	349
Clayton, Alabama	1884	5th	774
Clayton, New York	1887	5th	873
Cleveland, Ohio	1862		
Cleveland, Ohio	1868	1st	206
Cleveland, Ohio	1869	2nd	225
Cleveland, Ohio	1872	1st	313
Cleveland, Ohio	1872	2nd	348
Cleveland, Ohio	1872	2nd	358
Cleveland, Ohio	1874	1st	388
Cleveland, Ohio	1874	1st	389
Cleveland, Ohio	1877	3rd	563
Cleveland, Ohio	1881		
Cleveland, Ohio	1884	1st	803
Cleveland, Ohio	1884	1st	804
Cleveland, Ohio	1884	2nd	801
Cleveland, Ohio	1884	3rd	790
Cleveland, Ohio	1891	3rd	989
Clinton, Iowa	1867	2nd	122
Clintonville, Wisconsin	1899	1st	2690
Clyde, New York	1873	3rd	419
Coaticook, P.Q.	1887	5th	885
Cochran, Georgia	1875	4th	493
Coeymans, New York	1868	2nd	168
Cohoes, New York	1879	4th	605

Silsby Steam Fire Engines

City	Date	Size	Serial #
Coitland, New York	1876	3rd	543
Coldwater, Michigan	1872	3rd	247
Coldwater, Michigan	1882	1st	677
Colfax, Washington	1883	5th	743
Collingwood, Ontario	1871	3rd	299
Colon, Panama	1906	3rd	3109
Columbia, South Carolina	1871	3rd	270
Columbia, South Carolina	1893	4th	2202
Columbia, South Carolina	1894	4th	2302
Columbus, Georgia	1870	3rd	266
Columbus, Georgia	1881	5th	673
Columbus, Georgia	1893	3rd	2169
Columbus, Mississippi	1878	3rd	581
Columbus, Ohio	1861		28
Concord, New Hampshire	1882	4th	723
Conemaugh, Pennsylvania	1881	3rd	639
Conemaugh, Pennsylvania	1890	2nd	958
Conemaugh, Pennsylvania	1890	2nd	959
Coney Island, New York	1868	2nd	184
Coney Island, New York	1893	4th	2243
Corpus Christie, Texas	1873	3rd	420
Corry, Pennsylvania	1870	3rd	228
Corry, Pennsylvania	1882	3rd	736
Council Bluffs, Iowa	1868	2nd	183
Covington, Kentucky	1865	1st	69
Covington, Kentucky	1867	1st	128
Covington, Ohio	1870	3rd	229
Dallas, Texas	1874	3rd	433
Dallas, Texas	1880	3rd	630
Danielson, Connecticut	1878	4th	588
Danville, Illinois	1872	3rd	359
Danville, Illinois	1875	2nd	515
Danville, Pennsylvania	1871	3rd	286
Darien, Georgia	1883	5th	728
Darlington, South Carolina	1871	3rd	278
Darlington, South Carolina	1885	5th	826
Dartmouth, Nova Scotia	1878	4th	593
Dayton, Ohio	1862		
Dayton, Ohio	1863		
Dayton, Ohio	1865	1st	196
Dayton, Ohio	1874	1st	468
Dayton, Ohio	1874	1st	469
Dayton, Washington	1882	4th	694

City	Date	Size	Serial #
DeGraff, Ohio	1880	5th	639
Delaware, Ohio	1870	3rd	258
Delaware, Ohio	1874	2nd	478
Denver, Colorado	1880		
Denver, Colorado	1889	2nd	922
Denver, Colorado	1889	2nd	938
Denver, Colorado	1890	2nd	978
Denver, Colorado	1890	2nd	979
Denver, Colorado	1891	4th	997
Deseranto, Ontario	1875	4th	497
Detroit, Michigan	1883	3rd	748
Detroit, Michigan	1886	1st	853
Detroit, Michigan	1886	4th	859
Detroit, Michigan	1887	4th	865
Detroit, Michigan	1887	4th	893
Detroit, Michigan	1888	4th	900
Dexter, New York	1877	4th	571
Donaldsonville, Louisiana	1882	6th	698
Downington, Pennsylvania	1892	4th	2133
Dresden, Ontario	1879	3rd	622
DuBois, Pennsylvania	1882	3rd	734
DuBois, Pennsylvania	1889	4th	924
DuBois, Pennsylvania	1895	4th	2374
Dubuque, Iowa	1867	2nd	144
Dubuque, Iowa	1868	1st	191
Dubuque, Iowa	1881	1st	668
Dubuque, Iowa	1895	2nd	2331
Duluth, Minnesota	1870	3rd	263
Duluth, Minnesota	1872	3rd	308
Durand, Wisconsin	1876	4th	534
Durango, Colorado	1882	5th	690
East Liverpool, Ohio	1889	2nd	962
East Portchester, New York	1903	5th	2918
East Portland, Oregon	1883		
East Saginaw, Michigan	1870		
East Stoughton, Massachusetts	1880		
East Templeton, Massachusetts	1894		
Eastern Michigan Asylum	1872	2nd	852
Easton, Pennsylvania	1879	5th	609
Eaton Rapids, Michigan	1874	5th	460
Egypt, Pennsylvania	1875	3rd	589
El Paso, Texas	1890	2nd	
El Paso, Texas	1893	3rd	2153

Silsby Steam Fire Engines

City	Date	Size	Serial #	City	Date	Size	Serial #
Elgin, Illinois	1869	3rd	207	Fort Worth, Texas	1877	4th	549
Elgin, Illinois	1872	1st	324	Fort Worth, Texas	1890	2nd	953
Elizabeth City, North Carolina	1873	3rd	413	Fort Worth, Texas	1890	5th	955
Elizabeth City, North Carolina	1902	2nd	2888	Fortress Monroe, Virginia	1872		
Elkhart, Indiana	1867	3rd	153	Fostoria, Ohio	1877	3rd	564
Elkland, Pennsylvania	1872		355	Fostoria, Ohio	1883	3rd	753
Ellensburg, Washington	1889	3rd	946	Framingham, Massachusetts	1885	2nd	812
Elmer, Ohio	1866	3rd	118	Framingham, Massachusetts	1886	3rd	848
Elmira, New York	1865	2nd	79	Frankfort, New York	1877	3rd	565
Elmira, New York	1868	1st	198	Frederick, Maryland	1877	3rd	547
Elyria, Ohio	1876	3rd	373	Frederickton, N.B.	1874	3rd	476
Enfield, Massachusetts	1900	4th	2734	Freeport, Illinois	1867	2nd	146
Englewood, Illinois	1884			Freeport, Illinois	1874	2nd	461
Englishtown, New Jersey	1905	4th	3038	Freeport, New York	1872	5th	349
Ennis, Texas	1884	3rd	792	Fresno, California	1883	4th	727
Erie, Pennsylvania	1867	2nd	154	Gainesville, Georgia	1886	5th	842
Erie, Pennsylvania	1878	3rd	577	Gallipolis, Ohio	1871	2nd	327
Erie, Pennsylvania	1882	3rd	705	Galveston, Texas	1866	3rd	105
Eufaula, Alabama	1883	5th	742	Galveston, Texas	1867	2nd	125
Eureka, California	1870	3rd	259	Galveston, Texas	1867	2nd	130
Eureka, California	1872	1st	398	Galveston, Texas	1870	1st	230
Evansville, Indiana	1867	2nd	136	Galveston, Texas	1875	3rd	517
Evansville, Indiana	1885	2nd	536	Galveston, Texas	1887	4th	901
Everett, Pennsylvania	1880	4th	636	Gardiner, Maine	1880	3rd	638
Fairhaven, Washington	1890	4th	957	Gardiner, Maine	1882	4th	708
Fairport, New York	1878	3rd	587	Genesco, New York	1876	3rd	520
Fall River, Massachusetts	1874	2nd	459	Geneva, New York	1865	2nd	99
Faribault, Minnesota	1872			Gettysburg, Pennsylvania	1886	2nd	841
Farmington, Maine	1886	4th	818	Gloucester, Massachusetts	1884	3rd	783
Fayetteville, North Carolina	1882	5th	834	Gloucester, Massachusetts	1885	2nd	835
Fenton, Michigan	1879			Goderich, Ontario	1873	3rd	426
Ferbus Falls, Minnesota	1882	4th	714	Goldsboro, North Carolina	1882	5th	701
Findlay, Ohio	1871	3rd	291	Gowanda, New York	1871	3rd	279
Findlay, Ohio	1875	3rd	573	Grand Rapids, Michigan	1867	2nd	180
Flint, Michigan	1867	3rd	143	Grand Rapids, Michigan	1872	1st	335
Flint, Michigan	1879	2nd	618	Grand Rapids, Michigan	1872	2nd	338
Florence, South Carolina	1882	5th	680	Grand Rapids, Michigan	1877	3rd	
Fort Leavenworth, Kansas	1864	2nd	62	Great Neck, New York	1904	4th	3013
Fort Leavenworth, Kansas	1879	2nd	623	Greencastle, Indiana	1874	4th	479
Fort Leavenworth, Kansas	1901	3rd	2795	Greencastle, Pennsylvania	1878	3rd	568
Fort Madison, Iowa	1872	3rd	418	Greenville, Mississippi	1885	5th	819
Fort Wayne, Indiana	1869	1st	217	Greenville, Mississippi	1885	5th	819
Fort Wayne, Indiana	1873	1st	394	Greenville, Ohio	1871	3rd	282

Silsby Steam Fire Engines

City	Date	Size	Serial #
Greenville, Ohio	1871	3rd	282
Greenville, Ohio	1881	3rd	671
Greenville, Pennsylvania	1880	4th	650
Griffin, Georgia	1870	3rd	241
Griffin, Georgia	1880	4th	627
Grinnell, Iowa	1867		
Grinnell, Iowa	1885	3rd	875
Guayaguil, Ecuador	1896	1st	2474
Guelph, Ontario	1868	3rd	172
Hagerstown, Maryland	1880	4th	644
Hamburg, Pennsylvania	1877	3rd	560
Hamilton, Ohio	1863	2nd	65
Hamilton, Ohio	1865	1st	72
Hamilton, Ohio	1869	2nd	224
Hammond, Indiana	1872	2nd	340
Hampshire, Illinois	1870		
Hannibal, Missouri	1867	2nd	122
Hanover, Pennsylvania	1882	4th	688
Harlan, Iowa	1878	2nd	584
Harrisburg, Pennsylvania	1887	3rd	883
Hartford, Connecticut	1883	3rd	750
Havana, Cuba	1874	2nd	611
Havana, Cuba	1880	5th	975
Haverhill, Massachusetts	1882	3rd	692
Hazelton, Pennsylvania	1885	2nd	833
Hazelton, Pennsylvania	1897	4th	2495
Helena, Montana	1874	5th	459
Helena, Montana	1880	5th	620
Hempstead, Long Island, New York	1882	5th	712
Hillsboro, Texas	1885	5th	878
Holliston, Massachusetts	1871	3rd	284
Holliston, Massachusetts	1875	4th	499
Homer, New York	1873		
Honeoye Falls, New York	1885	5th	806
Honesdale, Pennsylvania	1870	3rd	249
Honesdale, Pennsylvania	1874	3rd	483
Honey Grove, Texas	1899	3rd	2034
Hopkinsville, Kentucky	1869	3rd	202
Hopkinsville, Kentucky	1884	4th	771
Horicon, Wisconsin	1885	4th	811
Hornellsville, New York	1874	3rd	442
Horseheads, New York	1873	3rd	416
Hot Springs, Arkansas	1877	3rd	555

City	Date	Size	Serial #
Houghton, Michigan	1873	2nd	430
Houma, Louisiana	1887	5th	878
Houston, Texas	1865	3rd	98
Houston, Texas	1867	2nd	126
Houston, Texas	1876	4th	527
Houston, Texas	1876	4th	542
Hudson, Wisconsin	1872	3rd	360
Huntington, Pennsylvania	1872	3rd	384
Huntsville, Alabama	1867	3rd	149
Huntsville, Alabama	1885	4th	830
Hyde Park, New York	1888	5th	764
Ilion, New York	1865	3rd	78
Ilion, New York	1876	3rd	528
Ilion, New York	1876	3rd	531
Indianapolis, Indiana	1860		
Indianapolis, Indiana	1867	1st	159
Indianapolis, Indiana	1870	1st	233
Ingersoll, Ontario	1873	3rd	423
Ishpenning, Michigan	1874	3rd	453
Ishpenning, Michigan	1882	2nd	683
Ithaca, New York	1871	3rd	304
Ithaca, New York	1872	3rd	315
Jackson, Michigan	1865	1st	74
Jackson, Michigan	1884	3rd	741
Jackson, Michigan	1885	2nd	807
Jackson, Michigan	1892	2nd	2154
Jackson, Mississippi	1884	5th	777
Jackson, Ohio	1874		451
Jackson, Ohio	1886	3rd	854
Jacksonville, Florida	1871	3rd	280
Jacksonville, Illinois	1887	4th	894
Jacksonville, Illinois	1891	4th	1015
Janesville, Wisconsin	1868	2nd	179
Janesville, Wisconsin	1876	2nd	534
Jeanerette, Louisiana	1885	5th	824
Jefferson City, Missouri	1871	3rd	285
Jefferson, Texas	1870	3rd	237
Jefferson, Wisconsin	1884	3rd	581
Jefferson, Wisconsin	1895	3rd	2215
Johnson's Creek, Wisconsin	1871	3rd	296
Johnstown, Pennsylvania	1889		
Joliet, Illinois	1869	3rd	209
Joliet, Illinois	1869	3rd	230

Silsby Steam Fire Engines

City	Date	Size	Serial #
Joliet, Illinois	1877	1st	581
Jonesville, Michigan	1886	5th	866
Kansas City, Missouri	1868	2nd	161
Kansas City, Missouri	1872	2nd	365
Kemptville, Ontario	1881	3rd	659
Kennett Square, Pennsylvania	1903	4th	2722
Kenosha, Wisconsin	1875	3rd	464
Kent, Ohio	1875	3rd	511
Kenton, Ohio	1871	3rd	289
Keokuk, Iowa	1870	3rd	247
Key West, Florida	1886	4th	869
Knoxville, Tennessee	1867	2nd	157
Knoxville, Tennessee	1878	4th	599
Knoxville, Tennessee	1893	3rd	2140
La Crosse, Wisconsin	1867	2nd	125
La Crosse, Wisconsin	1873	2nd	421
La Salle, Illinois	1873	3rd	383
Lafayette, Indiana	1864		
Lafayette, Indiana	1877	2nd	546
Lake Charles, Louisiana	1885	5th	832
Lake City, Minnesota	1875	3rd	492
Lake Linden, Michigan	1871	3rd	295
Lake, Illinois	1883	3rd	766
Lake, Illinois	1884	3rd	769
Lake, Illinois	1886	4th	845
Lanark, Ontario	1866	1st	93
Lancaster, Ohio	1869	2nd	189
Lancaster, Ohio	1874	4th	510
Lancaster, Ohio	1875	4th	512
Lansing, Michigan	1872	3rd	337
Lapeer, Michigan	1878	5th	591
Laramie, Wyoming	1882	5th	696
Larchmont, New York	1896	5th	2985
Laredo, Texas	1890	5th	971
Laurens, South Carolina	1887	5th	879
Lawrenceburg, Indiana	1874	4th	479
Le Mars, Iowa	1882	4th	711
Leavenworth, Kansas	1865	2nd	62
Leavenworth, Kansas	1866	1st	101
Leavenworth, Kansas	1868	2nd	212
Lebanon, Ohio	1872	3rd	329
Leesburg, Florida	1886	5th	849
Leonore, Illinois	1884	2nd	793

City	Date	Size	Serial #
Lewisburg, Pennsylvania	1874	2nd	437
Lewistown, Pennsylvania	1877	3rd	563
Lexington, Kentucky	1864		
Lexington, Kentucky	1868	1st	194
Lexington, Kentucky	1875	2nd	524
Lexington, Massachusetts	1895	5th	2373
Lima, Ohio	1872	3rd	356
Lincoln, Nebraska	1872	3rd	328
Lincoln, Nebraska	1880	1st	652
Lincoln, Nebraska	1895	1st	2394
Little Falls, New York	1877	3rd	565
Little Rock, Arkansas	1877	3rd	558
Lock Haven, Pennsylvania	1872	2nd	362
Lock Haven, Pennsylvania	1874	2nd	434
Logansport, Indiana	1870	3rd	219
London, Ohio	1871	3rd	288
Long View, Texas	1872	4th	357
Long View, Texas	1878	4th	367
Lorain, Ohio	1887	4th	893
Louisiana, Missouri	1870	3rd	239
Louisiana, Missouri	1881	3rd	656
Lowell, Massachusetts	1860		
Lowell, Massachusetts	1861		30
Ludlow, Vermont	1883	5th	725
Lynchburg, Virginia	1877	4th	557
Lyons, New York	1870	3rd	242
Macon City, Missouri	1871		
Macon, Georgia	1867	2nd	152
Macon, Georgia	1872	3rd	353
Macon, Georgia	1875	4th	493
Madison, Indiana	1868		
Madison, Indiana	1878	3rd	518
Mahanoy, Pennsylvania	1872	3rd	326
Mahanoy, Pennsylvania	1885	2nd	829
Malden, Massachusetts	1880	2nd	635
Malden, Massachusetts	1886	3rd	860
Malone, New York	1880	3rd	624
Manchester, Iowa	1875	2nd	514
Mansfield, Ohio	1866	2nd	119
Marblehead, Massachusetts	1880	2nd	629
Marietta, Georgia	1881	4th	655
Marietta, Ohio	1871	3rd	279
Marietta, Ohio	1872	3rd	379

Silsby Steam Fire Engines

City	Date	Size	Serial #
Marietta, Ohio	1877	4th	579
Marietta, Pennsylvania	1872	3rd	351
Marine City, Michigan	1874	3rd	455
Marion, Michigan	1879	2nd	618
Marion, Ohio	1871	3rd	276
Marion, Ohio	1872	3rd	233
Marshall, Texas	1884	4th	796
Martinsburg, West Virginia	1870	3rd	251
Marysville, California	1862	1st	39
Marysville, California	1862		54
Marysville, California	1870	3rd	255
Marysville, California	1878	1st	583
Mason, Michigan	1885	5th	820
Maspeth, New York	1873	3rd	424
Matanzas, Cuba	1890	4th	972
Matawan, New Jersey	1876	3rd	531
Mauch Chunk, Pennsylvania	1875	4th	494
McKinney, Texas	1887	5th	872
Meadville, Pennsylvania	1866		
Meadville, Pennsylvania	1873	2nd	414
Mechanicsburg, Pennsylvania	1870		
Mechanicsburg, Pennsylvania	1886	3rd	870
Medina, Ohio	1877	4th	577
Memphis, Tennessee	1865	1st	95
Memphis, Tennessee	1871	1st	301
Memphis, Tennessee	1876	2nd	502
Memphis, Tennessee	1876	2nd	533
Menasha, Wisconsin	1886	3rd	855
Merced, California	1883	5th	734
Mercersburg, Pennsylvania	1874	3rd	415
Merida, Mexico	1890	5th	986
Meriden, Connecticut	1884	3rd	776
Meridian, Mississippi	1882	3rd	706
Meridian, Mississippi	1887	4th	875
Meridian, Mississippi	1887	5th	874
Merrimack, Massachusetts	1886	5th	847
Mexico City, Mexico	1878		
Mexico City, Mexico	1878		
Mexico, New York	1887	5th	877
Middleport, New York	1895	5th	2372
Middlesborough, Kentucky	1872	3rd	316
Mill Hall, Pennsylvania	1892	3rd	1018
Millbury, Massachusetts	1883	5th	731

City	Date	Size	Serial #
Millbury, Massachusetts	1883	5th	732
Milton, Pennsylvania	1876	3rd	521
Milton, Pennsylvania	1893	4th	2231
Moberly, Missouri	1873	3rd	404
Mobile, Alabama	1866	3rd	102
Mobile, Alabama	1866	3rd	110
Mobile, Alabama	1869	2nd	176
Mobile, Alabama	1869	3rd	206
Mobile, Alabama	1874	4th	487
Monmouth, Illinois	1868	3rd	191
Monmouth, Illinois	1870	3rd	569
Monmouth, Illinois	1882	4th	681
Monroe, Louisiana	1874	3rd	431
Monroe, Louisiana	1892	4th	2118
Monroe, Michigan	1875	3rd	484
Monroe, North Carolina	1886	5th	556
Montgomery, Alabama	1865	2nd	86
Montgomery, Alabama	1871	3rd	283
Montgomery, Alabama	1877	3rd	576
Montgomery, Pennsylvania	1873	3rd	402
Moravia, New York	1881	5th	682
Morgan City, Louisiana	1890	5th	987
Moscow, Russia	1872	3rd	331
Mount Carmel, Pennsylvania	1905	3rd	3031
Mount Holly, New Jersey	1880	4th	634
Mount Vernon, Ohio	1868	2nd	178
Mt. Clemens, Michigan	1884	4th	784
Muncy, Pennsylvania	1874	5th	456
Muskegon, Michigan	1868	3rd	181
Myerstown, Pennsylvania	1883	5th	743
Naperville, Illinois	1887	4th	895
Natchez, Mississippi	1870	3rd	252
Natchez, Mississippi	1887	4th	887
Natchitoches, Louisiana	1891	5th	1008
Nebraska City, Nebraska	1868	3rd	170
Neenah, Wisconsin	1869	3rd	222
Negaunee, Michigan	1873	2nd	427
New Albany, Indiana	1871	2nd	290
New Bedford, Massachusetts	1879	2nd	618
New Bern, North Carolina	1879	4th	604
New Britain, Connecticut	1883	4th	747
New Britain, Connecticut	1888	3rd	913
New Brunswick, New Jersey	1885	3rd	834

Silsby Steam Fire Engines

City	Date	Size	Serial #
New Haven, Connecticut	1883	2nd	733
New Haven, Connecticut	1886	2nd	846
New Haven, Connecticut	1894	2nd	2255
New Iberia, Louisiana	1883	5th	746
New Iberia, Louisiana	1886	4th	864
New Orleans, Louisiana	1865	2nd	77
New Orleans, Louisiana	1865	2nd	86
New Orleans, Louisiana	1867	3rd	131
New Orleans, Louisiana	1867	3rd	132
New Orleans, Louisiana	1883	3rd	755
New Orleans, Louisiana	1886	3rd	94
New Philadelphia, Ohio	1867	3rd	141
New Philadelphia, Ohio	1883	4th	744
New Rochelle, New York	1885	5th	810
New York, New York	1860		
New York, New York	1861		
New York, New York	1881	3rd	669
New York, New York	1881	4th	613
New York, New York	1893	3rd	2231
Newark, Ohio	1866	2nd	120
Newcastle, Delaware	1887	4th	876
Newport, New Hampshire	1885	3rd	831
Newton, Pennsylvania	1870	3rd	238
Nicholson, Pennsylvania	1905	5th	3033
Nicolet, Wisconsin	1877		
Norfolk, Virginia	1892	2nd	2138
Norristown, Pennsylvania	1884	3rd	775
North Brookfield, Massachusetts			
Northampton, Massachusetts	1889	3rd	935
Norwalk, Wisconsin	1882	4th	711
Norway, Michigan	1882	4th	702
Norwich, Connecticut	1891	4th	1004
Nyack, New York	1883	3rd	714
Nyack, New York	1895	5th	2411
Oakland, California	1872	2nd	367
Oakland, California	1875	2nd	519
Oberlin, Ohio	1866	3rd	118
Ocean City, New Jersey	1877	3rd	548
Ocean Grove, New Jersey	1900	4th	2758
Oconomowoc, Wisconsin	1879	3rd	612
Oconto, Wisconsin	1872	3rd	275
Oil City, Pennsylvania	1872	3rd	342
Old Orchard, Maine	1883	5th	735
Old Point Comfort, Virginia	1872	4th	357
Old Point Comfort, Virginia	1875	2nd	524
Olean, New York	1881	4th	653
Olympia, Washington	1883	5th	761
Omaha, Nebraska	1867	3rd	124
Omaha, Nebraska	1870	2nd	250
Omaha, Nebraska	1870	2nd	264
Opelika, Alabama	1872	3rd	590
Opelika, Alabama	1878		
Opelousas, Louisiana	1882	6th	722
Opsechee, Michigan	1863		
Orange, Massachusetts	1883	2nd	730
Orangeburg, South Carolina	1880	5th	520
Oresibe, Puerto Rico	1899	5th	2649
Oshkosh, Wisconsin	1866	2nd	106
Oshkosh, Wisconsin	1869	2nd	245
Oshkosh, Wisconsin	1874	3rd	443
Ossining, New York	1875	3rd	575
Oswego, New York	1865		
Oswego, New York	1867	2nd	137
Oswego, New York	1868	3rd	167
Oswego, New York	1881	2nd	660
Oswego, New York	1882	4th	709
Oswego, New York	1884	3rd	
Ottawa, Illinois	1872	3rd	378
Ottawa, Illinois	1893	5th	2710
Ottawa, Kansas	1872	3rd	343
Ottawa, Ohio	1883	5th	785
Ottawa, Ontario	1874	3rd	448
Ottumwa, Iowa	1867	2nd	158
Ovid, New York	1873	3rd	354
Owenton, Kentucky	1886	5th	863
Owosso, Michigan	1876	3rd	572
Oxford, Massachusetts	1884	5th	767
Oxford, New York	1888	5th	925
Oxford, Pennsylvania	1880	5th	648
Oyster Bay, New York	1895	5th	2375
Paducah, Kentucky	1869		
Painesville, Ohio	1871	3rd	272
Palatka, Florida	1882	5th	720
Palmyra, New York	1868	3rd	180
Paris, Texas	1877	5th	553
Paris, Texas	1886	3rd	844

Silsby Steam Fire Engines

City	Date	Size	Serial #
Pasadena, California	1887	2nd	943
Paterson, New Jersey	1884	3rd	782
Paterson, New Jersey	1890	3rd	974
Paterson, New Jersey	1891	3rd	996
Paw Paw, Michigan	1880	4th	640
Pekin, Illinois	1868	3rd	186
Penn Yan, New York	1872	3rd	346
Pensacola, Florida	1879	5th	606
Pensacola, Florida	1891		
Peru, Indiana	1874	3rd	474
Peterborough, Ontario	1871	3rd	292
Peterborough, Ontario	1872	3rd	309
Philadelphia, Pennsylvania	1885	2nd	840
Philadelphia, Pennsylvania	1886	1st	921
Philadelphia, Pennsylvania	1888	2nd	928
Philadelphia, Pennsylvania	1888	2nd	929
Philadelphia, Pennsylvania	1888	2nd	930
Philadelphia, Pennsylvania	1888	2nd	931
Philadelphia, Pennsylvania	1888	2nd	932
Philadelphia, Pennsylvania	1888	2nd	937
Philadelphia, Pennsylvania	1889	1st	941
Philadelphia, Pennsylvania	1889	2nd	938
Philadelphia, Pennsylvania	1889	2nd	939
Philadelphia, Pennsylvania	1889	2nd	940
Philadelphia, Pennsylvania	1889	2nd	942
Philadelphia, Pennsylvania	1890	2nd	946
Philadelphia, Pennsylvania	1890	2nd	965
Philadelphia, Pennsylvania	1890	2nd	969
Philadelphia, Pennsylvania	1890	4th	961
Philadelphia, Pennsylvania	1891	2nd	973
Philadelphia, Pennsylvania	1891	2nd	990
Philadelphia, Pennsylvania	1891	2nd	991
Philadelphia, Pennsylvania	1891	3rd	994
Philadelphia, Pennsylvania	1891	4th	992
Philadelphia, Pennsylvania	1891	4th	993
Philadelphia, Pennsylvania	1892	2nd	995
Philadelphia, Pennsylvania	1892	2nd	2112
Philadelphia, Pennsylvania	1892	2nd	2115
Philadelphia, Pennsylvania	1892	2nd	2119
Philadelphia, Pennsylvania	1892	2nd	2120
Philadelphia, Pennsylvania	1892	4th	2111
Philadelphia, Pennsylvania	1893	2nd	2192
Philadelphia, Pennsylvania	1893	2nd	2346

City	Date	Size	Serial #
Philadelphia, Pennsylvania	1893	4th	2193
Philadelphia, Pennsylvania	1893	4th	2199
Philadelphia, Pennsylvania	1893	4th	2200
Philadelphia, Pennsylvania	1894	2nd	227
Philadelphia, Pennsylvania	1894	4th	2272
Philadelphia, Pennsylvania	1895	2nd	2343
Philadelphia, Pennsylvania	1895	2nd	2345
Philadelphia, Pennsylvania	1895	2nd	2347
Philadelphia, Pennsylvania	1895	2nd	2355
Philadelphia, Pennsylvania	1895	2nd	2356
Philadelphia, Pennsylvania	1897	4th	2498
Phillipsburg, New Jersey	1877	3rd	550
Phillipsburg, New Jersey	1894	5th	2291
Pictou, Nova Scotia	1878	2nd	522
Pine Bluff, Arkansas	1877	4th	559
Pittsfield, Massachusetts	1885	3rd	817
Pittsfield, Massachusetts	1885	3rd	818
Pittston, Pennsylvania	1876	3rd	517
Pomeroy, Ohio	1868	3rd	166
Pontiac, Illinois	1873	3rd	475
Pontiac, Michigan	1865		
Pontiac, Michigan	1872	2nd	332
Port Arthur, Texas	1871	3rd	271
Port Clinton, Ohio	1871	3rd	289
Port Townsend, Washington	1889	3rd	948
Portage, Wisconsin	1877		
Portland, Maine	1883	3rd	751
Portland, Oregon	1864	3rd	87
Portland, Oregon	1867	3rd	138
Portland, Oregon	1873	2nd	394
Portland, Oregon	1881	4th	674
Portland, Oregon	1883	5th	760
Portsmouth, Ohio	1867	2nd	155
Pottstown, Pennsylvania	1871	3rd	281
Pottstown, Pennsylvania	1891	3rd	1002
Pottstown, Pennsylvania	1898	3rd	2175
Poughkeepsie, New York	1860		5
Poughkeepsie, New York	1872	1st	352
Princeton, New Jersey	1902	4th	2941
Providence, Rhode Island	1860	1st	3
Providence, Rhode Island	1860	2nd	4
Providence, Rhode Island	1861	1st	5
Providence, Rhode Island	1861	1st	7

Silsby Steam Fire Engines

City	Date	Size	Serial #
Providence, Rhode Island	1861	3rd	6
Providence, Rhode Island	1866	1st	115
Providence, Rhode Island	1871	2nd	274
Providence, Rhode Island	1872	1st	336
Providence, Rhode Island	1872	2nd	335
Providence, Rhode Island	1890	3rd	970
Providence, Rhode Island	1891	3rd	1000
Providence, Rhode Island	1893	3rd	2165
Quincy, Illinois	1866	2nd	114
Quincy, Illinois	1868	3rd	162
Quincy, Illinois	1877	2nd	552
Quincy, Illinois	1882	1st	715
Racine, Wisconsin	1866	2nd	100
Racine, Wisconsin	1871	2nd	269
Racine, Wisconsin	1877	2nd	543
Rahway, New Jersey			
Ravenna, Ohio	1870	3rd	327
Reading, Pennsylvania	1875	2nd	
Reading, Pennsylvania	1881	1st	678
Reading, Pennsylvania	1891	3rd	2139
Red Bluff, California	1880	5th	641
Red Wing, Minnesota	1871	3rd	273
Regula, Cuba	1894	5th	2301
Reidsville, North Carolina	1883	4th	763
Republic, Michigan	1868	3rd	171
Richland Center, Wisconsin	1887	5th	897
Richmond, Indiana	1860		
Richmond, Indiana	1871	3rd	300
Richmond, Indiana	1872	3rd	348
Richmond, Virginia	1881	3rd	667
Richmond, Virginia	1882	2nd	707
Richwood, Ohio	1875	4th	498
Rochester, Minnesota	1870	3rd	231
Rochester, New York	1861		
Rochester, New York	1869	2nd	200
Rochester, New York	1873	2nd	390
Rochester, New York	1873	2nd	391
Rochester, New York	1891	2nd	1009
Rochester, New York	1891	2nd	1010
Rock Hill, South Carolina	1887	5th	885
Rockport, Massachusetts	1885	3rd	814
Rockport, Massachusetts	1888	3rd	909
Rockville, Connecticut	1882	3rd	689
Rockville, Connecticut	1888	3rd	916
Rocky Mount, North Carolina	1896	5th	2471
Rome, Georgia	1867	3rd	147
Rome, New York	1884	4th	778
Roslyn, New York	1903	5th	2917
Rye, New York	1900	5th	2775
Saginaw, Michigan	1867	3rd	151
Sagua, La Grande, Cuba	1883	5th	759
Salamanca, New York	1880	4th	642
Salem, Indiana	1878	4th	589
Salem, New Jersey	1878	4th	582
Salem, Ohio	1869	3rd	20
Salem, Oregon	1882	4th	713
Salisbury, Massachusetts	1878	2nd	495
Salisbury, Massachusetts	1879	3rd	616
Salt Lake City, Utah	1872	2nd	371
Salt Lake City, Utah	1888	4th	917
San Antonio, Texas	1873	3rd	413
San Antonio, Texas	1876	4th	542
San Antonio, Texas	1884	3rd	791
San Jose, California	1866	2nd	112
San Jose, California	1888	2nd	920
San Luis Obisbo, California	1890	3rd	960
Sandusky, Ohio	1869	1st	213
Santa Clara, Cuba	1882	5th	700
Santiago, Cuba	1882	5th	703
Saratoga Springs, New York	1866	2nd	113
Schuylerville, New York	1870	3rd	239
Scranton, Pennsylvania	1874	2nd	477
Scranton, Pennsylvania	1875	3rd	508
Scranton, Pennsylvania	1892	2nd	2131
Sedalia, Missouri	1868	3rd	164
Sedalia, Missouri	1884	3rd	773
Selins Grove, Pennsylvania	1872	3rd	325
Selma, Alabama	1868	2nd	193
Selma, Alabama	1872	2nd	340
Selma, Alabama	1880	3rd	651
Seneca Falls, New York	1860		
Seneca Falls, New York	1868	3rd	173
Seneca Falls, New York	1881	4th	655
Seneca Falls, New York	1889	4th	950
Shamokin, Pennsylvania	1881	4th	661
Shanghai, China	1874	3rd	444

Silsby Steam Fire Engines

City	Date	Size	Serial #
Sharon, Pennsylvania	1873	3rd	385
Sheboygan, Wisconsin	1873	3rd	405
Sheffield, Pennsylvania	1881	2nd	660
Shelburne Falls, Massachusetts	1888	5th	915
Shepherdstown, West Virginia	1885	5th	808
Sherbrooke, P. Q.	1875	2nd	495
Sherman, Texas	1873	3rd	414
Sherman, Texas	1878	2nd	524
Sherman, Texas	1884	3rd	798
Shreveport, Louisiana	1866	3rd	117
Shreveport, Louisiana	1877	3rd	581
Shreveport, Louisiana	1884	4th	800
Shreveport, Louisiana	1885	4th	837
Silver Creek, New York	1885	3rd	815
Sing Sing, New York	1876		
Sioux City, Iowa	1874	3rd	447
Sioux Falls, South Dakota	1882	3rd	718
Slatington, Pennsylvania	1891	2nd	1013
Smith's Falls, Ontario	1875	3rd	503
Somerville, Massachusetts	1883	3rd	740
Somerville, Massachusetts	1890	2nd	981
Somerville, Massachusetts	1893	3rd	2241
South Amboy, New Jersey	1891	4th	1003
South Ashburnham, Massachusetts	1891	3rd	1005
South Bend, Indiana	1867	2nd	166
Southport, Connecticut	1887	5th	872
Sparta, Wisconsin	1870	3rd	268
Spokane, Washington	1889	2nd	951
Spokane, Washington	1890	3rd	983
Spokane, Washington	1890	3rd	984
Spring City, Pennsylvania	1882	2nd	684
Spring Lake, Michigan	1867	3rd	132
Spring Lake, New Jersey	1891	4th	1011
Springfield, Illinois	1869	3rd	204
Springfield, Illinois	1882	4th	737
Springfield, Ohio	1865	1st	80
Springfield, Ohio	1865	2nd	73
Springfield, Ohio	1870	3rd	266
Springfield, Vermont	1882	5th	691
St. Augustine, Florida	1887	3rd	882
St. Augustine, Florida	1887	5th	889
St. Clair, Michigan	1873	2nd	430
St. Hyacinthe, P.Q.	1887	3rd	898

City	Date	Size	Serial #
St. Ignace, Michigan	1872	3rd	359
St. Johns, Michigan	1880	3rd	683
St. Johns, P.Q.	1876		
St. Joseph, Michigan	1873	3rd	412
St. Louis, Missouri	1865	1st	91
St. Louis, Missouri	1966	1st	404
St. Martinsville, Louisiana	1889	5th	954
St. Paul, Minnesota	1868	1st	214
St. Paul, Minnesota	1870	2nd	248
St. Paul, Minnesota	1872	1st	368
St. Paul, Minnesota	1872	1st	369
St. Paul, Minnesota	1887	3rd	880
Stapleton, Long Island, New York	1871	3rd	283
Stillwater, Minnesota	1872	3rd	344
Stoughton, Massachusetts	1880	4th	645
Stratford, Ontario	1874	3rd	470
Stuart, Iowa	1884	4th	786
Sumpter, South Carolina	1895	3rd	2348
Sunbury, Pennsylvania	1870	3rd	232
Sunbury, Pennsylvania	1874	3rd	441
Swampscott, Massachusetts	1883	4th	749
Syracuse, New York	1859		
Syracuse, New York	1885	3rd	816
Syracuse, New York	1888	2nd	903
Syracuse, New York	1897		
Tacoma, Washington	1889	2nd	950
Tacoma, Washington	1889	4th	945
Tacoma, Washington	1889	4th	947
Templeton, Massachusetts	1891	3rd	1014
Templeton, Massachusetts	1894	6th	2278
Thibodeau, Louisiana	1888	5th	905
Thomasville, Georgia	1883	4th	754
Tiffin, Ohio	1867	2nd	130
Tippicanoe, Ohio	1874	3rd	446
Titusville, Pennsylvania	1872	2nd	334
Tizer, Iowa	1865	2nd	79
Toledo, Ohio	1861	2nd	33
Toledo, Ohio	1861		13
Toledo, Ohio	1863	2nd	37
Toledo, Ohio	1868	2nd	195
Toledo, Ohio	1872	2nd	362
Toledo, Ohio	1886	3rd	843
Tonawanda, New York	1871	3rd	321

Silsby Steam Fire Engines

City	Date	Size	Serial #
Topeka, Kansas	1870	3rd	236
Toronto, Ontario	1861		
Toronto, Ontario	1866	1st	93
Toronto, Ontario	1871	1st	297
Torrington, Connecticut	1886	3rd	926
Towanda, Pennsylvania	1870	3rd	249
Towanda, Pennsylvania	1870	3rd	268
Townsend, Massachusetts	1886	2nd	812
Tremont, Pennsylvania	1878	4th	598
Trenton, Michigan	1879	3rd	614
Trenton, New Jersey	1864		
Trenton, New Jersey	1878	3rd	590
Trenton, New Jersey	1880	3rd	829
Troy, Alabama	1871	5th	661
Troy, New Hampshire	1873	3rd	407
Troy, Ohio	1870	3rd	229
Troy, Ohio	1875	4th	502
Tusket, Nova Scotia	1878	4th	593
Tyrone, Pennsylvania	1888	4th	911
Tyrone, Pennsylvania	1893	3rd	2213
Union Springs, New York	1880	3rd	625
Union, New Jersey	1883	5th	784
Upper Sandusky, Ohio	1867	2nd	134
Upper Sandusky, Ohio	18808	4th	643
Urbana, Illinois	1868	2nd	165
Utica, New York	1865	3rd	84
Valdosta, Georgia	1884	5th	794
Vancouver, Washington	1884	5th	787
Vicksburg, Mississippi	1867	3rd	133
Vicksburg, Mississippi	1869		203
Vicksburg, Mississippi	1870	3rd	235
Vicksburg, Mississippi	1872	3rd	364
Vinalhaven, Maine	1888	5th	912
Vinton, Iowa	1881	4th	670
Virginia City, Nevada	1872	3rd	341
Visalia, California	1888	4th	934
Wabasha, Minnesota	1888	4th	927
Waco, Texas	1874	3rd	415
Waco, Texas	1885	4th	827
Waco, Texas	1888	3rd	906
Wakefield, Massachusetts	1882	4th	693
Walla Walla, Washington	1871	3rd	287
Walla Walla, Washington	1882	4th	697

City	Date	Size	Serial #
Wappingers Falls, New York	1902	4th	2915
Ware, Massachusetts	1885	4th	821
Warren, Ohio	1868	2nd	168
Warren, Ohio	1881	2nd	672
Warren, Pennsylvania	1873	3rd	429
Warsaw, Indiana	1868	3rd	175
Washington, D.C.	1870	3rd	226
Washington, D.C.	1880	3rd	681
Washington, D.C.	1892	3rd	2157
Washington, North Carolina	1888	5th	899
Washington, Pennsylvania	1872		361
Waterbury, Connecticut	1880	3rd	628
Waterbury, Connecticut	1883	3rd	756
Waterloo, New York	1872	3rd	372
Waterloo, New York	1873	2nd	399
Waterloo, Wisconsin	1874	2nd	461
Watertown, New York	1873	3rd	491
Watertown, New York	1883	3rd	765
Watertown, Wisconsin	1876	2nd	526
Waterville, New York	1877		
Watsontown, Pennsylvania	1874	3rd	440
Waukegan, Illinois	1874	3rd	452
Waverly, New York	1874	3rd	382
Waxahachie, Texas	1883	4th	741
Waynesboro, Pennsylvania	1880	5th	649
Weatherford, Texas	1884	4th	785
Weatherly, Pennsylvania	1893	5th	2330
Weedsport, New York	1879	5th	610
Weimar, Texas	1877	2nd	549
Wellesville, New York	1872	2nd	334
West Branch, Michigan	1882	1st	677
West Brookfield, Massachusetts	1888	5th	910
West Chester, Pennsylvania	1883	4th	739
West De Pera, Wisconsin	1875	3rd	504
West Hazelton, Pennsylvania	1893	4th	2243
West Point, Georgia	1885	5th	819
Westfield, Massachusetts	1871	3rd	317
Wheeling, West Virginia	1884	3rd	779
White River Junction, Vermont	1893	5th	2257
Whitehall, Michigan	1874	3rd	445
Whitehaven, Pennsylvania	1877	3rd	544
Whitesboro, New York	1865	3rd	78
Whitestown, New York	1865		

Silsby Steam Fire Engines

City	Date	Size	Serial #
Willard, New York	1872		
Wilmington, Delaware	1872	3rd	380
Wilmington, Delaware	1892	2nd	2117
Wilmington, North Carolina	1868	2nd	192
Wilmington, North Carolina	1874	5th	481
Wilmington, North Carolina	1886	3rd	857
Wilmington, North Carolina	1887	4th	886
Wilson, North Carolina	1887	5th	914
Winchendon, Massachusetts	1891	3rd	1001
Winchester, Kentucky	1886	5th	862
Winchester, New Hampshire	1894	4th	2293
Winchester, Virginia	1874	5th	481
Winchester, Virginia	1876	5th	585
Winnipeg, Manitoba	1874	2nd	471
Winnipeg, Manitoba	1874	3rd	455

City	Date	Size	Serial #
Winnipeg, Manitoba	1882	1st	676
Winona, Minnesota	1870	2nd	240
Winstead, Connecticut	1884	5th	799
Winterset, Iowa	1881	6th	665
Wooster, Ohio	1868	3rd	163
Worcester, Massachusetts	1860	2nd	2
Worcester, Massachusetts	1861	1st	35
Worcester, Massachusetts	1867	2nd	145
Worcester, Massachusetts	1873	3rd	407
Worcester, Massachusetts	1874	2nd	462
Yantic, Connecticut	(See Norwich, CT)		
Yarmouth, Nova Scotia	1880	4th	626
York, Pennsylvania	1870	3rd	252
York, Pennsylvania	1905	2nd	3028
Youngstown, Ohio	1868	2nd	169

The engineer keeps a constant vigil on the gauges of this Amoskeag at a fire in Lewiston, Maine in 1890.

Cole Brothers Steam Fire Engines
Pawtucket, Rhode Island

Cole Brothers 1867-1880

Information compiled by:

Harold S. Walker, P. E.
Edward R. Tufts

Total Number of Engines Built: 60
Total Number of Engines Listed 48
Unaccounted for 12

Sizes:

1st Size .... 6,500 lbs.
2nd Size .... 5,500 lbs.
3rd Size .... 4,500 lbs.

Prices:
Ranged from $4,000 to $5,000.

Cole Brothers Steam Fire Engines
(1867 - 1880)

City	Date	Size	Serial #	City	Date	Size	Serial #
Bloomington, Illinois				Pawtucket, Rhode Island	1867	3rd	
Bristol, Rhode Island				Providence, Rhode Island			
Central Falls, Rhode Island	1868			Providence, Rhode Island			
Chelsea, Massachusetts				Providence, Rhode Island			
Chicago, Illinois	1872			Providence, Rhode Island			
Chicago, Illinois	1873			Quincy, Illinois			
Chicago, Illinois	1875			Richmond, Virginia			
Clinton, Massachusetts		3rd		Rome, New York			
Cumberland, Maryland				Rome, New York			
Fort Atkinson, Wisconsin				Shelbyville, Kentucky			
Foxboro, Massachusetts	1870	3rd		Southbridge, Massachusetts			
Frankfort, Kentucky	1868	2nd		Southbridge, Massachusetts			
Hyde Park, Massachusetts		4th		Stonington, Connecticut			
Hyde Park, Massachusetts		4th		Taunton, Massachusetts	1872		
Lancaster, Pennsylvania	1870	4th		Utica, New York	1865		
Manitowec, Wisconsin				Utica, New York	1867		
Manitowec, Wisconsin				Vincennes, Indiana	1869	2nd	
Marblehead, Massachusetts		2nd		Warren, Rhode Island			
Milford, Massachusetts	1868	2nd		Webster, Massachusetts	1868	3rd	
Natick, Massachusetts		2nd		Wheeling, West Virginia			
Newark, New Jersey		3rd		Wheeling, West Virginia			
Norwalk, Connecticut				Winchendon, Massachusetts		2nd	
Oneida, New York				Xenia, Ohio			
Oswego, New York				York, Pennsylvania	1873		

Clapp & Jones Steam Fire Engines
Hudson, New York

Information compiled by:

Harold S. Walker, P. E.
Edward R. Tufts

Clapp & Jones Steam Fire Engines
(1862 - 1891)

City	Date	Size	Serial #
Alameda, California	1891		
Albany, Georgia	1891	3rd	
Albany, New York	1884	2nd	
Albany, New York	1891	2nd	
Albany, Oregon	1875		
Albany, Oregon	1891		
Alpena, Michigan	1871		
Anderson, South Carolina	1866		
Antigo, Wisconsin	1887		
Appleton, Wisconsin	1872		
Armour, Dole & Co., Chicago, Illinois	1874		
Ashtabula, Ohio	1873		
Astoria, Oregon	1874		
Astoria, Oregon	1887		
Athens, New York	1871		
Atlanta, Georgia	1871		
Atwater, Minnesota	1890		
Augusta, Georgia	1868		
Baltimore, Maryland	1885	3rd	
Baltimore, Maryland	1885	3rd	
Baltimore, Maryland	1886	2nd	472
Baltimore, Maryland	1888	3rd	503
Baltimore, Maryland	1890	1st	
Barnesville, Georgia	1879		
Barre, Ontario	1871		
Bayonne, New Jersey	1874	2nd	
Bayonne, New Jersey	1887	2nd	
Bellefonte, Pennsylvania	1875		
Berkeley, Virginia	1890		
Bethlehem, Pennsylvania	1869	3rd	510
Bethlehem, Pennsylvania	1874	4th	
Blissfield, Michigan	1876		
Boston, Massachusetts	1873	4th	
Boston, Massachusetts	1888	3rd	498
Boston, Massachusetts	1890	1st	542
Boston, Massachusetts	1890	1st	548
Boston, Massachusetts	1890	1st	550
Boston, Massachusetts	1890	1st	560
Boston, Massachusetts	1890	2nd	531
Boston, Massachusetts	1890	2nd	532
Boston, Massachusetts	1891	3rd	566
Boston, Massachusetts	1891	3rd	567
Brattleboro, Vermont	1876	5th	134
Brattleboro, Vermont	1876	5th	135
Brazilian Government	1883		
Briarcliff Farms, New Jersey	1883		
Brooklyn, New York	1881	4th	375
Brooklyn, New York	1886	3rd	506
Buckingham & Co., Chicago, Illinois	1874		
C. B. & Q. Railroad	1872		
Camden, New Jersey	1890		
Canastota, New York	1876		
Carrollton, Michigan	1887		
Castleton, New York	1871		
Catskill, New York	1872		83
Charleston, South Carolina	1866	4th	
Charleston, South Carolina	1866	4th	
Charleston, South Carolina	1870	4th	
Charleston, South Carolina	1871	4th	
Charleston, South Carolina	1883	4th	
Charleston, South Carolina	1884	2nd	
Charleston, South Carolina	1884	2nd	
Chatham, Ontario	1871		
Chenango, New York	1872	3rd	
Chester, Vermont	1889		
Chillicothe, Ohio	1874		
Chillicothe, Ohio	1887		
Chilton, Wisconsin	1872		
Circleville, Ohio	1887		
City Island, New York	1890		
Cleveland, Ohio	1875	1st	
Cleveland, Ohio	1885	X1st	
Clintonville, Wisconsin	1886		
Clyde, Ohio	1878		
Coatesville, Pennsylvania	1877		
Columbia City, Indiana	1877		
Columbia, Pennsylvania	1868		
Columbia, South Carolina	1890		
Columbus, Georgia	1873	3rd	
Columbus, Mississippi	1887		
Corunna, Michigan	1887		
Crisfield, Maryland	1886		
Cutler, Ontario	1886		
Davenport, Iowa	1866		
Defiance, Ohio	1872	4th	
Depere, Wisconsin	1872		

Clapp & Jones Steam Fire Engines

City	Date	Size	Serial #
Dover, New Jersey	1885		
Easton, Pennsylvania	1870		
Elizabethtown, Pennsylvania	1879		
Evansville, Indiana	1874		
Evansville, Indiana	1887		
Fall River, Massachusetts	1890	1st	562
Fort Edward, New York	1874		
Fredericksburg, Maryland	1878		
Fremont, Ohio	1873		
Frenchtown, New Jersey	1888		
Geneva, Ohio	1874		
Gifford & Ruddock, Manistee, Michigan	1874		
Gilberton, Pennsylvania	1892		
Glens Falls, New York	1891		
Grand Haven, Michigan	1869		
Grand Haven, Michigan	1886		
Grand Rapids, Michigan	1873		
Green Bay, Wisconsin	1872		
Greenbush, New York	1871	4th	
Greenville, Michigan	1872		
Hamilton, Ontario	1883	1st	
Harrison, New Jersey	1879		
Hartford, Connecticut	1880	2nd	
Hartford, Connecticut	1890	2nd	571
Havana, Cuba	1876		
Hawaiian Government	1878		
Hawaiian Government	1878		
Hillsdale, Michigan	1874		
Hillsdale, Michigan	1887		
Hoboken, New Jersey	1888		
Holgate, Ohio	1889		
Honolulu, Territory of Hawaii	1891		
Hoquiam, Washington	1890		
Hudson, New York	1868		
Hudson, New York	1868		
Hudson, New York	1869		
Huntington, Indiana	1873		
Hurley, Wisconsin	1886		
Hurontown, Michigan			
Independence, Iowa	1874		
Indianapolis, Indiana	1874		
Iron Mountain, Michigan	1884		
Ithaca, New York	1874	4th	6

City	Date	Size	Serial #
Ithaca, New York	1887		
J. Estey & Co. Brattleboro	1876	5th	
J. I. Case Threshing Machine Co., Racine, Wisconsin	1882		
Jacksonville, Florida	1872	3rd	
Jersey City, New Jersey	1873		
Jersey City, New Jersey	1874		
Jersey City, New Jersey	1887		
Kenosha, Wisconsin	1887		
Kinderhook, New York	1882		
Kingston, New York	1867		
Kingston, Pennsylvania	1889		
Kokomo, Indiana	1872	3rd	
Lancaster, Pennsylvania	1888	2nd	
Lancaster, Pennsylvania	1888	2nd	
Lancaster, Pennsylvania	1888	2nd	
Lansing, Michigan	1873		
Lansingburgh, New York	1875		82
Laprairie, Quebec	1877		
Larium, Michigan	1891	4th	
Lebanon, Pennsylvania	1872	3rd	
Levis, Quebec	1877		
Lima, Ohio	1872		
Logansport, Indiana	1873		
Long Branch, New Jersey	1886		
Long Branch, New Jersey	1886		
Long Island City, New York	1888	3rd	
Lynchburg Virginia	1874		
Lynchburg, Virginia	1887		
Macon, Georgia	1873	4th	
Manchester, Indiana	1888		
Manistee, Michigan	1872	2nd	
Marathon, New York	1889		
Marinetta, Wisconsin	1884		
Marshall, Minnesota	1890		
Marysville, California	1887		
Massilon, Ohio	1874		
Melrose, Massachusetts	1891	3rd	536
Mexican Government	1874		
Mexican Government	1887		
Middleburg, New York	1887		
Minneapolis, Minnesota	1874		
Minneapolis, Minnesota	1887	2nd	
Minneapolis, Minnesota	1888	1st	

Clapp & Jones Steam Fire Engines

City	Date	Size	Serial #
Minneapolis, Minnesota	1888	2nd	
Minneapolis, Minnesota	1890	2nd	
Mobile, Alabama	1868	2nd	
Mobile, Alabama	1868	2nd	
Mobile, Alabama	1872		
Monroe, Michigan	1868		
Monroeville, Ohio	1878		
Montague, Michigan	1873		
Montreal, Quebec	1877		
Montreal, Quebec	1890	1st	
Morristown, New Jersey	1873		
Muncie, Indiana	1874		
Muncie, Indiana	1874		
Napoleon, Ohio	1872		
New Bedford, Massachusetts	1873		116
New Brunswick, New Jersey	1874		
New Brunswick, New Jersey	1887		
New York City, New York	1880	1st	351
New York City, New York	1880	2nd	352
New York City, New York	1881	4th	359
New York City, New York	1881	4th	362
New York City, New York	1881	4th	365
New York City, New York	1881	4th	368
New York City, New York	1881	4th	370
New York City, New York	1881	4th	371
New York City, New York	1881	4th	375
New York City, New York	1882	2nd	380
New York City, New York	1882	2nd	381
New York City, New York	1882	2nd	383
New York City, New York	1882	2nd	385
New York City, New York	1882	5th	397
New York City, New York	1883	2nd	415
New York City, New York	1883	4th	409
New York City, New York	1883	4th	417
New York City, New York	1883	5th	413
New York City, New York	1883		405
New York City, New York	1883		406
New York City, New York	1884	4th	430
New York City, New York	1884	4th	432
New York City, New York	1884	4th	433
New York City, New York	1884	4th	434
New York City, New York	1884	4th	436
New York City, New York	1884	4th	438

City	Date	Size	Serial #
New York City, New York	1884	5th	452
New York City, New York	1885	2nd	463
New York City, New York	1886	2nd	473
New York City, New York	1887	1st	491
New York City, New York	1890	1st	544
New York City, New York	1891	1st	558
New York City, New York	1891	1st	559
Newport, Rhode Island	1873		103
Newton, New Jersey	1873		
North Manchester, Indiana	1885		
North Tonawanda, New York	1881		
Northampton, Massachusetts	1870		
Norwich, New York	1871		
Nyack, New York	1874		
Nyack, New York	1887		
Oakland, California	1888	3rd	
Ocean Grove, New Jersey	1886		
Ogdensburg, New York	1887	3rd	
Omro, Wisconsin	1891		
Ontonagon, Michigan	1874		
Oswego, New York	1874		
Oswego, New York	1887		
Palmer, Massachusetts	1885	4th	465
Passaic, New Jersey	1886	3rd	
Paterson, New Jersey	1874		
Paterson, New Jersey	1887		
Paterson, New Jersey	1887		
Pentwater, Michigan	1871		
Peoria, Illinois	1874		
Peoria, Illinois	1887		
Peru, Indiana	1872		
Pittsfield, Massachusetts	1872	4th	
Pittsfield, Massachusetts	1872	4th	
Pocomoke City, Maryland	1888		
Port Deposit, Maryland	1885		
Port Henry, New York	1875		131
Port Huron, Michigan	1867		
Portage La Prairie, Manitoba	1877		
Portland, Maine	1890	2nd	526
Portland, Oregon	1887		
Pottsville, Pennsylvania	1875		
Pottsville, Pennsylvania	1875		
Poughkeepsie, New York	1872		

Clapp & Jones Steam Fire Engines

City	Date	Size	Serial #
Quebec City, Quebec	1876		
Racine, Wisconsin	1871		
Racine, Wisconsin	1882		
Racine, Wisconsin	1885		
Racine, Wisconsin	1885		
Reading, Pennsylvania	1871	2nd	
Reading, Pennsylvania	1874		
Reading, Pennsylvania	1887		
Red Jacket, Michigan	1875		
Reno, Nevada	1874		
Richmond, Virginia	1888	3rd	502
Rio de Janeiro, Brazil	1874		
Rio de Janeiro, Brazil	1887		
Rochester, New York	1869	2nd	
Rochester, New York	1889	3rd	
Rockaway Beach, New York	1889		
Rockland Lake, New York	1889		
Romeo, Michigan	1871		
Rondout, New York	1874		
Rondout, New York	1887		
Rondout, New York	1887		
Sacketts Harbor, New York	1889		
Salem, New York	1875		140
Salem, Ohio	1874		
Salem, Ohio	1887		
San Francisco, California	1874		
San Francisco, California	1887		
San Jose, California	1874		
San Jose, California	1887		
Sarnia, Ontario	1868		
Saugerties, New York	1873		
Schenectady, New York	1874		
Schenectady, New York	1887		
Scranton, Pennsylvania	1874		
Scranton, Pennsylvania	1887		
Shreveport, Louisiana	1874		
Shreveport, Louisiana	1887		
Smith Paper Co. Lee, Massachusetts	1879		
South Easton, Pennsylvania	1867		
Spanish Government	1874		
Spanish Government	1887		
Spring Lake, Michigan	1885		
St. Conegal, Canada	1874		

City	Date	Size	Serial #
St. Conegal, Canada	1887		
St. Paul, Minnesota	1885	X1st	
Standard Oil Co.	1874		
Stroudsburg, Pennsylvania	1872		172
Sussex, New Jersey	1873		
Syracuse, New York	1885		
Syracuse, New York	1891		
Syracuse, New York	1891		
Tacoma, Washington	1874		
Tacoma, Washington	1887		
Thomson, Georgia	1888		
Titusville, Pennsylvania	1871		
Toledo, Ohio	1873		
Toledo, Ohio	1874	2nd	
Toledo, Ohio	1887		
Trenton, New Jersey	1868	3rd	
Troy, New York	1872		
Troy, New York	1874	2nd	
Troy, Pennsylvania	1872		
United States Government	1874		
United States Government	1887		
Utica, New York	1874		
Utica, New York	1887		
Vallejo, California	1878		
Valleyfield, Quebec	1878		
Valpariso, Chile	1874		
Valpariso, Chile	1887		
Vaughn, Wisconsin	1887		
Vera Cruz, Mexico	1880		
Virginia City, Nevada	1873		
Wallaceburg, Ontario	1883		
Wapakoneta, Ohio	1873		
Washington Court House, Ohio	1875		
Washington, D.C.	1883	4th	
Washington, D.C.	1884	4th	7
Washington, D.C.	1885	4th	10
Washington, D.C.	1888	2nd	
Washington, D.C.	1889	1st	
Washington, D.C.	1889	2nd	
Washington, D.C.	1889	3rd	
West Bay City, Michigan	1872		
West New Brighton, New York	1872		
What Cheer, Iowa	1874		

Clapp & Jones Steam Fire Engines

City	Date	Size	Serial #
What Cheer, Iowa	1887		
Williamsport, Michigan	1887		
Williamsport, Pennsylvania	1872		
Wilmington, Delaware	1873		
Wilmington, Delaware	1879		
Wilmington, Delaware	1888	2nd	

City	Date	Size	Serial #
Wilmington, Ohio	1875		
Winona, Wisconsin	1871		
Woodland, California	1876	3rd	
Yokohama, Japan	1874		
Yokohama, Japan	1887		
Ypsilanti, Michigan	1873	3rd	

Amoskeag Steam Fire Engines
Manchester, New Hampshire

Amoskeag Manufacturing Co. 1859-1879
Manchester, New Hampshire (Serial Numbers 1 - 545)

Manchester Locomotive Works 1879-1902
Manchester, New Hampshire (Serial Numbers 546-770)

American Locomotive Co. 1902-1908
Manchester, New Hampshire (Under contract with the
International Power Co. who by purchase owned
the exclusive rights to the "Amoskeag" name
and the right to build the engines.) (Serial Numbers 771-839)

International Power Co. 1908-1913
(At the plant of their affiliate,
The American & British Mfg. Co.
at the Corliss Works, Providence, Rhode Island.)
(Serial Numbers 840-853)

Types of Engines:

1	Rotary Pump	1858-1865	11
2	Double Round Tank	1860-1866	55
3	Single Round Tank	1860-1864	3
4	Single U-Tank	1860-1866	60
5	Single Harp Tank	1861-1879	118
6	Double Straight Frame	1866-1885	118
7	Double Straight Frame Self-Propellers	1868	2
8	Double Crane Neck Frame	1870-1913	447
9	Double Crane Neck Frame Self-Propeller	1873-1906	22
10	Single Crane Neck Frame	1879-1907	5
11	Single Short Frame	1878-1897	10
12	Fireboat Pumps		3
		Total	853

Information compiled by:

Harold S. Walker, P. E.
Edward R. Tufts

Amoskeag Steam Fire Engines
(1859 - 1913)

City	Date	Size	Serial #	City	Date	Size	Serial #
		1st	501	Ashland, Massachusetts	1871	3rd	369
		3rd	689	Astoria, Oregon	1879	2nd	543
			801	Athol, Massachusetts	1868	2nd	288
			802	Athol, Massachusetts	1871	2nd	365
			803	Atlanta, Georgia	1866	3rd	184
	1866	2nd	207	Atlanta, Georgia	1867	2nd	233
	1871	3rd	368	Atlanta, Georgia	1885	2nd	606
	1880	4th	539	Auburn, Maine	1871	2nd	352
	1906		791	Augusta, Georgia	1867	3rd	222
???, Massachusetts	1866	2nd	196	Augusta, Maine	1865	2nd	113
?????, Massachusetts	1870	3rd	336	Augusta, Maine	1867	2nd	232
???piapo, Chile	1869	3rd	325	Augusta, Maine	1867	2nd	237
???ston, Pennsylvania	1869	3rd	331	Aurora, Illinois	1869	1st	314
Adrian, Michigan	1867	1st	254	Baltimore, Maryland	1908		835
Albany, New York	1867	2nd	244	Bangor, Maine	1871	2nd	372
Albany, New York	1867	2nd	258	Bath, Maine	1866	2nd	153
Albany, New York	1867	2nd	274	Bath, Maine	1873	2nd	422
Albany, New York	1867	2nd	275	Bath, Maine	1873	2nd	423
Albany, New York	1871	2nd	367	Benecia, California	1868	2nd	305
Albany, New York	1871	2nd	385	Bergen, New Jersey	1869	3rd	332
Albany, New York	1873	2nd	464	Bergen, New Jersey	1869	3rd	333
Albany, New York	1873	2nd	465	Berlin, New Hampshire	1905	2nd	783
Alexandria, Virginia	1862	2nd	49	Beverly, Massachusetts	1866	2nd	187
Alexandria, Virginia	1863	2nd	66	Biddeford, Maine	1868	2nd	292
Allegheny City, Pennsylvania	1863	1st	73	Biddeford, Maine	1869	2nd	310
Allegheny City, Pennsylvania	1864	1st	87	Biddeford, Maine	1909		846
Allegheny City, Pennsylvania	1871	2nd	366	Boston, Massachusetts	1859	1st	3
Allegheny, Pennsylvania	1869	2nd	309	Boston, Massachusetts	1859	1st	4
Allegheny, Pennsylvania	1874	2nd	488	Boston, Massachusetts	1860	1st	8
Allegheny, Pennsylvania	1874	2nd	489	Boston, Massachusetts	1860	1st	9
Allegheny, Pennsylvania	1877	2nd	512	Boston, Massachusetts	1860	1st	10
Allegheny, Pennsylvania	1882	2nd	566	Boston, Massachusetts	1860	2nd	17
Allentown, Pennsylvania	1882	2nd	563	Boston, Massachusetts	1861	1st	35
Altoona, Pennsylvania	1867	2nd	239	Boston, Massachusetts	1862	2nd	51
Altoona, Pennsylvania	1868	2nd	285	Boston, Massachusetts	1864	1st	96
Altoona, Pennsylvania	1868	2nd	286	Boston, Massachusetts	1866	2nd	167
Altoona, Pennsylvania	1903	2nd	774	Boston, Massachusetts	1867	1st	252
Altoona, Pennsylvania	1907	1st	834	Boston, Massachusetts	1867	1st	270
Amesbury, Massachusetts	1900	2nd	755	Boston, Massachusetts	1867	1st	273
Amoor, Russia	1862	1st	47	Boston, Massachusetts	1867	2nd	263
Andover, Massachusetts	1883	4	579	Boston, Massachusetts	1869	1st	328
Andover, Massachusetts	1901	4	765	Boston, Massachusetts	1870	1st	337
Annapolis, Maryland	1866	2nd	200	Boston, Massachusetts	1870	1st	350

Amoskeag Steam Fire Engines

City	Date	Size	Serial #	City	Date	Size	Serial #
Boston, Massachusetts	1870	1st	354	Brooklyn, New York	1868	3rd	265
Boston, Massachusetts	1872	1st	416	Brooklyn, New York	1869	1st	316
Boston, Massachusetts	1874	1st	484	Brooklyn, New York	1869	2nd	307
Boston, Massachusetts	1879	2nd	534	Brooklyn, New York	1870	2nd	322
Boston, Massachusetts	1882	2nd	562	Brooklyn, New York	1870	2nd	338
Boston, Massachusetts	1882	2nd	569	Brooklyn, New York	1871	2nd	381
Boston, Massachusetts	1883	X1st	578	Brooklyn, New York	1872	2nd	382
Boston, Massachusetts	1884	2nd	591	Brooklyn, New York	1872	2nd	383
Boston, Massachusetts	1886	2nd	619	Brooklyn, New York	1872	2nd	395
Boston, Massachusetts	1890	3rd	652	Brooklyn, New York	1873	2nd	421
Boston, Massachusetts	1890	3rd	663	Brooklyn, New York	1873	2nd	427
Boston, Massachusetts	1890	3rd	664	Brooklyn, New York	1873	2nd	428
Boston, Massachusetts	1890	3rd	665	Brooklyn, New York	1873	2nd	429
Boston, Massachusetts	1896	1st	725	Brooklyn, New York	1874	1st	486
Boston, Massachusetts	1896	2nd	720	Brooklyn, New York	1874	2nd	473
Boston, Massachusetts	1896	2nd	721	Brooklyn, New York	1876	2nd	507
Boston, Massachusetts	1897	DX-1	727	Brooklyn, New York	1877	2nd	528
Boston, Massachusetts	1897	DX1st	736	Brooklyn, New York	1880	2nd	546
Boston, Massachusetts	1901	2nd	760	Brooklyn, New York	1882	2nd	568
Boston, Massachusetts	1901	X1st	761	Brooklyn, New York	1883	2nd	585
Boston, Massachusetts	1904	X1st	778	Brooklyn, New York	1884	2nd	590
Boston, Massachusetts	1906	1st	785	Brooklyn, New York	1884	2nd	594
Boston, Massachusetts	1906	X1st	784	Brooklyn, New York	1885	2nd	598
Boston, Massachusetts	1907	1st	820	Brooklyn, New York	1885	2nd	599
Boston, Massachusetts	1907	DX1st	808	Brooklyn, New York	1885	2nd	600
Boston, Massachusetts	1909	1st	841	Brooklyn, New York	1889	2nd	654
Boston, Massachusetts	1909	1st	842	Brooklyn, New York	1889	2nd	655
Boston, Massachusetts	1911	2nd	850	Brooklyn, New York	1890	2nd	658
Boston, Massachusetts	1912	2nd	851	Brooklyn, New York	1890	2nd	659
Bradley Beach, New Jersey	1908		840	Brooklyn, New York	1890	2nd	660
Bridgeport, Connecticut	1864	1st	84	Brooklyn, New York	1891	2nd	667
Bridgeport, Connecticut	1865	2nd	125	Brooklyn, New York	1891	2nd	668
Bridgeport, Connecticut	1865	3rd	124	Brooklyn, New York	1891	2nd	669
Bridgeport, Connecticut	1883	2nd	575	Brooklyn, New York	1892	2nd	684
Brockton, Massachusetts	1879	2nd	541	Brooklyn, New York	1892	2nd	685
Brockton, Massachusetts	1899	2nd	738	Brooklyn, New York	1893	2nd	696
Brookfield, Massachusetts	1899	4	743	Brooklyn, New York	1893	2nd	697
Brookline, Massachusetts	1873	2nd	454	Brooklyn, New York	1894	1st	707
Brookline, Massachusetts	1892	2nd	681	Brooklyn, New York	1894	1st	708
Brooklyn, New York	1861	2nd	32	Brooklyn, New York	1894	1st	709
Brooklyn, New York	1861	2nd	38	Buffalo, New York	1875	2nd	498
Brooklyn, New York	1868	1st	299	Buffalo, New York	1893	2nd	695
Brooklyn, New York	1868	2nd	276	Buffalo, New York	1894	1st	705

Amoskeag Steam Fire Engines

City	Date	Size	Serial #
Buffalo, New York	1894	1st	706
Buffalo, New York	1896	1st	717
Buffalo, New York	1896	1st	718
Calais, Maine	1871	2nd	358
Calumet, Michigan	1882	4	553
Cambridge, Massachusetts	1862	2nd	56
Cambridge, Massachusetts	1863	2nd	71
Cambridge, Massachusetts	1864	2nd	95
Cambridge, Massachusetts	1869	2nd	308
Cambridge, Massachusetts	1872	1st	379
Cambridge, Massachusetts	1873	2nd	468
Cambridge, Massachusetts	1876	2nd	510
Cambridge, Massachusetts	1883	1st	584
Cambridge, Massachusetts	1891	1st	671
Cambridge, Massachusetts	1895	2nd	711
Cambridge, Massachusetts	1896	3rd	719
Camden, Maine	1893	3rd	694
Camden, New Jersey	1864	3rd	92
Camden, New Jersey	1864	3rd	99
Camden, New Jersey	1868	2nd	287
Camden, New Jersey	1869	2nd	318
Camden, New Jersey	1869	2nd	319
Camden, New Jersey	1908	2nd	838
Camden, New Jersey	1908	2nd	839
Canton, Ohio	1868	2nd	277
Carlisle, Pennsylvania	1882	3rd	564
Charleston, South Carolina	1867	2nd	236
Charleston, South Carolina	1870	1st	329
Charleston, South Carolina	1870	2nd	321
Charleston, South Carolina	1870	3rd	334
Charlestown, Massachusetts	1862	2nd	53
Charlestown, Massachusetts	1865	1st	136
Charlestown, Massachusetts	1866	2nd	202
Charlestown, Massachusetts	1872	1st	415
Chelsea, Massachusetts	1860	2nd	14
Chelsea, Massachusetts	1862	2nd	59
Chelsea, Massachusetts	1872	2nd	420
Chelsea, Massachusetts	1904	2nd	775
Chelsea, Massachusetts	1909	2nd	847
Chelsea, Massachusetts	1909	2nd	848
Chester, Pennsylvania	1885	2nd	605
Chicago, Illinois	1860	1st	7
Chicago, Illinois	1860	2nd	23

City	Date	Size	Serial #
Chicago, Illinois	1861	2nd	27
Chicago, Illinois	1864	1st	85
Chicago, Illinois	1865	1st	139
Chicago, Illinois	1865	1st	141
Chicago, Illinois	1866	1st	140
Chicago, Illinois	1866	2nd	208
Chicago, Illinois	1867	1st	256
Chicago, Illinois	1867	2nd	209
Chicago, Illinois	1867	2nd	259
Chicago, Illinois	1872	1st	380
Chicago, Illinois	1872	2nd	394
Chicago, Illinois	1877	1st	503
Chicago, Illinois	1877	1st	521
Chicago, Illinois	1877	1st	522
Chicago, Illinois	1907		810
Chicago, Illinois	1907		813
Chicago, Illinois	1907		814
Cleveland, Ohio	1874	2nd	497
Cleveland, Ohio	1879	2nd	544
Clinton, Massachusetts	1897	3rd	732
Clinton, New Jersey	1892	4	678
Columbia, Pennsylvania	1867	2nd	248
Columbus, Wisconsin	1886	3rd	624
Concord, New Hampshire	1862	1st	50
Concord, New Hampshire	1867	2nd	211
Concord, New Hampshire	1883	2nd	574
Concord, New Hampshire	1890	1st	670
Davenport, Iowa	1865	2nd	155
Dayton, Ohio	1867	2nd	238
Dedham, Massachusetts	1873	2nd	456
Des Moines, Iowa	1868	1st	280
Detroit, Michigan	1860	1st	22
Detroit, Michigan	1860	1st	26
Detroit, Michigan	1861	1st	30
Detroit, Michigan	1865	2nd	101
Detroit, Michigan	1865	2nd	128
Detroit, Michigan	1868	2nd	261
Detroit, Michigan	1872	1st	401
Detroit, Michigan	1872	2nd	408
Detroit, Michigan	1873	1st	447
Detroit, Michigan	1873	2nd	430
Detroit, Michigan	1876	1st	500
Detroit, Michigan	1876	2nd	508

Amoskeag Steam Fire Engines

City	Date	Size	Serial #
Detroit, Michigan	1877	2nd	524
Detroit, Michigan	1891	1st	673
Detroit, Michigan	1892	X1st	686
Detroit, Michigan	1892	X1st	687
Detroit, Michigan	1893	X1st	701
Detroit, Michigan	1907		804
Detroit, Michigan	1907		805
Detroit, Michigan	1907		809
Dover, New Hampshire	1865	1st	130
Dover, New Hampshire	1865	3rd	129
Dover, New Hampshire	1875	2nd	504
Dover, New Hampshire	1884	2nd	593
Easton, Pennsylvania	1865	2nd	112
Easton, Pennsylvania	1907	4	827
Elizabeth, New Jersey	1871	3rd	344
Elizabeth, New Jersey	1888	3rd	635
Elizabeth, New Jersey	1890	3rd	650
Ellis Island, New York	1867	1st	268
Elmira, New York	1864	3rd	91
Elmira, New York	1868	1st	300
Elyria, Ohio	1906		790
Erie, Pennsylvania	1864	3rd	105
Erie, Pennsylvania	1892	2nd	682
Everett, Massachusetts	1878	4	530
Everett, Massachusetts	1891	2nd	675
Everett, Massachusetts	1897	2nd	731
Exeter, New Hampshire	1873	2nd	458
Fairfield, Maine	1882	3rd	571
Fall River, Massachusetts	1859	1st	5
Fall River, Massachusetts	1860	1st	25
Fall River, Massachusetts	1865	1st	138
Fitchburg, Massachusetts	1867	2nd	215
Flint, Michigan	1872	2nd	409
Fond Du Lac, Wisconsin	1863	2nd	72
Fond Du Lac, Wisconsin	1866	2nd	197
Fond Du Lac, Wisconsin	1874	1st	495
Fort Wayne, Indiana	1878	1st	538
Framingham, Massachusetts	1897	2nd	733
Framingham, Massachusetts	1900	2nd	753
Framingham, Massachusetts	1904	2nd	777
Franklin, New Hampshire	1880	3rd	550
Frederickton, New Brunswick	1868	2nd	293
Fremont, Ohio	1865	2nd	116

City	Date	Size	Serial #
Gardner, Massachusetts	1906	1st	797
Georgetown, District of Columbia	1867	2nd	220
Georgetown, Massachusetts	1875	3rd	478
Georgetown, South Carolina	1870	3rd	343
Glasgow, Nova Scotia	1877	2nd	525
Gloucester, Massachusetts	1873	2nd	443
Gloucester, Massachusetts	1879	2nd	545
Governors Island, New York	1867	2nd	231
Green Bay, Wisconsin	1868	2nd	294
Halifax, Nova Scotia	1860	2nd	20
Halifax, Nova Scotia	1861	2nd	37
Halifax, Nova Scotia	1888	2nd	638
Halifax, Nova Scotia	1893	2nd	691
Hallowell, Maine	1880	3rd	551
Hampton, Virginia	1875	2nd	505
Hampton, Virginia	1886	2nd	620
Hannibal, Missouri	1870	2nd	346
Harrisburg, Pennsylvania	1861	2nd	39
Harrisburg, Pennsylvania	1867	1st	225
Harrisburg, Pennsylvania	1907	2nd	828
Hartford, Connecticut		2nd	515
Hartford, Connecticut	1861	2nd	45
Hartford, Connecticut	1863	2nd	64
Hartford, Connecticut	1863	2nd	67
Hartford, Connecticut	1863	2nd	75
Hartford, Connecticut	1868	2nd	290
Hartford, Connecticut	1871	2nd	386
Hartford, Connecticut	1876	1st	502
Hartford, Connecticut	1889	DX1st	644
Hartford, Connecticut	1900	2nd	754
Hartford, Connecticut	1904	3rd	781
Hartford, Connecticut	1907	2nd	806
Hartford, Connecticut	1907	2nd	807
Hartford, Connecticut		DX1st	764
Haverhill, Massachusetts	1866	3rd	176
Haverhill, Massachusetts	1870	2nd	351
Haverhill, Massachusetts	1873	3rd	446
Hilton Head, North Carolina	1865	2nd	115
Hilton Head, North Carolina	1865	2nd	133
Hingham, Massachusetts	1905	2nd	782
Hoboken, New Jersey	1873	3rd	432
Hoboken, New Jersey	1888	2nd	637
Hoboken, New Jersey	1897	2nd	734

Amoskeag Steam Fire Engines

City	Date	Size	Serial #	City	Date	Size	Serial #
Hoboken, New Jersey	1897	2nd	735	Lewiston, Maine	1868	2nd	304
Hoboken, New Jersey	1907	2nd	832	Lewiston, Maine	1877	1st	483
Holyoke, Massachusetts	1866	2nd	181	Lima, Peru	1869	3rd	323
Holyoke, Massachusetts	1870	2nd	339	Lima, Peru	1889	2nd	648
Holyoke, Massachusetts	1907	1st	815	Little Rock, Arkansas	1867	2nd	217
Honolulu, Hawaii	1884	2nd	588	London, England	1862	1st	55
Honolulu, Hawaii	1884	2nd	589	London, England	1862	3rd	44
Honolulu, Hawaii	1900	3rd	749	London, Ontario	1867	3rd	223
Hudson, New Jersey	1869	3rd	326	London, Ontario	1873	2nd	459
Hull, Massachusetts	1905	2nd	780	Los Angeles, California	1872	2nd	393
Hyde Park, Illinois	1889	DX1st	645	Los Angeles, California	1873	2nd	431
Hyde Park, New York	1884	3rd	595	Los Angeles, California	1887	2nd	626
Hyde Park, New York	1884	3rd	596	Los Angeles, California	1893	2nd	690
Indianapolis, Indiana	1874	1st	481	Lowell, Massachusetts	1883	2nd	573
Jeffersonville, Indiana	1871	2nd	374	Lowell, Massachusetts	1888	2nd	636
Jersey City, New Jersey	1865	3rd	131	Lowell, Massachusetts	1890	1st	653
Jersey City, New Jersey	1867	3rd	264	Lowell, Massachusetts	1892	1st	680
Jersey City, New Jersey	1870	2nd	342	Lowell, Massachusetts	1907	1st	817
Jersey City, New Jersey	1870	2nd	345	Lynn, Massachusetts	1864	2nd	82
Jersey City, New Jersey	1873	1st	419	Lynn, Massachusetts	1866	2nd	186
Jersey City, New Jersey	1885	2nd	614	Lynn, Massachusetts	1869	1st	271
Jersey City, New Jersey	1897	3rd	728	Lynn, Massachusetts	1873	1st	418
Jersey City, New Jersey	1898	2nd	737	Lynn, Massachusetts	1883	1st	559
Johnstown, Pennsylvania	1867	2nd	235	Lynn, Massachusetts	1895	1st	677
Johnstown, Pennsylvania	1890	2nd	656	Lynn, Massachusetts		X1st	779
Johnstown, Pennsylvania	1890	2nd	657	Madison, Wisconsin	1866	2nd	206
Keene, New Hampshire	1883	2nd	580	Madison, Wisconsin	1870	2nd	341
Keokuk, Iowa	1866	3rd	198	Manchester, Massachusetts	1885	4	552
Laconia, New Hampshire	1875	2nd	499	Manchester, Massachusetts	1902	3rd	771
Lake Linden, Michigan	1892	4	676	Manchester, New Hampshire	1859	1st	1
Lake Linden, Michigan	1897	4	729	Manchester, New Hampshire	1860	1st	11
Lancaster, Pennsylvania	1869	2nd	311	Manchester, New Hampshire	1860	2nd	13
Lawrence, Kansas	1868	2nd	289	Manchester, New Hampshire	1865	2nd	121
Lawrence, Massachusetts	1860	1st	15	Manchester, New Hampshire	1867	2nd	257
Lawrence, Massachusetts	1862	2nd	48	Manchester, New Hampshire	1874	1st	485
Lawrence, Massachusetts	1862	3rd	43	Manchester, New Hampshire	1876	1st	518
Lawrence, Massachusetts	1864	3rd	100	Manchester, New Hampshire	1886	2nd	615
Lawrence, Massachusetts	1871	1st	355	Manchester, New Hampshire	1887	2nd	631
Lawrence, Massachusetts	1885	1st	610	Manchester, New Hampshire	1888	3rd	629
Lawrence, Massachusetts	1889	2nd	643	Manchester, New Hampshire	1893	2nd	692
Lawrence, Massachusetts	1889	2nd	647	Manchester, New Hampshire	1907		830
Lebanon, Pennsylvania	1866	2nd	210	Mare Island, California	1870	1st	349
Leominster, Massachusetts	1871	2nd	356	Mare Island, California	1872	1st	413

Amoskeag Steam Fire Engines

City	Date	Size	Serial #
Marlborough, New Hampshire	1895	4	712
Marshall, Michigan	1871	2nd	375
Medford, Massachusetts	1861	2nd	40
Medford, Massachusetts	1889	2nd	642
Menominee, Michigan	1874	1st	480
Menominee, Michigan	1884	2nd	597
Merrimac, Massachusetts	1884	3rd	583
Michigan City, Indiana	1909		844
Milford, Massachusetts	1873	2nd	435
Milton, Massachusetts	1887	3rd	628
Milwaukee, Wisconsin	1861	1st	31
Milwaukee, Wisconsin	1862	1st	60
Milwaukee, Wisconsin	1863	1st	77
Milwaukee, Wisconsin	1866	1st	152
Milwaukee, Wisconsin	1866	1st	171
Milwaukee, Wisconsin	1869	2nd	320
Milwaukee, Wisconsin	1872	1st	378
Milwaukee, Wisconsin	1877	1st	523
Milwaukee, Wisconsin	1877	2nd	511
Minneapolis, Minnesota	1874	2nd	490
Minneapolis, Minnesota	1882	2nd	572
Minneapolis, Minnesota	1883	2nd	581
Minneapolis, Minnesota	1884	1st	587
Mobile, Alabama	1867	2nd	216
Moline, Illinois	1869	1st	313
Moncton, New Brunswick	1883	3rd	577
Morris, Illinois	1868	1st	298
Nantucket, Massachusetts	1907	4	799
Nashua, New Hampshire		2nd	213
Nashua, New Hampshire	1867	1st	253
Nashua, New Hampshire	1870	1st	330
Nashua, New Hampshire	1873	1st	470
Nashua, New Hampshire	1896	1st	722
New Bedford, Massachusetts	1860	1st	6
New Bedford, Massachusetts	1860	1st	16
New Bedford, Massachusetts	1864	1st	90
New Bedford, Massachusetts	1866	1st	144
New Bedford, Massachusetts	1869	1st	327
New Bedford, Massachusetts	1882	2nd	567
New Bedford, Massachusetts	1884	2nd	592
New Bedford, Massachusetts	1884	2nd	603
New Bedford, Massachusetts	1890	2nd	662
New Bern, North Carolina	1865	3rd	127

City	Date	Size	Serial #
New Brunswick, New Jersey		3rd	175
New Haven, Connecticut	1861	1st	34
New Orleans, Louisiana	1865	1st	145
New Orleans, Louisiana	1865	2nd	106
New Orleans, Louisiana	1865	2nd	117
New Orleans, Louisiana	1868	1st	281
New Orleans, Louisiana	1869	2nd	312
New Orleans, Louisiana	1869	2nd	317
New Orleans, Louisiana	1872	1st	402
New Orleans, Louisiana	1872	2nd	396
New Orleans, Louisiana	1872	2nd	410
New Orleans, Louisiana	1872	2nd	411
New Orleans, Louisiana	1872	3rd	404
New Orleans, Louisiana	1872	3rd	405
New Orleans, Louisiana	1873	2nd	436
New Orleans, Louisiana	1873	3rd	406
New Orleans, Louisiana	1873	3rd	424
New Orleans, Louisiana	1874	2nd	474
New Orleans, Louisiana	1874	2nd	475
New Orleans, Louisiana	1876	1st	482
New Orleans, Louisiana	1884	3rd	602
New Orleans, Louisiana	1885	3rd	616
New Orleans, Louisiana	1887	3rd	627
New Orleans, Louisiana	1899	3rd	742
New Orleans, Louisiana	1900	3rd	745
New Orleans, Louisiana	1900	3rd	746
New Orleans, Louisiana	1900	3rd	747
New Orleans, Louisiana		DX1st	744
New York, New York		2nd	295
New York, New York		2nd	296
New York, New York	1860	2nd	19
New York, New York	1861	2nd	28
New York, New York	1861	3rd	36
New York, New York	1865	1st	137
New York, New York	1865	1st	142
New York, New York	1865	1st	143
New York, New York	1865	2nd	147
New York, New York	1865	2nd	148
New York, New York	1865	2nd	157
New York, New York	1865	2nd	158
New York, New York	1866	1st	191
New York, New York	1866	1st	192
New York, New York	1866	1st	193

Amoskeag Steam Fire Engines

City	Date	Size	Serial #
New York, New York	1866	1st	194
New York, New York	1866	1st	195
New York, New York	1866	2nd	159
New York, New York	1866	2nd	160
New York, New York	1866	2nd	161
New York, New York	1866	2nd	162
New York, New York	1866	2nd	163
New York, New York	1866	2nd	164
New York, New York	1866	2nd	165
New York, New York	1866	2nd	166
New York, New York	1866	2nd	185
New York, New York	1867	2nd	226
New York, New York	1867	2nd	227
New York, New York	1867	2nd	228
New York, New York	1867	2nd	229
New York, New York	1867	2nd	230
New York, New York	1868	2nd	301
New York, New York	1868	2nd	302
New York, New York	1871	2nd	359
New York, New York	1871	2nd	360
New York, New York	1871	2nd	361
New York, New York	1871	2nd	362
New York, New York	1871	2nd	363
New York, New York	1872	1st	284
New York, New York	1873	2nd	437
New York, New York	1873	2nd	438
New York, New York	1873	2nd	439
New York, New York	1873	2nd	440
New York, New York	1873	2nd	441
New York, New York	1873	2nd	455
New York, New York	1874	1st	491
New York, New York	1874	1st	492
New York, New York	1874	1st	493
New York, New York	1874	1st	494
New York, New York	1875	1st	513
New York, New York	1875	1st	514
New York, New York	1876	3rd	516
New York, New York	1877	3rd	517
New York, New York	1877	3rd	519
New York, New York	1877	3rd	520
New York, New York	1879	1st	527
New York, New York	1895	3rd	714
New York, New York	1895	3rd	715

City	Date	Size	Serial #
New York, New York	1898	4	739
New York, New York	1898	4	740
New York, New York	1898	4	741
Newark, New Jersey	1860	1st	21
Newark, New Jersey	1864	1st	94
Newark, New Jersey	1865	1st	123
Newark, New Jersey	1866	2nd	168
Newark, New Jersey	1887	2nd	625
Newark, New Jersey	1887	2nd	632
Newark, New Jersey	1891	2nd	661
Newark, New Jersey	1897	3rd	730
Newark, New Jersey	1899	2nd	748
Newark, New Jersey	1901	2nd	758
Newark, New Jersey	1901	2nd	762
Newark, New Jersey	1901	2nd	763
Newark, New Jersey	1902	2nd	768
Newark, New Jersey	1902	2nd	769
Newark, New Jersey	1906	1st	787
Newark, New Jersey	1906	X1st	786
Newark, New Jersey	1907		826
Newark, New Jersey	1909		845
Newburgh, New York	1871	3rd	376
Newburgh, New York	1873	3rd	433
Newburyport, Massachusetts	1867	2nd	242
Newburyport, Massachusetts	1867	2nd	243
Newburyport, Massachusetts	1873	2nd	466
Newport, Kentucky	1868	1st	282
Newport, Rhode Island	1866	2nd	188
Newport, Rhode Island	1867	1st	269
Newport, Rhode Island	1867	2nd	241
Newton, Massachusetts	1871	2nd	373
Newton, Massachusetts	1874	2nd	462
Newton, Massachusetts	1892	3rd	679
Niles, Ohio	1874	2nd	496
Norfolk, Pennsylvania	1870	1st	348
Norfolk, Virginia	1865	2nd	132
Norfolk, Virginia	1866	2nd	154
Norfolk, Virginia	1866	2nd	204
Norfolk, Virginia	1867	3rd	221
Norfolk, Virginia	1873	3rd	445
Norfolk, Virginia	1894	1st	703
Norristown, Pennsylvania	1865	2nd	156
Norristown, Pennsylvania	1888	2nd	633

Amoskeag Steam Fire Engines

City	Date	Size	Serial #
North Andover, Massachusetts	1872	2nd	399
North Andover, Massachusetts	1901	5	766
North Brookfield, Massachusetts	1888	3rd	634
Norwich, Connecticut	1861	1st	29
Oakland, California	1868	3rd	266
Oakland, California	1877	2nd	506
Oakland, California	1900	3rd	752
Ogdensburg, New York	1866	2nd	189
Ogdensburg, New York	1867	2nd	245
Oklahoma City, Oklahoma	1906		794
Omaha, Nebraska	1868	2nd	306
Orange, New Jersey	1873	2nd	457
Oshkosh, Wisconsin	1867	1st	272
Ottawa, Ontario	1870	2nd	353
Owego, New York	1866	2nd	182
Park, New Jersey	1862	2nd	58
Passaic, New Jersey	1900	2nd	759
Passaic, New Jersey	1907		811
Patterson, New Jersey	1881	2nd	561
Peabody, Massachusetts	1903	2nd	773
Pensacola, Florida	1866	2nd	205
Peoria, Illinois	1864	2nd	104
Pepperell, Massachusetts	1891	3rd	672
Philadelphia, Pennsylvania	1860	2nd	24
Philadelphia, Pennsylvania	1861	1st	42
Philadelphia, Pennsylvania	1863	1st	76
Philadelphia, Pennsylvania	1863	1st	80
Philadelphia, Pennsylvania	1863	2nd	68
Philadelphia, Pennsylvania	1863	2nd	69
Philadelphia, Pennsylvania	1863	2nd	74
Philadelphia, Pennsylvania	1864	1st	88
Philadelphia, Pennsylvania	1864	1st	89
Philadelphia, Pennsylvania	1864	1st	93
Philadelphia, Pennsylvania	1864	1st	102
Philadelphia, Pennsylvania	1864	2nd	79
Philadelphia, Pennsylvania	1865	1st	118
Philadelphia, Pennsylvania	1865	2nd	135
Philadelphia, Pennsylvania	1865	2nd	146
Philadelphia, Pennsylvania	1865	2nd	149
Philadelphia, Pennsylvania	1866	3rd	183
Philadelphia, Pennsylvania	1867	1st	251
Philadelphia, Pennsylvania	1873	1st	448
Philadelphia, Pennsylvania	1907		829

City	Date	Size	Serial #
Pittsburgh, Pennsylvania	1861	2nd	33
Pittsburgh, Pennsylvania	1861	2nd	41
Pittsburgh, Pennsylvania	1862	2nd	57
Pittsburgh, Pennsylvania	1863	1st	81
Pittsburgh, Pennsylvania	1863	2nd	78
Pittsburgh, Pennsylvania	1865	2nd	114
Pittsburgh, Pennsylvania	1867	2nd	219
Pittsburgh, Pennsylvania	1867	2nd	262
Pittsburgh, Pennsylvania	1868	2nd	278
Pittsburgh, Pennsylvania	1872	3rd	403
Pittsburgh, Pennsylvania	1873	2nd	452
Pittsburgh, Pennsylvania	1873	2nd	453
Pittsburgh, Pennsylvania	1873	3rd	450
Pittsburgh, Pennsylvania	1873	3rd	451
Pittsburgh, Pennsylvania	1874	3rd	477
Pittsburgh, Pennsylvania	1882	3rd	570
Pittsburgh, Pennsylvania	1883	3rd	582
Pittsburgh, Pennsylvania	1884	3rd	601
Pittsburgh, Pennsylvania	1885	1st	611
Pittsburgh, Pennsylvania	1885	3rd	607
Pittsburgh, Pennsylvania	1885	3rd	608
Pittsburgh, Pennsylvania	1886	3rd	617
Pittsburgh, Pennsylvania	1886	3rd	618
Pittsburgh, Pennsylvania	1889	DX1st	646
Pittsburgh, Pennsylvania	1893	1st	698
Pittsburgh, Pennsylvania	1893	1st	700
Pittsburgh, Pennsylvania	1896	1st	723
Pittsburgh, Pennsylvania	1896	1st	724
Pittsburgh, Pennsylvania	1900	1st	750
Pittsburgh, Pennsylvania	1900	2nd	751
Pittsburgh, Pennsylvania	1900	DX1st	756
Pittsburgh, Pennsylvania	1906	2nd	792
Pittsburgh, Pennsylvania	1906	2nd	793
Pittsburgh, Pennsylvania	1906	2nd	795
Plainfield, New Jersey	1867	3rd	224
Plainfield, New Jersey	1869	3rd	324
Plainfield, New Jersey	1886	3rd	623
Plymouth, Massachusetts	1893	3rd	699
Plymouth, Massachusetts	1913	2nd	853
Portland, Maine	1859	1st	2
Portland, Maine	1862	2nd	54
Portland, Maine	1871	1st	370
Portland, Maine	1873	1st	449

Amoskeag Steam Fire Engines

City	Date	Size	Serial #
Portland, Maine	1881	2nd	554
Portland, Maine	1885	2nd	612
Portland, Maine	1894	X1st	713
Portland, Maine	1903	DX1st	772
Portland, Maine	1906		788
Portland, Maine	1907	1st	833
Portland, Maine	1907	3rd	823
Portland, Maine	1908	1st	836
Portland, Maine	1908	1st	837
Portland, Maine	1910		849
Portland, New Brunswick	1872	2nd	392
Portland, New Brunswick	1877	2nd	526
Portland, Oregon	1873	2nd	460
Portland, Oregon	1873	2nd	461
Portland, Oregon	1878	4	537
Portsmouth, New Hampshire	1863	2nd	63
Portsmouth, New Hampshire	1866	2nd	203
Portsmouth, New Hampshire	1870	2nd	340
Portsmouth, New Hampshire	1879	2nd	542
Portsmouth, New Hampshire	1890	2nd	649
Portsmouth, New Hampshire	1972	1st	414
Portsmouth, Virginia	1870	3rd	335
Portsmouth, Virginia	1892	3rd	683
Pottstown, Pennsylvania	1907		821
Pottsville, Pennsylvania	1866	3rd	199
Pottsville, Pennsylvania	1883	3rd	576
Providence, Rhode Island	1872	3rd	377
Providence, Rhode Island	1907	3rd	800
Provincetown, Massachusetts	1889	3rd	639
Quincy, Massachusetts	1882	3rd	565
Quincy, Massachusetts	1912	1st	852
Randolph, Massachusetts	1879	2nd	540
Randolph, Massachusetts	1880	2nd	548
Reading, Pennsylvania	1865	1st	107
Reading, Pennsylvania	1865	2nd	150
Reading, Pennsylvania	1867	2nd	234
Reading, Pennsylvania	1868	1st	297
Reading, Pennsylvania	1887	2nd	630
Revere, Massachusetts	1907	2nd	824
Richmond, Virginia	1906	1st	798
Richmond, Virginia	1907	1st	816
Rock Island, Illinois	1866	1st	172
Rockland, Maine	1878	2nd	532

City	Date	Size	Serial #
Rockland, Massachusetts	1866	2nd	201
Rutland, Vermont	1868	2nd	303
Saco, Maine	1864	2nd	83
Saco, Maine	1871	1st	371
Sacramento, California	1872	2nd	400
Sacramento, California	1872	2nd	407
Sacramento, California	1874	2nd	471
Sacramento, California	1907		822
Salem, Massachusetts	1866	2nd	212
Salem, Massachusetts	1873	2nd	434
Salem, Massachusetts	1880	2nd	556
Salem, Massachusetts	1907	1st	812
San Francisco, California	1866	1st	173
San Francisco, California	1866	2nd	178
San Francisco, California	1866	2nd	179
San Francisco, California	1866	2nd	180
San Francisco, California	1866	2nd	190
San Francisco, California	1867	2nd	249
San Francisco, California	1867	2nd	250
San Francisco, California	1868	2nd	291
San Francisco, California	1869	3rd	267
San Francisco, California	1872	2nd	389
San Francisco, California	1872	2nd	390
San Francisco, California	1873	2nd	426
San Francisco, California	1873	2nd	442
San Francisco, California	1878	2nd	533
San Francisco, California	1879	3rd	535
San Francisco, California	1885	2nd	604
San Francisco, California	1885	3rd	609
San Francisco, California	1886	2nd	622
San Francisco, California	1894	1st	710
San Francisco, California	1895	2nd	716
San Jose, California	1880	2nd	547
San Jose, California	1890	3rd	651
Sandusky, Ohio	1864	2nd	98
Schenectady, New York	1867	2nd	246
Shanghai, China	1865	3rd	108
Skoegan, Maine	1881	3rd	558
Snohomish, Washington	1890	3rd	666
Somerville, New Jersey	1873	3rd	425
Springfield, Massachusetts	1862	2nd	52
Springfield, Massachusetts	1862	2nd	61
Springfield, Massachusetts	1862	2nd	62

Amoskeag Steam Fire Engines

City	Date	Size	Serial #
Springfield, Massachusetts	1865	1st	126
Springfield, Massachusetts	1871	2nd	391
Springfield, Massachusetts	1873	2nd	463
Springfield, Massachusetts	1893	2nd	693
Springfield, Massachusetts	1907	1st	818
Springfield, Massachusetts	1907	1st	819
Springfield, Massachusetts		X1st	704
St. John, New Brunswick	1863	2nd	65
St. John, New Brunswick	1863	2nd	70
St. John, New Brunswick	1864	1st	103
St. John, New Brunswick	1874	2nd	487
St. Joseph, Missouri	1865	2nd	120
St. Joseph, Missouri	1872	2nd	397
St. Paul, Minnesota	1884	2nd	586
St. Paul, Minnesota	1907	2nd	825
St. Stephens, New Brunswick	1871	2nd	357
Stamford, Connecticut	1906	1st	796
Staten Island, New York	1873	3rd	444
Steven's Point, Wisconsin	1874	2nd	476
Stevens Point, Wisconsin	1885	2nd	613
Stockton, California	1874	2nd	469
Stoneham, Massachusetts	1891	2nd	674
Swanzey, New Hampshire	1901	4	767
Sydney, Australia	1865	3rd	122
Syracuse, New York	1865	1st	151
Syracuse, New York	1866	2nd	169
Syracuse, New York	1867	1st	255
Syracuse, New York	1871	2nd	384
Tacoma, Washington	1889	3rd	640
Taunton, Massachusetts	1865	3rd	119
Taunton, Massachusetts	1866	2nd	177
Taunton, Massachusetts	1866	3rd	134
Taunton, Massachusetts	1873	2nd	467
The Dalles, Oregon	1879	3rd	529
Thompsonville, Connecticut	1867	2nd	247
Titusville, Pennsylvania	1868	1st	283
Toledo, Ohio	1867	1st	174
Tompkinsville, New York		2nd	688
Townsend, Massachusetts	1875	3rd	479
Townsend, Massachusetts	1909	2nd	843

City	Date	Size	Serial #
Trenton, New Jersey	1864	2nd	97
Trenton, New Jersey	1864	3rd	86
Trenton, New Jersey	1880	2nd	549
Trenton, New Jersey	1881	3rd	557
Trenton, Ontario	1882	X1st	560
Troy, New York	1860	1st	12
Troy, New York	1860	2nd	18
Troy, New York	1862	1st	46
Troy, New York	1867	2nd	214
Troy, New York	1876	1st	502
Troy, New York	1876	2nd	509
Troy, New York	1880	2nd	555
Vancouver, British Columbia	1906	DX1st	789
Virginia City, Nevada	1872	2nd	412
Wakefield, Massachusetts	1907		831
Waltham, Massachusetts	1871	2nd	364
Waltham, Massachusetts	1902	2nd	770
Washington, D.C.	1865	2nd	109
Washington, D.C.	1865	2nd	110
Washington, D.C.	1865	2nd	111
Washington, D.C.	1869	1st	315
Washington, D.C.	1886	2nd	621
Washington, D.C.	1896	2nd	726
Watertown, Massachusetts	1867	2nd	218
Watertown, New York	1900	2nd	757
West Point, New York	1872	3rd	387
West Point, New York	1872	3rd	388
Wilkes Barre, Pennsylvania	1870	2nd	347
Wilkes Barre, Pennsylvania	1874	2nd	472
Williamsport, Pennsylvania	1867	2nd	240
Williamsport, Pennsylvania	1867	2nd	260
Wilmington, Delaware	1866	2nd	170
Wilmington, Delaware	1889	2nd	641
Windsor, Nova Scotia	1868	2nd	279
Woburn, Massachusetts	1893	2nd	702
Woodstock, New Brunswick	1872	2nd	398
Woodstock, New Brunswick	1882	3rd	536
Worcester, Massachusetts	1873	1st	417
Yarmouth, Nova Scotia	1878	2nd	531
York, Pennsylvania	1904	1st	776

Lee & Larnard Steam Fire Engines
New York, New York
(1858 - 1864)

Information compiled by:
Edward R. Tufts

City	Date	Size	Serial #
New Orleans, Louisiana	1861		
New Orleans, Louisiana	1861		
New Orleans, Louisiana	1861		
New Orleans, Louisiana	1861		
New York, New York	1859		
New York, New York	1859		
New York, New York	1859		
New York, New York	1860		
New York, New York	1860		
New York, New York	1864		
New York, New York	1868	2nd	
Philadelphia, Pennsylvania	1859		
Philadelphia, Pennsylvania	1860		
Philadelphia, Pennsylvania	1860	2nd	
Philadelphia, Pennsylvania	1860	2nd	
Reading, Pennsylvania	1860		

Note:
There were 3 Lee & Larned self-propellers. They were the first truly self-propelled apparatus, with no horses needed. The first was 1858, the J.C. Cary; followed by the John G. Storms, in the same year; and the Southwark, for Philadelphia in 1859. This last engine was returned to Lee & Larned, and was renamed the Niagara (sometimes mistakenly thought of as 4th propeller). It was used as a demonstrator, but it broke down at a muster in Troy, NY in 1860 and was scrapped.

G. & J. Chapman Steam Fire Engines
Philadelphia, Pennsylvania
(1860 - 1864)

Information compiled by:
Edward R. Tufts

City	Date	Size	Serial #
Philadelphia, Pennsylvania	1860	2nd	
Philadelphia, Pennsylvania	1860	2nd	
Philadelphia, Pennsylvania	1863	2nd	
Philadelphia, Pennsylvania	1863	2nd	
Philadelphia, Pennsylvania	1863	2nd	
Philadelphia, Pennsylvania	1863	2nd	
Philadelphia, Pennsylvania	1863	2nd	
Wilmington, Delaware	1864	2nd	

Reaney & Neafie Steam Fire Engines
Philadelphia, Pennsylvania
(1857 - 1867)

Information compiled by:

Edward R. Tufts

City	Date	Size	Serial #
Augusta, Georgia	1859	2nd	11
Baltimore, Maryland	1858	1st	2
Baltimore, Maryland	1859		5
La Atravida, Cuba	1867	2nd	28
Lancaster, Pennsylvania	1867	2nd	26
Madison, Indiana	1859	2nd	14
Mobile, Alabama	1865	2nd	23
Nashville, Tennessee	1860	2nd	18
New Orleans, Louisiana	1864	2nd	21
Norfolk, Virginia	1866	2nd	25
Philadelphia, Pennsylvania	1857	1st	1
Philadelphia, Pennsylvania	1858	3rd	3
Philadelphia, Pennsylvania	1858	X1st	4
Philadelphia, Pennsylvania	1859	1st	6
Philadelphia, Pennsylvania	1859	2nd	7
Philadelphia, Pennsylvania	1859	2nd	8
Philadelphia, Pennsylvania	1859	2nd	9
Philadelphia, Pennsylvania	1859	2nd	10
Philadelphia, Pennsylvania	1859	2nd	12
Philadelphia, Pennsylvania	1859	2nd	15
Philadelphia, Pennsylvania	1859	2nd	16
Philadelphia, Pennsylvania	1863	2nd	19
Philadelphia, Pennsylvania	1865	2nd	24
Providence, Rhode Island	1859	2nd	13
San Francisco, California	1864	2nd	22
St. Louis, Missouri	1864	2nd	20
Washington, D.C.	1860	2nd	17
Washington, D.C.	1867	2nd	27

James B. Johnson/Portland Company Steamer
Portland, Maine
(1858 - 1870)

Information compiled by:
Michael LaPlante

City	Date	Size	Serial #
Albany, New York	1864		
Bangor, Maine	1861		
Bangor, Maine	1865		
Bridgeport, Connecticut	1864-65		
Fitchburg, Massachusetts	1864		
Gloucester, Massachusetts	1864		
Gloucester, Massachusetts	1864		
Grand Trunk Railroad, Portland yard	1860		
Lewiston, Maine	1866		
Lynn, Massachusetts	1863-64		
Malden, Massachusetts	1864		
New Haven, Connecticut	1860		
New Haven, Connecticut	1861		
New York, New York	1861		
New York, New York	1861		
Newburyport, Massachusetts	1864-65		

City	Date	Size	Serial #
Norristown, Pennsylvania	1865		
Philadelphia, Pennsylvania	1860		
Portland, Maine	1861		
Portland, Maine	1864		
Portland, Maine	1865		
Portland, Maine	1865		
Portland, Maine	1869-70		
Portsmouth, New Hampshire	1864		
Salem, Massachusetts	1858		
Salem, Massachusetts	1859		
Salem, Massachusetts	1861		
Salem, Massachusetts	1866		
Santiago, Chile	1864		
Schnectady, New York	1865		
West Chester, Pennsylvania	1867		

Photo from the collection of J.R. Hunneman, Jr. Photo by Harold Walker, 1915.

Hunneman No. 744, the Enterprise No. 2. This steamer was sold to Beverly, Massachusetts in September, 1881. It was the last steamer built in the Hunneman shop.

Hunneman Steamers
Boston, Massachusetts
(1866-1881)

Information compiled by:
Edward R. Tufts

City	Date	Size	Serial #
Beverly, Massachusetts	1881		S-744
Blackstone, Massachusetts	1875		S-737
Boston, Massachusetts	1872		S-720
Boston, Massachusetts	1872		S-722
Boston, Massachusetts	1872		S-724
Boston, Massachusetts	1873		S-734
Brighton, Massachusetts	1873		S-731
Danvers, Massachusetts	1874		S-735
Dorchester, Massachusetts	1867		S-687
Fall River, Massachusetts	1868		S-699
Fall River, Massachusetts	1873		S-729
Leicester, Massachusetts	1883		S-743
Lowell, Massachusetts	1866		S-684
Lowell, Massachusetts	1868		S-697
Mystic Bridge, Connecticut	1875		S-739

City	Date	Size	Serial #
New Haven, Connecticut	1867		S-688
New Haven, Connecticut	1869		S-702
New Haven, Connecticut	1879		S-738
New London, Connecticut	1867		S-692
New London, Connecticut	1867		S-693
Newton, Massachusetts	1868		S-690
Plymouth, Massachusetts	1872		S-706
Somerville, Massachusetts	1866		S-678
Spencer, Massachusetts	1872		S-715
Stoneham, Massachusetts	1870		S-710
West Roxbury, Massachusetts	1871		S-711
West Roxbury, Massachusetts	1872		S-718
Westboro, Massachusetts	1868		S-698
Winchester, Massachusetts	1873		S-726

Index

❦

Note: The 4,200 steam fire engines
listed in the Appendix, beginning on page 217,
are not included in this index, but are listed
alphabetically by city for each make.

Page numbers in italics denote pictures or drawings.

1904 American-LaFrance Cosmopolitan Steamer

The Cosmopolitan was the smallest steamer built for use by fire departments. Its 250 gpm capacity made it useful only for the smallest communities or in very narrow streets. However, the Cosmopolitan needed only one man to operate it, which made it more efficient than the manpower-driven hand pumper. This Cosmopolitan was built in 1904 for Claremore, OK, and later served in Millersburg, KY. The apparatus, designed by Charles H. Fox, later of Ahrens-Fox fame, is 6 feet high, 7 feet long, and 3 feet 8 inches wide. It weighs about 1,900 pounds, and its original price was $1,500. Of the 21 built between 1902 and 1912, seven still exist today. The 1904 American-LaFrance Cosmopolitan Steamer is part of the Freightliner antique fire apparatus collection. (This apparatus was restored by Firefly Restorations, Hope, Maine.)

An early steamer fighting a fire in Cincinnati, the city of its manufacture.

Bibliography

American-LaFrance
First Water, The History of American-LaFrance. 1972.

Clarke, Robert
History of the Cincinnati Fire Department.
Cincinnati: The Robert Clarke Co., 1895.

Cromie, Robert
The Great Chicago Fire
Nashville, Tennessee: Rutledge Hill Press, 1994.

Daly, George Anne and Robrecht, John J.
An Illustrated Handbook of Fire Apparatus
Philadelphia, Pennsylvania: INA Corporation Archives Department. 1972.

Ditzel, Paul C.
Fire Engines Firefighters
New York: Bonanza Books. 1984.

Hass, Ed
The Dean of Steam Fire Engine Builders.
Sunnyvale, California: Kes-Print, Inc., 1986.

Heath, Richard L.
Fighting The Fire Engine Trust: The Nott Fire Engine Company of Minneapolis.
St. Paul: Minnesota History, Spring 1987.

Holzman, Robert S.
The Romance of Firefighting
New York: Harper & Brothers. 1956.

King, William T.
History of the American Steam Fire Engine.
Chicago: Davies, 1896.

Meek, Clarence E.
Saga Of The Steamer.
Fire Engineering Magazine, June 1957.

Morris, John V.
Fires and Firefighters
New York: Bramhall House. 1955.

Peckham, John M.
Fighting Fire With Fire
Newfoundland, New Jersey: Walter R. Haessner and Associates, Inc. 1972.

Rhode, Dr. Robert T.
When Steam Was King... and Cincinnati Was Queen.
Lancaster, Pennsylvania: Stemgas Publishing Co. January/February 1996.

Roper, Stephen
Handbook of Modern Steam Fire-Engines.
Philadelphia: Claxton, Remsen & Haffelfinger, 1876.

Author Unknown:

Amoskeag Steam Fire Engines
Manchester, New Hampshire: Manchester Historic Association. 1990.

The Famous Amoskeag Steamers.
Manchester, New Hampshire: The Manchester Historic Association, Special Bulletin No. 1.

Fire Fighting of Long Ago
Maynard, Massachusetts: Chandler Press, 1988.

The Volunteer Fire Department of Old New York
Scotia, New York: Americana Review. 1962.

Note:

Much additional reference material was in the form of unpublished papers and manuscripts by the following firefighting historians, whose gracious assistance is gratefully acknowledged, and who are listed in alphabetical order:

Nancy Kohnen	William Patton Schott
Mike LaPlante	Bill Schwartz
Matt Lee	Ken Soderbeck
David Lewis	Ed Tufts
John Peckham	Harold Walker
Ken Peterson	Al Wills
John Robrecht	

STEAM FIRE ENGINE "MISSOURI"
built by
ABEL SHAWK, INVENTOR & PATENTEE
"YOUNG AMERICA WORKS."
CINCINNATI, OHIO.

Scale 1½ inches to a foot.

Other Books in the
Fire Service History Series
from Fire Buff House Publishers

- **CHEMICAL FIRE ENGINES** by W. Fred Conway
  The only book ever written about these amazing engines that for half a century put out 80% of all fires in spite of the fact that they never did perform as advertised! Hard cover. 128 pages, over one hundred photographs and drawings.

- **FIREBOATS** by Paul Ditzel
  The definitive work on the history of marine firefighting - a book so real you can almost hear and feel the engines and pumps throbbing! Relive the thrilling accounts of fireboats in action at spectacular fires. Hardcover. Over one hundred pictures.

- **FIRE ALARM!** by Paul Ditzel
  The story of fire alarm telegraphy - a nostalgic overview of fire alarm transmission in America. Includes the incredible story of an obscure telegraph operator, John N. Gamewell, who built a vast fire alarm empire with a 90% market share. Hard cover. Hundreds of pictures.

- **LOS ANGELES FIRE DEPARTMENT** by Paul Ditzel
  The fascinating complete history of the Los Angeles Fire Department. America's foremost fire historian details the major fires during the city's history, including the Bel-Air brush fire disaster, and the Central Library blaze. Oversize book with 250 pages and hundreds of photographs of fires and apparatus. Soft cover.

- **A FIRE CHIEF REMEMBERS** by Battalion Chief Edwin F. Schneider (Ret.)
  The poignant, touching, moving account of his FDNY career. Now 82 years of age, Chief Schneider looks back at the series of incredible events in his 34 year career climb from buff to chief. Soft cover. Illustrated.

- **LAGUARDIA'S FIRE CHIEF** by Kathleen Walsh Packard
  The fascinating biography of New York City Fire Chief/Fire Commissioner Patrick Walsh, who served under the mercurial mayor, Fiorello LaGuardia. Chief Walsh and Mayor LaGuardia would race to see who could get to the fire first. This account of Chief Walsh's storybook career is written by his granddaughter. Soft cover. Illustrated.

- **DISCOVERING AMERICA'S FIRE MUSEUMS** by W. Fred Conway
  A comprehensive guidebook describing 150 museums in the United States and Canada displaying vintage fire apparatus, equipment, and memorabilia. Includes a history of firefighting apparatus and equipment from Colonial times to the present. 188 pages, 200 illustrations. Soft cover.

- **FIREFIGHTING LORE** by W. Fred Conway
  Probably the most unusual book of firefighting history ever written, it recounts dozens of amazing, strange, and incredible stories from firefighting's past and present - every one true. Soft cover. Illustrated.

- **INVENTING THE AMERICAN FIRE ENGINE** by M.W. Goodman, M.D.
  More than 200 inventors are profiled to show their contributions to the evolution of fire engines from primitive hand tubs to today's awesome state-of-the-art apparatus. Includes nearly 400 photographs and patent drawings spanning three centuries. Hard cover.

- **HUNNEMAN'S AMAZING FIRE ENGINES** by Edward R. Tufts
  The hand fire engines built by Paul Revere's apprentice, William C. Hunneman changed firefighting in Colonial America. The story of Hunneman and his fire engines is a fascinating chapter of Americana. Full size. Soft cover. Illustrated.

These books are available wherever fire books are sold, or you may order direct from the publisher.

Fire Buff House Publishers
P.O. Box 711, New Albany, IN 47151-0711
1-800-234-1804